Supplement to Basic Practice of Statistics

11th edition Update
D'Arcy P. Mays, III

Mc Graw Hill Education

9 0 SCI SCI 19 18 17

ISBN-13: 978-1-259-42552-3
ISBN-10: 1-259-42552-5

Learning Solutions Consultant: Valerie Walo
Project Manager: Vanessa Arnold
Cover Photo Credits: 87835733.tif – NA

Preface

This workbook is designed to be a supplement to the fifth edition of David Moore's A Basic Practice of Statistics. It is a required book for STAT 210 Basic Practice of Statistics taught at Virginia Commonwealth University, an introductory level course that is taken by students from many majors. The course is taught in three 50-minute lectures per week.

Each chapter of the workbook consists of five components. The text involves definitions, important concepts, formulas and their interpretations. Class examples are incorporated in each section and provide the students an opportunity to apply the concept just discussed. At the end of each chapter is a section entitled "additional reading and examples" that the students should read outside of class. For some chapters this includes instructions for using a TI-83/84 calculator. This is followed by a suggested list of practice problems that the students should work outside of class. Solutions can be found in the back of the supplement. Finally, activities are included throughout the workbook, providing the students with hands-on experience in applying the concepts learned.

The author hopes that the student finds this workbook to be helpful and welcomes any comments and suggestions.

Acknowledgments

The author would like to acknowledge the contribution of other Virginia Commonwealth University statistics faculty members and graduate students for their suggestions on items to include in the workbook and guidance in choosing topics for the course. Their feedback and suggestions for improvement have made this workbook an easier tool for students to use. In particular, recognition is given to Amy Kimbrough and Mita Basu for input on the items included and revised, and to Alex Cameron and Brianna Huffman for reviewing the manuscript and working some of the practice problem solutions.

Finally, I acknowledge the comments, suggestions, complaints, and compliments of past students that have been incorporated into the revision of the supplement. With the purpose of the supplement being to advance the understanding and appreciation of statistics, the opinions of past (and current) students are the real measure of the effectiveness and usefulness of the project.

Table of Contents

I. Introduction and Basic Definitions

In Moore: Read beginning of Chapter 1 (pages 3 – 6), and page 202

Statistics is a science that involves the extraction of information from numerical data obtained during an experiment or from a sample. It involves the <u>design</u> of the experiment or sampling procedure and the collection of the data, the <u>analysis</u> of the data, and making <u>inferences</u> (statements) about larger groups based on the data that was collected.

Definitions:

1. **Population**: the entire group of individuals (subjects) about which the researcher wants information.
   1. All U.S. citizens
   2. All male students at this university
   3. All sections of all courses taught this semester at this university

2. **Parameter**: some <u>characteristic</u> of the population that the researcher wants to measure.
   1. <u>Proportion</u> of U.S. citizens who voted in the last Presidential election
   2. <u>Average</u> (<u>mean</u>) height of all male students at this university
   3. <u>Proportion</u> of all sections of all courses taught by adjunct (part-time) faculty

Typically parameters are denoted using Greek letters, and this convention will be used in the remainder of this book. For example, the mean (average) of a population is often denoted with the Greek letter μ (read mu) and the proportion of a population that are "successes" is often denoted with the Greek letter π (read pi). Other parameters will be introduced as the book progresses.

Often a population is so large that it is nearly impossible to contact or measure every subject, and hence the true value of the parameter is usually unknown. So instead we must select a <u>representative sample</u> of the population and only contact or measure the subjects in the sample. The definition of "representative" will be provided in the next chapter.

3. **Sample**:   a subset of the population that we examine in order to gather information.

   If the population were all male students at this university, then the male students in this class would be a sample of this population.

4. **Statistic**: a descriptive measure, usually computed from a sample, which can be expressed or evaluated <u>numerically.</u>

> If the population were all male students at this university, and the male students in this class a sample of this population, then the <u>average height</u> of the male students in this class would be a statistic.

Typically statistics are denoted with symbols involving regular English letters, and this convention will be used in the remainder of this book. For example, the mean (average) of a sample is often denoted by the symbol $\overline{X}$ (read X-bar) and the proportion of a sample that are "successes" is often denoted by the symbol $\hat{p}$ (read p-hat). Other statistics will be introduced as the book progresses.

5. **Inference**: a statement about a population based on the data collected in a sample. One type of inference is using a sample statistic to <u>estimate</u> a population parameter.

> The average height of the male students in this class (a statistic, $\overline{X}$) can be used to <u>estimate</u> the average height of all male students at this university (a parameter, μ).

Example 1

The 2008 Summer Olympic Games took place in Beijing, China from August 8 until August 24. Of the 195 countries in the world, 192 of them participated, with only Brunei, Kosovo and Vatican City not participating. Additionally, 12 territories participated (including American Samoa, Aruba, Bermuda, British Virgin Islands, Cayman Islands, Cook Islands, Guam, Hong Kong, Netherlands Antilles, Palestine, Puerto Rico and U. S. Virgin Islands). Hence there were a total of 204 countries and territories that were competing and eligible to win Olympic medals, and it is of interest to gather information about these 204 competing countries and territories. Certain things, such as the numbers of gold, silver and bronze medals won and the number of athletes participating in the Olympic games, were easy to determine for each country or territory, but other information could not be collected for all countries and territories. The number of gold medals won by each country and territory competing the 2008 Summer Olympic Games is easy to determine, and a total of 81 different countries and territories had at least one athlete win a gold medal. A random sample of 20 competing countries or territories was selected for further analysis. 13 of these 20 countries and territories, or 65% had at least one athlete win a gold medal, and 93% of the athletes in these 20 countries and territories answered that they enjoyed the Beijing Olympics. Interestingly, 7 of the 20 countries and territories in the sample were located in South America.

Describe the population of interest in this study.

Describe the sample in this study.

Identify each of the following as being a parameter or a statistic.

(a) 204, the number of competing countries and territories

(b) 20, the number of competing countries and territories selected for further analysis

(c) 65%, the percentage of the 20 countries or territories that had at least one athlete win a gold medal

(d) 93%, the percentage of the athletes in the 20 countries and territories that enjoyed the Beijing Olympics

(e) 81, the number of all competing countries and territories that had at least one athlete win a gold medal

(f) 7, the number of the 20 countries and territories that were located in South America

6. **Distribution**: a listing of all the possible values that a characteristic can take and the number (or percentage) of times that each value occurs. A major component of statistics involves describing the distribution of a set of data.

      1.   Consider gender of a student. Students are either male or female, and if we count the number of each that would give us the distribution.

      2.   Consider grades on a test worth 100 points. We can count the number of students who make grades between 0 and 9, between 10 and 19, etc through grades between 90 and 100. The 10-point intervals would be the values of the characteristic and the number of students in each interval would complete the distribution.

Two key components of statistics involve learning how to describe a distribution, and also learning properties of commonly used distributions. There are sections and chapters devoted to each of these things later in the book.

We generally deal with two branches of statistics:

1. **Descriptive statistics** is the branch of statistics concerned with <u>numerical</u> and <u>graphical</u> techniques for describing one or more characteristics of a population and for comparing characteristics among populations. The first part of this book, beginning with chapter III, will focus on descriptive statistics.

2. **Inferential statistics** is the branch of statistics in which we use data and statistics computed from a sample to make inferences (statements) about a population. Often the inference is based on some descriptive statistic

that has already been computed or created. The second part of this book, beginning with chapter VII, will focus on inferential statistics.

A goal of statistics is to measure some characteristic about a subject or set of subjects. To assure more accurate results, we usually either measure the characteristic on several subjects (the sample), or if only one subject is available, we repeat the measurement several times. This is called **replication** or **repetition** and it is in repeated experiments that statistics become important.

Definitions:

1. When the measurements of some characteristic do <u>not</u> change in repeated trials over time, then the characteristic is called a **constant**.

    1. Number of days in January each year (always 31)

    2. Number of minutes in an hour (always 60)

2. When the measurements of some characteristic vary (change) from trial to trial, then the characteristic is called a **variable**.

    1. Heights of students

    2. Grades on a test

In statistics, we are primarily concerned with the observation of <u>variables</u> — if we know beforehand what the measurement is going to be, as is the case with constants, then there is no reason to make repeated measurements.

Variables are classified into two categories:

1. A **qualitative** (or **categorical**) **variable** is a variable whose measurements vary in kind or name but not in degree, meaning that they cannot be arranged in order of magnitude. Hence one level of a qualitative variable cannot be considered greater or better than another level.

    1. Gender — male or female

    2. Eye color — you can name the eye color

    3. Social security number – a number is used to <u>identify</u> (name) a person

2. A **quantitative variable** is a variable whose measurements vary in magnitude from trial to trial, meaning some order or ranking can be applied.

    1. Number of students in a particular class

    2. Weight of a typical student

    3. Grades on a test

Quantitative variables are further classified as being discrete or continuous.

1. A **discrete quantitative variable** is a variable whose measurements can assume only a <u>countable</u> number of possible values.

    1. Number of students in a particular class
    2. Number of cars in a parking deck
    3. Grades on a test

2. A **continuous quantitative variable** is a variable whose measurements can assume any one of a countless number of values in a line interval. It is usually either a <u>measurable</u> quantity or something that is <u>calculated</u> such as rates, averages, proportions, and percentages.

    1. Weight of a typical student
    2. Percentage of students who pass a course

Example 2

Identify each of the following characteristics as being a constant, a qualitative variable, a discrete quantitative variable, or a continuous quantitative variable.

(a). College major

(b). Number of dependents claimed on a tax form

(c). Number of people serving as President of the United States at any one time

(d). Average age of students in a class

(e). Zip code

(f). Suicide rate

Additional Reading and Examples

1. A fundamental component of statistics is the ability to understand and recognize the difference and relationship between a population and a sample. In most problems the data that we have is a sample of the population, and our goal is to use this data to make statements about the population.

2. Greek letters will be used to denote parameters and symbols involving regular English letters will be used to denote statistics.

3. The type of analysis to be performed on a set of data is dependent on the type of data that we have collected. Hence being able to identify whether a variable is qualitative or quantitative, and for quantitative variables whether it is discrete or continuous, is important to assure that the appropriate analysis is done.

4. Radon is a radioactive gas that is generally present in harmless amounts in nature. However, in certain dwellings radon gas is known to be present in quantities that may be harmful to humans, particularly in basements of buildings where air is stagnant. The Environmental Protection Agency (EPA) sets standards for environmental emissions from hazardous substances. According to the July 1995 issue of Consumer Reports, the EPA has suggested that radon levels exceeding 4.0pc/l (picocurie per liter) are associated with an increased risk of lung cancer. Of interest is to estimate the percentage of all dwellings in which the radon concentration poses an increased risk of lung cancer. Data is available for a sample of 51 residential buildings owned by a local real estate developer.

The **population** consists of all dwellings in which humans may enter and which could therefore pose a health risk. The specific **parameter** of interest is the percentage of all these dwellings that have a radon concentration above 4.0 pc/l. To estimate this percentage a **sample** of 51 residential building is selected, and the percentage of these 51 dwellings that have radon concentrations above 4.0 pc/l can be computed. This sample percentage is a **statistic** and can be used to estimate the percentage of all dwellings with radon concentrations above 4.0 pc/l (the **inference**).

The owner of the dwelling is a **qualitative** variable, because we can only name the owner. The actual radon concentration is measured and hence is a **continuous quantitative** variable. The number of dwellings with radon concentrations exceeding 4.0pc/l is countable and hence is a **discrete quantitative variable**. However, the percentage of the dwellings with radon concentrations exceeding 4.0 pc/l can take an uncountable number of possible values and hence is a **continuous quantitative variable**. The number of dwellings is countable and hence is a **discrete quantitative variable**.

5. On January 20, 1986 the National Aeronautics and Space Administration (NASA) experienced a great tragedy, as the space shuttle Challenger exploded less than two minutes from take off killing all on board. Could this tragedy have been avoided? To answer this question the Rogers Commission, headed by then Secretary of State William Rogers, studied the accident and the events that led to the fatal launching. Their investigation determined the cause of the accident, and their findings were published in the two volume *Report of the Presidential Commission on the Space Shuttle Challenger Accident (1986)*.

Through the use of statistics, the report indicates that the flight should never have taken place and hence the explosion could have been avoided. To illustrate this, we must first understand some information on how the space shuttle operates. A space shuttle uses two booster rockets consisting of several pieces whose connections are sealed with rubber O-rings, with the booster rockets lifting the shuttle into orbit. Each booster has three primary O-rings, for a total of six on the entire shuttle.

Using data collected from previous flights, NASA had determined that the performance of the O-rings was quite sensitive to the temperature. Due to their rubber makeup, the O-rings will change shape when a compression is placed on them. The previous data has revealed that when this compression is removed, a warm O-ring will recover its shape, while a cold O-ring will not. When an O-ring does not recover its shape the joints will not be sealed, and hence a gas leak is quite possible.

Prior to the Challenger launch, the coldest launch temperature had been 53 degrees Fahrenheit. The forecasted temperature for January 20, 1986 was only 31 degrees. Prior to the flight, the NASA engineers discussed the conditions for the flight and decided to proceed with the launch. Unfortunately a statistician was not involved in the discussion, because using only the data available at the time of the launch and some very simple statistical analyst, the failure of the flight likely could have been predicted. The statistical analysis follows.

Of the previous 23 flights, 16 of them were completed with no O-rings being damaged. The minimum temperature of these 16 flights was 66 degrees, with an average temperature of 72.5 degrees. On five of the flights, one O-ring was damaged, and on the other two flights two O-rings were damaged. The temperatures for these seven flights ranged from 53 to 75 degrees, with an average temperature of 63 .7 degrees. The data clearly indicate that there is a strong relationship between launch temperature and O-ring damage, with colder temperatures associated with a higher chance of O-ring damage. Using a more advanced statistical technique referred to as logistic regression, a function could be estimated that would predict the probability of O-ring damage given the temperature at the time of the launch. Using the data available from the previous 23 launches, the predicted probability of O-ring damage for a launch temperature of 31 degrees is .96. Hence given the data available at the time of the launch, the engineers could have predicted the near-certain O-ring damage that allowed the gas leak whose combustion resulted in the explosion of the Challenger.

A more exhaustive discussion of this material can be found in the 1989 paper "Risk Analysis of the Space Shuttle: Pre-Challenger Prediction of Failure," by S. Dalal, E. Fowlkes, and B. Hoadley, which appeared in *Journal of the American Statistical Association.*

TI-83/84 Calculator

In many of the remaining chapters instructions will be given to use a T1-83/84 calculator. In this chapter we begin with instructions for entering data.

1. Press the **STAT** button; then under the EDIT on-screen menu select **1:Edit**.
2. You should get a window that looks like this:

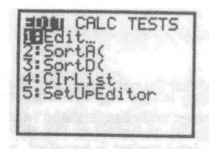 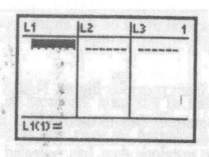

If your list contains data, you can remove the data in an individual list by moving the cursor up (using the up-arrow button) to select the name of the list you want to clear and then press the **CLEAR** button followed by the **ENTER** button. Your list should now be clear.

To clear data in all lists, select the memory command **2nd** + (two separate keys) then select **4:ClrAllLists** from the on-screen menu. When **ClrAllLists** appears on the screen, press **ENTER**. All of your lists should now be clear.

3. Enter your data set into a list by typing in the first value, press **ENTER**, then type in the next value, press **ENTER**, and continue doing so until all values are in the list. Be sure to press **ENTER** after every data value (including the final value). You can use the up-arrow and down-arrow buttons to scroll through your list to be sure that all of the data values were entered correctly. Replace any incorrect value with the correct value and press **ENTER**.

4. If you have grouped data (data values and frequencies), then you would enter the data values into one list and the frequencies into the next list. For example, if the number 57 occurs 3 times, enter 57 into list L1 and enter 3 into list L2.

5. If you mistakenly delete any one of your six lists (by pressing **DEL** instead of **CLEAR** when trying to clear a list), you may retrieve it by pressing **STAT**, then select **EDIT**, then select **5: SetUpEditor**. When **SetUpEditor** appears on the screen, press **ENTER**. Now all of your six lists should be available.

Practice Problems:

I.1. A local city council is interested in determining the percentage of people who live in the city that would be in favor of spending the money necessary to finance the renovation of the city's sports arena. They randomly sampled 250 city residents and asked each of them whether they would favor investing their tax dollars for such a purpose. Identify the population, parameter, sample, and statistic in this experiment, and briefly explain the inference that is taking place.

I.2. Identify each of the following characteristics as being a constant, a qualitative variable, a discrete quantitative variable or a continuous quantitative variable. Support your choice.

(a). Type of illness   (b). Birth rate   (c). Number of pets owned

(d). Daily rainfall   (e). Marital status   (f). Temperature of classroom (°F)

I.3. A local church congregation consists of 318 members, and the total offering collected during 1998 was $76,002. This works out to a mean contribution of $239 per member. The church is now faced with the task of putting a new roof on the church building. A sample of 30 congregation members was selected to form a "roof committee", and the mean contribution of these 30 members to the church in 1998 was $275. The church has received only one bid to repair the roof, and 24 out of the 30 "roof committee" members, or 80%, approve allowing this company to do the work.

According to the paragraph above, identify each of the following as being a parameter or a statistic.

(a) 30   (b) 80%   (c) $239   (d) $275   (e) 318   (f) $76,002

Identify each of the following characteristics as being a constant, a qualitative variable, a discrete quantitative variable, or a continuous quantitative variable. Support your choice.

(g). Number of congregation members present each Sunday.

(h). Sunday school class to which each member belongs.

(i). Percentage of the congregation members in favor of the repair proposal.

(j). Average age of church attendees each Sunday.

(k). Number of years that a person has been a member of the church.

I.4. As we will learn later the standard deviation is a measure of spread in a data set and being able to correctly identify whether a value is the population standard deviation (and hence a parameter) or the sample standard deviation (and hence a statistic) is very important. For each of the following there is a standard deviation highlighted. Identify whether this is the standard deviation of the population or of the sample.

(a). A national grocery store chain reports that the mean amount spent on groceries per trip by all of its customers is $75.45 with a standard deviation of $15.00. The chain recently opened stores in the

Richmond, Virginia area and claim that the mean amount spent on groceries per trip by customers in their stores is less than the national mean. To test this claim a simple random sample of 200 Richmond area customers is selected and the amount spent on groceries during their last national grocery store chain shopping trip determined. The mean amount spent by this sample of customers is $71.89.

(b). In an attempt to determine the appropriate methods of publicizing the Annual Giving campaign, YMCA officials are obtaining demographic information about the potential contributors. One of these demographic characteristics is the age of the contributor. The mean age of all adults in the surrounding area is known to be 48.3 years. The YMCA selected a simple random sample of 29 contributors to the YMCA Annual Giving campaign and determined the age of each. The mean age of this sample of 29 contributors was 45.4 years with a standard deviation of 6.2 years.

(c). According to the Butterball website, Butterball turkeys typically range from 10 to 25 pounds. Of interest is to estimate the mean weight of all Butterball turkeys that were sold for Thanksgiving 2004. To estimate this, a simple random sample of 51 Butterball turkeys sold between November 1 and November 24, 2004 were selected and their weights recorded. The mean weight of this sample of 51 Butterball turkeys was 18.7 pounds, with a standard deviation of 2.4 pounds.

(d). The United States Congress consists of 100 Senators and 435 members of the House of Representatives. A historian who is writing a book about the 107th Congress is interested in the intelligence of the members of Congress. One approach to measure the intelligence is to give a standard intelligence test to the members of Congress. The test that is to be used is scaled such that all scores are between 0 and 200, and such that the standard deviation of all scores is 20 points.

I.5. On January 27, 2000 Bill Clinton delivered his last State of the Union Address. Among those invited to be in attendance were the 535 members of Congress, which comprise the population. Of the 535 members of Congress, 487, or 91%, were in attendance. Political experts were interested in the opinions that members of Congress have about the speech and about the current status of the nation. To gather this information, they randomly sampled 20 members of Congress. Of these 20 members, 12 were Democrats and 8 were Republicans. 14 gave President Clinton favorable marks for his speech, and 19, or 95%, gave the current status of the nation a positive rating. The average age (in years) of the 20 members in the sample was 73.

Identify each of the following as being a parameter or a statistic.

(a) 20   (b) 535   (c) 91%   (d) 95%   (e) 12 Democrats   (f) 73

Identify each of the following characteristics as being a constant, a qualitative variable, a discrete quantitative variable, or a continuous quantitative variable. Support your choice.

(g). Percentage of each elected Congress less than 65 years of age

(h). State from which a Congressperson was elected

(i). Number of Democrats attending each Congressional meeting

June 16, 2014

Most Americans Remain Satisfied With Healthcare System

Little change in satisfaction since mid-March

by Frank Newport

http://www.gallup.com/poll/171680/americans-remain-satisfied-healthcare-system.aspx

PRINCETON, NJ -- Sixty-six percent of Americans in the first half of June are satisfied with the way the healthcare system is working for them, in line with attitudes since mid-March. Gallup's seven-day rolling average on this measure shows confidence during that time has varied only slightly, increasing to 70% in mid-April, just after the enrollment period ended for purchasing insurance under the provisions of the Affordable Care Act. That modest increase was short-lived; satisfaction has averaged about 65% since mid-May.

Are you satisfied or dissatisfied with how the healthcare system is working for you?

Seven-day rolling average

% Satisfied

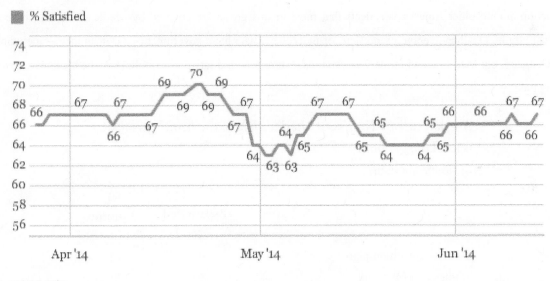

GALLUP

Gallup began asking this question nightly on March 21 as a continuous measure of the way changes in the nation's healthcare system are affecting average Americans. There are no comparable data for 2013 or previous years, before the ACA's individual insurance mandate helped lead to a significant drop in the uninsured population in the U.S. However, these readings serve as a baseline for assessing the effect the ACA is having on people's healthcare experiences as they interact with the system going forward. Americans' satisfaction with the healthcare system is highly related to their health insurance status, although having health insurance does not guarantee satisfaction. Nearly three in 10 Americans with insurance say they are dissatisfied with the way the healthcare system is working for them. Among those without insurance --currently about 13.4% of Americans -- six in 10 are dissatisfied.

Are you satisfied or dissatisfied with how the healthcare system is working for you?

	Satisfied	Dissatisfied	No opinion
	%	%	%
National adults	66	32	2
Have health insurance	71	28	1
Do not have health insurance	36	60	4

March 21-June 14, 2014

GALLUP

Higher percentages of Americans aged 65 and older are satisfied (79%) with how the system is working, with satisfaction ranging from 61% to 66% among those between the ages of 18 and 49. This elevated level of satisfaction among older Americans reflects that most in this group are covered by Medicare. Along these same lines, slightly higher-than-average proportions of individuals who have government-paid insurance -- including not only Medicare, but Medicaid and military or veterans insurance -- are satisfied with the way the healthcare system is treating them.

Are you satisfied or dissatisfied with how the healthcare system is working for you?
By healthcare status

	Satisfied	Dissatisfied	No opinion
	%	%	%
Employer or union plan	70	29	1
Medicare or Medicaid	76	23	1
Military or veterans	77	21	2
Plan paid by self	66	33	2
Something else	70	27	3
Do not have insurance	36	60	4

March 21-June 14, 2014

GALLUP

Politics Have an Effect Above and Beyond Insurance Status

This measure of healthcare satisfaction does not mention the ACA or any other details about what the U.S. healthcare system entails, and is, effectively, politically neutral. Still, politics shade the results, with Democrats and Democratic-leaning independents somewhat more likely to say they are satisfied than are Republicans and Republican leaners. While health insurance status is clearly the most significant predictor of satisfaction, partisan identification still has an effect beyond basic insurance status. There is a 16-point satisfaction gap between Republicans and Democrats among those with health insurance, and a nine-point gap among those without it.

Implications

About 13% of the U.S. adult population remains uninsured at this point, even after the institution of the ACA's individual mandate and the availability of insurance through government health exchanges. These uninsured Americans are half as likely as those with insurance to say they are satisfied with the way the healthcare system is working for them. Still, one in three Americans without insurance are satisfied, and almost as many of those with insurance are dissatisfied, indicating that there is more involved in satisfaction than having insurance.

More Americans with government-paid insurance are satisfied with the way the system is working than is true for those with private plans. The data do not provide a way of separating out those newly insured through the exchanges. These individuals are just now beginning to see how well these plans work in their personal situations, and all of them will need to re-enroll when the exchanges open up again in mid-November. This ongoing measure of Americans' healthcare satisfaction will provide an assessment of any effect of these changes going forward.

Americans' high level of satisfaction with how the healthcare system is treating them suggests that healthcare is not in a crisis for most Americans. At the same time, that 30% of the adult population -- more than 70 million people -- is not satisfied with the healthcare system underscores the need for improvement.

Some Americans who are dissatisfied with the way the healthcare system is treating them may be expressing their displeasure with particular doctors, hospitals, billing issues, or medical procedures -- aspects that have little to do with the broader issue of how healthcare coverage is provided. The differing satisfaction levels between those with insurance and those without, and between those with federal and those with private plans, however, indicate that the way this coverage is provided is obviously related to healthcare satisfaction.

Survey Methods

Results for this Gallup poll are based on telephone interviews conducted March 21-June 14, 2014, with a random sample of 42,566 adults, aged 18 and older, living in all 50 U.S. states and the District of Columbia. For results based on the total sample of national adults, the margin of sampling error is ±1 percentage point at the 95% confidence level.

Interviews are conducted with respondents on landline telephones and cellular phones, with interviews conducted in Spanish for respondents who are primarily Spanish-speaking. Each sample of national adults includes a minimum quota of 50% cellphone respondents and 50% landline respondents, with additional minimum quotas by time zone within region. Landline and cellular telephone numbers are selected using random-digit-dial methods. Landline respondents are chosen at random within each household on the basis of which member had the most recent birthday.

Samples are weighted to correct for unequal selection probability, nonresponse, and double coverage of landline and cell users in the two sampling frames. They are also weighted to match the national demographics of gender, age, race, Hispanic ethnicity, education, region, population density, and phone status (cellphone only/landline only/both, and cellphone mostly). Demographic weighting targets are based on the most recent Current Population Survey figures for the aged 18 and older U.S. population. Phone status targets are based on the most recent National Health Interview Survey. Population density targets are based on the most recent U.S. census. All reported margins of sampling error include the computed design effects for weighting. In addition to sampling error, question wording and practical difficulties in conducting surveys can introduce error or bias into the findings of public opinion polls.

June 11, 2014

Smaller Majority of Americans View Hillary Clinton Favorably

At 54%, her favorability has slipped since February

by Justin McCarthy

http://www.gallup.com/poll/171290/smaller-majority-americans-view-hillary-clinton-favorably.aspx

WASHINGTON, D.C. -- Hillary Clinton's favorability rating has dropped slightly, although a majority of Americans continue to view her in a positive light. As Clinton publicizes her new memoir, "Hard Choices," 54% of Americans view her favorably. This is down from 59% in February, and significantly less than the ratings she received as secretary of state, which were consistently above 60%.

The latest findings come from a Gallup poll conducted June 5-8. Though Clinton has said she will not announce whether she'll run for president until at least later this year, her latest book has been widely framed as a preamble to another presidential bid and a move typical of White House hopefuls. Clinton already has the support of many elected officials and Democratic Party representatives if she chooses to run. Americans have named her their Most Admired Woman 18 times. Clinton's current favorability rating is the lowest it has been since August 2008 (54%), when she was preparing to deliver a speech at the Democratic National Convention endorsing then-Sen. Barack Obama, who defeated her in a hard-fought primary battle for the party's 2008 presidential nomination.

After recovering from a contentious Democratic primary race that strapped her with campaign debt, Clinton's favorability soared while she served as secretary of state during Obama's first term. As she continued in her role, as many as two-thirds of Americans (66%) viewed her favorably, in consecutive polls in 2011 and 2012 -- a rating she surpassed only once before, at 67% in December 1998, shortly after her husband, President Bill Clinton, was impeached. In her nonpolitical role as secretary of state, Clinton enjoyed extremely high ratings from her fellow Democrats, but saw her ratings increase among Republicans as well. She peaked with Republicans during this period in mid-2012, when 41% viewed her favorably. Her favorability fell with the GOP, as it did with independents, after the September 2012 attacks on the U.S. compound in Benghazi, Libya. As Democratic elected officials continue to encourage her to run for president, her name has become further politicized, thus making her less favorable to non-Democrats.

GOP operatives and media pundits have publicly questioned whether her health and age (Clinton is now 66) could hinder her ability to serve as president. Additionally, the House of Representatives has formed a select committee to investigate the attack in Benghazi. And as she wades into Obama's controversial decision to trade five Taliban prisoners held at Guantanamo Bay for U.S. soldier Bowe Bergdahl, Clinton's performance as one of Obama's top cabinet members will likely undergo greater scrutiny.

Bill Clinton, who in the same poll receives a 64% favorable rating, has commanded majority favorability from Americans during most of his time as president and in post-presidential life. While some may view his high favorability ratings as an advantage for Hillary if she decides on another presidential run, Bill's favorability did take a hit when he joined her on the 2008 campaign trail.

By January 2008 -- a year after Hillary announced her candidacy -- his favorability hit a five-year low of 50%, barely ahead of Hillary's 48%. In fact, for much of Hillary's career since Bill's presidency, their favorability ratings have been closely related.

Their latest favorability ratings are separated by 10 percentage points and, with the exception of a 12-point difference in March 2007, are as far apart as they've been since Hillary independently entered the political fray as a candidate for the U.S. Senate from New York. During Hillary's first term as New York's junior senator, her favorability was closely linked to that of her husband. But for the first three years of her second term, from 2005-2007, their ratings differed by five to 12 percentage points. Then, in early 2008, when Bill became a proxy campaigner for Hillary in her bid for the presidency, his favorability fell and their ratings converged.

Hillary Clinton's era of higher favorability appears to be ending even before she announces whether she will run for president. Americans typically rate non-political figures higher than political ones on this measure, and her favorable ratings before, during, and after being secretary of state are consistent with that phenomenon. Though her husband's influence is far from Hillary's greatest selling point, he may be better positioned to help her on the campaign trail than he was last time, with his favorability up five points from what it was in mid-2006. But if Hillary does run, the boost she receives from him may be limited if it is similar to 2008, with his past favorability so closely married to her own in the backdrop of a presidential campaign.

Survey Methods

Results for this Gallup poll are based on telephone interviews conducted June 5-8, 2014, with a random sample of 1,027 adults, aged 18 and older, living in all 50 U.S. states and the District of Columbia. For results based on the total sample of national adults, the margin of sampling error is ±4 percentage points at the 95% confidence level.

Interviews are conducted with respondents on landline telephones and cellular phones, with interviews conducted in Spanish for respondents who are primarily Spanish-speaking. Each sample of national adults includes a minimum quota of 50% cellphone respondents and 50% landline respondents, with additional minimum quotas by time zone within region. Landline and cellular telephone numbers are selected using random-digit-dial methods. Landline respondents are chosen at random within each household on the basis of which member had the most recent birthday.

Samples are weighted to correct for unequal selection probability, nonresponse, and double coverage of landline and cell users in the two sampling frames. They are also weighted to match the national demographics of gender, age, race, Hispanic ethnicity, education, region, population density, and phone status (cellphone only/landline only/both, and cellphone mostly). Demographic weighting targets are based on the most recent Current Population Survey figures for the aged 18 and older U.S. population. Phone status targets are based on the most recent National Health Interview Survey. Population density targets are based on the most recent U.S. census. All reported margins of sampling error include the computed design effects for weighting. In addition to sampling error, question wording and practical difficulties in conducting surveys can introduce error or bias into the findings of public opinion polls.

II. Producing Data

To perform any type of statistical procedure we require data. Data can be generated by many different methods, including simulation. This chapter will focus on two methods of acquiring data: first sampling from a population, and second creating a study or experiment to generate data. We discuss several sampling and experimental designs and the concepts related to each.

A. Sampling Designs

In Moore: Read Chapter 8 (pages 201 – 217)

Recall that a population is a large set of subjects that we want to make statements about, and that in many cases time, cost, or inconvenience make it impossible to contact or measure every member of the population. For example, suppose the population consists of all students at this university. While getting some information about all students may be possible through the registration office, contacting each student would be very difficult, if not impossible.

In this case we must actually contact a sample of the population and use the data in the sample to make inferences about the population. The students in this class would be a subset of the population and hence would be considered a sample, and contacting only the students in this class would be much easier than contacting all students at the university.

We want the sample to be as representative of the population as possible, and hence free of bias. A sample is said to be **representative** of the population if the characteristics of the population that are important are nearly the same in the sample. For example, if the population of all students at this university was 60% female and 40% male, then the sample would be representative in terms of the gender of the student if it were approximately 60% female and 40% male.

Bias exists when some subjects or outcomes are systematically favored over others. Types of bias that can be introduced into sampling include the following:

(1). **Selection bias**: exists when one or more types of subjects are systematically excluded from the sample. This undercoverage results in the sample representing a smaller group of individuals that does not contain individuals like those systematically excluded from the sample. Hence when inferences are made back to the population, the inferences can only be made to the subset of the population that is represented in the sample. Inferences cannot be made to the subset of the population that were systematically excluded from the sample.

As an example, suppose the population consists of all students at this university, and of interest is the opinion of students regarding an increase in student fees to pay for an expansion of the basketball arena. Contacting all students for their opinions is not possible, so instead a sample of 200 students in attendance at a basketball game is selected and they are asked their opinion. This would likely create selection bias because the opinions of students not attending the basketball game were not included. Most likely those attending the basketball game would be more willing to support an increase in fees for this purpose, while those who do not have an interest in basketball would be less likely to support such a fee increase. Instead of using the 200 responses to make inferences about the opinion of <u>all</u> students, the 200 responses can only be used to make inferences about the opinion of all students <u>who attend basketball games</u>. Opinions of students who do not attend the basketball games are not represented and hence inference cannot be made about these students – this is the <u>undercoverage</u>.

(2). **Nonresponse bias**: exists when individuals chosen for the sample cannot be contacted or fail (or refuse) to respond. This happens often in surveys or polls and creates a problem when those who do not respond are different from those who do respond.

As an example, suppose the U. S. Government is interested in the opinions of citizens regarding the rights of illegal aliens in this county. They select a sample of 500 citizens (using the procedure defined below as stratified random sampling) that involves a representative number of citizens from each racial and ethnic group. However, suppose all the Latino Americans chosen for the sample refuse to respond. If the opinions of the Latino American citizens are different from the opinions of other citizens, then this would create a nonresponse bias.

(3). **Response bias**: exists when the respondents give inaccurate information (especially on questions that involve legal or social behavior issues) or if the interviewer influences the subject to respond in a certain way due to the wording of the question.

As an example, consider the question "have you ever committed a crime that involved inflicting injury to the body of another person?" There are many situations where a person answering this question, even if the correct answer is yes, may respond no due to social pressures or other concerns. This would generate a response bias.

As another example, suppose the Department of Transportation wants to compare opinions about perceived safety among passengers on different airlines. One of the questions asked of the passengers was the following: "Do you feel safer flying on Delta Airlines as opposed to one of the other airlines?" This question would cause a response bias in favor of Delta Airlines because it is the only airline mentioned in the question. A more general question, such as "rate how safe you feel flying your usual air carrier" or "on which airline do you feel safest when flying" would give a more trustworthy set of responses.

There are many different sampling procedures, some free of bias and some that involve bias. In what follows we discuss five such sampling procedures. In each case there is a population of interest, we are contacting or measuring a subset of the population (the sample), and using the data in the sample to make inferences about the population. It should be noted that even in the best planned sampling designs it is possible for random chance in the responses that can generate one or more types of bias.

1. Haphazard Samples

A **haphazard sample** involves selecting a sample by some convenient mechanism that does not involve randomization. One example would include campus surveys, where a student group may stand outside an academic building and ask students to answer a short questionnaire as they enter or leave the building. If a person does not have a class in the appropriate academic building at the appropriate day and time, then he or she will have no chance of being in the sample. Another example would include mall or grocery store surveys, where questionnaires are distributed to people as they walk through the mall or in and out of the store. If a person is not in the mall or at the store that day they have no chance of being in the sample.

2. Volunteer Response Samples

A **volunteer response sample** exists when people volunteer to be part of a study. Examples include telephone call-in polls, Internet surveys, and many other convenience (nonrandom) sampling designs. The problem with volunteer samples is that they often over-represent people with strong opinions, most often negative opinions.

Haphazard and volunteer response samples are particularly prone to large bias as no randomization procedure is used to assure a fair or representative sample. A sample that avoids (or reduces) bias will be representative of the population and will involve choosing subjects randomly as opposed to haphazardly or voluntarily. Hence we should use **probability sampling designs** in which each member of the population has a positive and equal probability (chance) of being selected for the sample. We now consider three such probability sampling designs.

3. Simple Random Sampling

With **simple random sampling** we attempt to make a list of all possible individuals in the population and randomly choose n of the subjects in such a way that every set of n subjects has an equal chance to be in the sample (n is the sample size). This procedure is impartial, meaning the interviewer has no discretion as to who is selected. There are situations in which compiling a list of all members of the population is not possible, and as described below the procedure uses the best single list that can be determined.

The simple random sample is usually selected using a computer-based simulation program that will select a random sample from a known list of individuals. A **Table of Random Digits**, such as the one on page 337, can also be used to randomly select the subjects for the sample. To use the Table of Random Digits, determine the number of individuals in the population (call this number N), and then label the subjects in the population from 1 to N. Depending on the number of digits in N, randomly select n one-digit, two-digit, three-digit, four-digit, etc. numbers between 1 and N. Repeated selections are omitted and numbers outside the allowable range are skipped.

For example, when N = 80, randomly select n two-digit numbers between 01 and 80. If a number between 81 and 99 (or 00) is obtained, that number is skipped. As a second example, if N = 636, randomly select n three-digit numbers between 001 and 636 (omit numbers between 637 and 999, and 000). As a third example, suppose the population consists of 1000 subjects. One option would be to select n four-digit numbers between 0001 and 1000, omitting numbers between 1001 and 9999, plus 0000). However, in this special case we make use of the number 000 and randomly select n three-digit numbers between 000 and 999, with the number 000 corresponding to the subject labeled 1000.

Simple random sampling is the most used type of random sampling procedure, and will be one of the assumptions in all of the inference procedures discussed in later sections. Hence understanding both how to identify that a selected sample is a simple random sample, and knowing how to select a simple random sample, are essential components of understanding statistics.

A simple random sample is a random procedure, which is good, but it does not guarantee a representative sample. The simple random sampling procedure can be followed and the selected sample may favor one or more types of subjects over others. For example, in selecting states more Eastern states may be selected than Midwestern and Western states, or in selecting people more males may be selected than females. This is a problem when there is an important difference between the group (or groups) that are over-represented and the group (or groups) that are under-represented. This concern can be addressed by selecting a stratified random sample, which will be discussed after the following example.

Example 3

Suppose the population consists of the 50 states (and hence N = 50), which are listed in alphabetical order below. Entering at line 131, use the Table of Random Digits on page 337 to randomly choose a sample of 8 states.

Alabama	Hawaii	Massachusetts	New Mexico	South Dakota
Alaska	Idaho	Michigan	New York	Tennessee
Arizona	Illinois	Minnesota	North Carolina	Texas
Arkansas	Indiana	Mississippi	North Dakota	Utah
California	Iowa	Missouri	Ohio	Vermont
Colorado	Kansas	Montana	Oklahoma	Virginia
Connecticut	Kentucky	Nebraska	Oregon	Washington
Delaware	Louisiana	Nevada	Pennsylvania	West Virginia
Florida	Maine	New Hampshire	Rhode Island	Wisconsin
Georgia	Maryland	New Jersey	South Carolina	Wyoming

4. Stratified Random Sampling

To eliminate the problem of over-representation in simple random sampling, a stratified random sample may be selected. With **stratified random sampling** the population is naturally divided into two or more groups of similar subjects, called **strata**. A simple random sample is then chosen from each group, and these simple random samples are combined to give the complete sample. The number chosen from each group should correspond to the approximate percentage of the total population in each group – this will guarantee a more representative sample. At least one individual should be chosen from each group.

With a stratified random sample you lose a degree of the randomization that you have with a simple random sample, and since you must select a simple random sample from each group the process involves a few more steps. However, the advantage of a stratified random sample is that it will often be more representative than a simple random sample and hence the inferences that can be made about the population more reliable.

As an example, suppose the current enrollment at a particular university of 20000 undergraduate students consists of 6000 freshmen, 5000 sophomores, 4000 juniors, and 5000 seniors. A simple random sample of 200 students could include all from one class (all freshmen, for example), which would over-represent that class. Hence a stratified random sample may be preferred. To select a stratified random sample of 200 undergraduate students, the following steps are necessary.

First, the number of students to select from each class must be determined. The number of students in each class in divided by the population size (20000), and then this proportion is multiplied by the sample size (200) to give the number of students in the sample from each class. This is summarized in the table below.

Class	Class size	Proportion	Number in sample
Freshman	6000	6000/20000 = .30	200(.30) = 60
Sophomore	5000	5000/20000 = .25	200(.25) = 50
Junior	4000	4000/20000= .20	200(.20) = 40
Senior	5000	5000/20000 = .25	200(.25) = 50

Note that $60 + 50 + 40 + 50 = 200$, the requested sample size. Also, above the figures required no rounding. However, it is possible some rounding may be required, and if so it should be done such that the total sample size is the requested number (200 in this example) and at least one is selected from each group.

Now to select the students:

For the freshmen, there are 6000 so label them from 0001 to 6000. Choose a starting point in the Table of Random Digits (say line 101), and randomly select the first 60 four-digit numbers between 0001 and 6000.

For the sophomores, there are 5000 so label them from 0001 to 5000. Choose a <u>different</u> starting point in the Table of Random Digits (say line 111) and randomly select the first 50 four-digit numbers between 0001 and 5000.

For the juniors, there are 4000 so label them from 0001 to 4000. Choose a third <u>different</u> starting point in the Table of Random Digits (say line 121), and randomly select the first 40 four-digit numbers between 0001 and 4000.

Finally, for the seniors, there are 5000 so label them from 0001 to 5000. Choose a fourth <u>different</u> starting point in the Table of Random Digits (say line 131), and randomly select the first 50 four-digit numbers between 0001 and 5000.

Hence there is a simple random sample selected from each class, and the students from the four simple random samples are combined to form the stratified random sample.

5. Multistage Random Sampling

Another problem with simple random samples (and stratified random samples) is that they can on occasion be expensive, time-consuming and inconvenient to obtain. These problems may make the simple random sample impractical.

As an example, suppose we are interested in examining the study habits of typical American college students that require face-to-face visits with the students. The population consists of all American college students, which is so large that we must take a sample of the population. Suppose that there are 12,454,039 college students in the United States, and we want a sample of 225 students.

Simple random sampling would involve labeling the college students from 00000001 to 12454039 and randomly selecting 225 eight-digit numbers between 00000001 and 12454039. These 225 numbers would then be used to identify the 225 students for the sample, and then interviewers would travel to meet these 225 students. However, due to the size of the country, simple random sampling may be very expensive – the interviewers may have to travel all over the country (possibly to all 50 states) and to many different colleges (possibly 225 different colleges) to interview the students that are chosen.

An alternative to simple random sampling that uses randomization is multistage random sampling. With **multistage random sampling** the population is divided into groups of individuals and simple random sampling is used to randomly select <u>some</u> of these <u>groups</u>. Each group chosen is then further divided into smaller subgroups and simple random sampling is used to randomly select some subgroups within each group. Continue dividing the chosen groups into smaller subgroups and randomly selecting some of these subgroups. Finally, for each of the smallest subgroups we use simple random sampling to randomly select a group of individuals that will be measured (or interviewed). There must be at least <u>two</u> randomization stages, and unlike stratified random sampling individuals are <u>not</u> chosen from <u>each</u> group.

In the example above involving selecting a sample of 225 college students, multistage random sampling can be done as follows.

Stage 1 involves treating the 50 states as groups of students. Label the states from 01 to 50 (as in example 3 on page 21) and randomly choose 5 two-digit numbers between 01 and 50. Suppose this is done and the resulting states are California, Utah, Georgia, Indiana, and Virginia.

Stage 2 involves obtaining a list of all colleges in each of these 5 states. For each state, simple random sampling is used to select 3 colleges from each state. For example, in California we may select UCLA, USC, and Stanford; in Utah we may select Utah State, Brigham Young, and University of Utah; in Georgia we may select Georgia State, Georgia Southern, and Georgia Tech; in Indiana we may select Indiana University, Purdue, and Notre Dame; and finally in Virginia we may select University of Virginia, Virginia Tech, and Virginia Commonwealth University.

This produces 15 colleges and hence 15 subgroups of students. Stage 3 involves obtaining a schedule/list of classes for each of these 15 colleges. Then for each college simple random sampling can be used to select 3 classes. This will produce a list of 45 classes, being held at 15 colleges, located in 5 states. At this point the 45 classes are even smaller subgroups of students.

Finally, stage 4 involves using simple random sampling to select 5 students from each of the 45 classes. This will produce a multistage random sample of 225 students that must be contacted. The interviewers will only have to travel to 15 colleges located in only 5 states, and once on each campus will only have to visit three classes to meet the students. This would be less time consuming and less expensive than the simple random sample. Note that 5 x 3 x 3 x 5 = 225 students.

Example 4

For each of the following situations identify the type of sampling procedure used to generate the sample. Choices are haphazard sampling, volunteer response sampling, simple random sampling, stratified random sampling and multistage random sampling.

(a). The Better Business Bureau is investigating cleanliness complaints at McDonalds restaurants. The population consists of all McDonald's restaurants in the United States, and since they cannot visit all McDonalds restaurants they have decided to sample 80 McDonalds restaurants to visit and observe. To select this sample of 80 McDonalds restaurants the Better Business Bureau first randomly selected 8 states; in each of these 8 states they randomly selected 10 counties or cities with McDonalds restaurants; and then they randomly selected one McDonalds restaurant from each of these selected counties or cities.

(b). A large grocery store chain estimates that 37,654 customers are currently enrolled in their valued customer program (VCP) and these VCP customers make up the population of interest. To gather more information on the buying practices and attitudes of all VCP customers a local consumer group contacted a sample of 120 VCP customers. To obtain the sample of 120 customers, the local consumer group assigned a data collector to the entrance of a local store and had the data collector question the first 20 VCP customers they could get to answer their questions. This repeated over six consecutive days at six different stores, each at 10:00 AM.

(c). Of interest is the opinion of air passengers regarding their satisfaction with air travel. Hence the population consists of all passengers who flew on airlines with U.S. Call Signs during 2009. There are 49 airlines in the United States that at the beginning of 2010 had registered Call Signs, and 20 passengers were randomly selected from the lists of passengers who had flown on each of these 49 airlines, giving a total of 980 passengers in the sample.

(d). Churchill Downs Inc. is interested in the opinions of the 153,563 fans who attended the 135th running of the Kentucky Derby on May 2, 2009. To gather information, Churchill Downs Inc. obtained a list of ticket numbers distributed to the fans. For the 2009 running of the race, the ticket numbers ranged from 000001 to 153563. Contacting all 153,563 fans is not reasonable, so Churchill Downs Inc. decided to select a sample of 150 fans. To do so they associated each fan with their ticket number such that each fan had a unique number between 000001 and 153563. They then randomly selected 150 numbers in that range, determined the seat location of these 150 fans, and had field interviewers meet those fans at their seats.

Additional Reading and Examples

1. In most applications involving the selection of random samples, the selection is done using a random number generator in a computer. The Table of Random Digits does the same thing. It is important to identify each member in the population (or each member in a group if stratified random sampling is being used) with a unique number. The number of digits in these numbers should correspond with the number of digits in the population (or group) total. For example, if N = 6006, then use four-digit numbers, and if a particular group has 83 subjects, then use two-digit numbers. The only exception is the special case where the population size (or group size) is a multiple of 10, such as 10, 100, 1000, 10000 etc. In this case the last individual can be associated with a set of 0's, and one less digit can be used. For example, if the population size is 10000 (a five-digit number), four-digit numbers can be used with person 10000 corresponding to randomly chosen number 0000.

2. Advice columnist Ann Landers once asked her readers, "If you had it to do over again, would you have children?" A few weeks later her column was headlined "70% of Parents Say Kids Not Worth It." This conclusion was drawn because 70% of the nearly 10,000 parents who wrote in said they would not have children if they could make the choice again.

These data are worthless as indicators of opinion among all American parents because the data that Landers reported came from a **volunteer response sample**. The people who responded felt strongly enough to take the trouble to write Ann Landers. Their letters showed that many of them were angry with their children when the letters were written and hence these people do not fairly represent all parents. It is not surprising that a statistically designed opinion poll on the same issue a few months later found that 91% of parents would have children again. The large difference between the 70% in Ann Landers' sample who say they would not have children again and the 91% in the statistically designed sample that would have children again illustrates the bias that can be created by a volunteer response sample.

3. Manufacturers and advertising agencies often use interviews at shopping malls to gather information about the habits of consumers and the effectiveness of ads. Obtaining a sample of mall shoppers is fast and inexpensive, but the lack of randomness in this type of **haphazard sample** creates a sample that is not representative of the entire U.S. population. A sample of mall shoppers generally over-represents the rich, and those in the sample are more likely to be either teenagers or retired. Due to the subjectivity in selecting whom to interview (often neat, safe-looking individuals), selection bias can result. In summary, using a sample of mall shoppers to make inferences about all consumers is hazardous since the sample is likely not representative of the entire population.

4. The head of a foreign language department in a university wants to determine the proportion of the 2,045 first-year students in the university who took at least one course in German in high school. The department head considers it too costly and time consuming to consult each of the 2,045 students, so he selected a simple random sample of 20 students and asked each of them if they had taken a high school course in German.

Each student in the population is assigned a unique number from 0001 to 2045 (four-digit numbers). The department head then chooses 20 four-digit numbers between 0001 and 2045. Beginning at line 101 of the Table of Random Digits on page 337, these numbers are: 0331, 0586, 1515, 0490, 1900, 1893, 0238, 1320, 0215, 0887, 1193, 1486, 1957, 0675, 1717, 1958, 1695, 0387, 2012, and 1199.

These students are contacted and asked if they took a German course in high school. The results are as follows.

Student	German course	Student	German course
331	no	1193	no
586	yes	1486	no
1515	no	1957	no
490	no	675	yes
1900	no	1717	no
1893	no	1958	no
238	no	1695	no
1320	no	387	no
215	no	2012	yes
887	no	1199	no

Based on this simple random sample, the sample proportion (a **statistic**) of the students who took a German course in high school is 3/20 = .15. This sample proportion can be used to estimate the proportion of all 2,045 students who took a German course in high school (an **inference**).

5. A radio or television station that broadcasts a piece of music owes a royalty to the composer. The American Society of Composers, Authors, and Publishers (ASCAP) sells licenses that permit broadcast of works by any of its members. ASCAP must then pay the proper royalties to the composers whose music was played. Television networks keep program logs of all music played, but local radio and television stations do not. There are over a billion ASCAP-licensed performances each year, and hence a detailed accounting is too expensive and cumbersome. Hence sampling is required.

ASCAP divides its royalties among its members by taping a **stratified random sample** of broadcasts. The sample of local commercial radio stations, for example, consists of 60,000 hours of broadcast time each year. Radio stations are stratified by type of community (metropolitan, rural), geographic location (New England, Southern, Midwestern, Pacific), and the size of the license fee paid to ASCAP, which reflects the size of the audience. Tapes are made at random hours for randomly selected members of each group. Experts who can recognize almost every piece of music ever written review the tapes, and the composers are then paid according to their popularity.

6. National samples of households usually involve choosing the sample in stages. For example, government data on employment and unemployment are gathered by the Current Population Survey, which conducts interviews in about 60,000 households each month. It is not practical to maintain a list of all U.S. households from which a simple random sample could be selected. Moreover, the cost of sending interviewers to the widely scattered households in a simple random sample would be too high. The Current Population Survey therefore uses a **multistage random sample.** The final sample consists of groups of nearby households, obtained in the following four-stage procedure.

Stage 1: Take a sample from the 3,000 counties in the United States.
Stage 2: Select a sample of townships within each of the counties chosen.
Stage 3: Select a sample of blocks within each chosen township.
Stage 4: Take a sample of households within each of these blocks.

Hence data is collected at the household level, but only households from the counties selected in stage 1, from the townships selected in stage 2, and the blocks selected in stage 3 will be in the sample. This method will be less expensive and time-consuming than selecting households using simple random sampling.

7. A survey paid for by makers of disposable diapers found that 84% of the sample opposed banning disposable diapers. Here is the actual question posed.

It is estimated that disposable diapers account for less than 2% of the trash in today's landfills. In contrast, beverage containers, third-class mail, and yard wastes are estimated to account for about 21% of the trash in landfills. Given this, in your opinion, would it be fair to ban disposable diapers?

This question gives information on only one side of an issue, then asks an opinion. This almost certainly will create a **response bias**. A different question that described how long disposable diapers take to decay and how many tons they contribute to landfills each year would draw a quite different response.

B. Design of Experiments

In Moore: Read Chapter 9 (pages 223 – 239)

In addition to the sampling methods of generating data, data is also often produced by experimentation. The goal of this section is to design and carry out an experiment that will <u>evaluate the effect of some treatment or treatments</u>. We begin by defining the following terms, and as the terms are defined an example that involves evaluating the effects of a new blood pressure medication is presented.

Blood pressure is the force exerted by circulating blood on the walls of blood vessels and is one of the principal vital signs. During each heartbeat, blood pressure varies between a maximum pressure, called <u>systolic</u> pressure, and a minimum pressure, called <u>diastolic</u> pressure. A person's blood pressure is usually expressed in terms of the systolic pressure and diastolic pressure, with the "normal" measurement being 120/80. When one or both of the numbers are significantly higher than these figures, the person is determined to have "high blood pressure". In this example, the person is declared to have "high blood pressure" if his or her diastolic pressure measurement is 90 or above.

A clinical trial that would allow such an evaluation would require government approval, and notification of those participating of the details of the trial. They would give their signed consent to participate in the trial. Suppose the clinical trial in this example involves the comparison of the new blood pressure medication with that of the three leading blood pressure medications currently approved.

1. **Experimental Units**: The subjects (individuals, units) on which the measurements are made.

   Example: people medically identified as having high blood pressure, with high blood pressure defined to be an initial diastolic pressure measurement of 90 or higher.

2. **Treatment**: A specific experimental condition applied to the experimental units.

   Example: the new blood pressure medication being tested in the clinical trial would be a treatment, along with the three leading blood pressure medications currently approved.

3. **Response**: The characteristic that is measured on each experimental unit that the experimenter wants to evaluate.

   Example: the diastolic pressure measurement after the treatment is applied, or more likely the reduction in the diastolic pressure measure pre-medication and post-medication.

4. **Comparison**: All experiments must involve a <u>comparison</u> of the responses among two or more groups.

Example: one may want to compare the effects of a new blood pressure medication versus the effects of the three leading blood pressure medications and no medication.

5. **Treatment Group(s)**: The group or groups of experimental units who receive a treatment. If there are multiple treatments, then a separate treatment group would be defined for each.

Example: as described above there would be four treatment groups: one receiving the new blood pressure medication and three receiving each of the three leading blood pressure medications currently available.

6. **Control Group**: A group of experimental units who do not receive one of the treatments. If multiple treatment groups exist a control group is not required. However, if only one treatment group exists then a control group is required so that a comparison can be made.

Example: the people who receive no (active) medication would be the control group. If there is only one treatment group (only the new blood pressure medication was being evaluated) this is required in order to have a comparison. If there are two or more treatment groups (as indicated above) such a control group is not necessary.

7. **Placebo**: A fake treatment that is given to the experimental units in the control group which (hopefully) prevents them from knowing if they received the treatment or not. A placebo is not required if there are multiple treatments and a control group is not required. A placebo is given to eliminate the <u>placebo effect</u> which occurs when experimental units know to which treatment or control group they have been assigned and hence psychological effects can bias the results of the experiment or study.

Example: if there is a group of people not receiving any medication (a control group), these people should receive a fake treatment that looks similar to the actual medication treatments. This fake treatment/pill would contain no active medication, but would resemble the actual pills and would be the placebo.

8. **Replication**: Repetition of the experiment on many experimental units in each group, which should reduce chance variation in the results. The number in each group does not have to be the same, but there should be enough experimental units in each group to get an accurate assessment of the effect of the treatment or treatments. Replication can also occur if the entire experimental process is repeated multiple times, allowing a measure of the validity of the results.

Example: if 500 people are available for the experiment, randomly assign (see below) 100 people to each of the five groups. This will minimize the effects of one person that may have a reaction to the medication, be killed in an accident, or have some other event that would bias the results.

9. **Randomization**: The use of impersonal chance to assign experimental units to the groups. The experimental units should be randomly assigned to the treatment and control groups. As for sampling procedures, randomization helps reduce/eliminate biases that can lead to questions about the validity of the responses and the conclusions made from the experiment.

Example: if 500 people are available for the experiment, each could be assigned a three-digit number between 001 and 500, and the first 100 three-digit numbers randomly chosen between 001 and 500 correspond to the new blood pressure medicine, the next 100 three-digit numbers randomly chosen between 001 and 500 (ignoring those already selected) correspond to the first currently used blood pressure medication, the next 100 three-digit numbers randomly chosen between 001 and 500 (ignoring those already selected) correspond to the second currently used blood pressure medication, the next 100 three-digit numbers randomly chosen between 001 and 500 (ignoring those already selected) correspond to the third currently used blood pressure medication, and the final 100 correspond to the control group. This would guarantee the same number in each group. Another method of randomization is for each patient randomly generate a number 1 through 5, and the number determines which of the five groups the person is in. This would allow an unequal number of experimental units in each group, and the randomization would be done as patients enter the experiment.

10. **Blinding**: The experimental units should not know to which group they have been assigned. The placebo given to those in the control group helps assure blinding.

Example: the pills containing the new and currently used blood pressure medications, and the placebo, should be as similar as possible, and the randomization above should be done in such a way that the high blood pressure patients do not know which group they are in and hence which medication they are receiving.

11. **Double-blinding**: In addition to the experimental units not knowing to which group they have been assigned, those people who have contact with the experimental units also should not

know to which group the experimental units have been assigned. The person conducting the experiment would have to know which group each experimental unit is in, but this person should not have direct contact with the experimental units.

Example: the person who randomly selects the numbers should not have direct contact with the high blood pressure patients. When patient X is assigned to receive a particular type of medication (or placebo), these should be placed in an unlabeled bottle with proper instructions and then given to the person (doctor/nurse) consulting with the patient. Then neither the patient nor the doctor/nurse knows which medication that patient is receiving.

12. **Bias**: Anything, such as a factor not considered, that systematically favors certain outcomes over others and which causes the experimenter to question the validity of the results. To avoid bias, the treatment group(s) and the control group should be as similar as possible, except for the treatment (or placebo) assigned to each group.

Example: if the patients know to which group they have been assigned, the placebo effect could bias the results. Additionally, if instead of randomly assigning patients to groups, if the patients are assigned to groups based on the severity of the high blood pressure, the results will likely be biased.

13. **Confounding**: The existence of some factor other than the treatment that makes the treatment and control groups different. When such a factor exists, we say the treatment is confounded with that factor (the confounding factor). Confounding factors create bias.

Example: As described above for the example of bias, if the five groups are determined based on the severity of the high blood pressure, then the effect of the blood pressure medication (or placebo) is confounded with the level of the severity of the high blood pressure. This confounding creates the bias.

Using these definitions, we can now define the following:

A **controlled experiment** is a designed procedure in which we randomly select experimental units to be in the experiment and can control which are assigned to the treatment group(s) and which are assigned to the control group. A controlled experiment is usually run double-blind, involves replication, and involves the random assignment of the experimental units to the groups. A controlled experiment involves the **imposition of some treatment(s)** on the experimental units or subjects in order to observe some response. It is then possible to **compare** results to determine the effect that the treatment (or treatments) is having. A properly designed controlled experiment will create groups that are as similar as possible and hence will be, as much as possible, free of bias and confounding.

An **observational study** is a procedure in which we <u>cannot</u> (or do not) control which experimental units are assigned to the groups and hence only observe anecdotal evidence. With observational studies we can randomly select experimental units to be in the experiment, but we can only <u>observe</u> them as they are. The treatment (or treatments) is <u>not</u> actually imposed.

Observational studies have two major disadvantages:

(1)   There are almost always confounding factors present.

(2)   Observational studies show <u>association</u>, not causation. This means that the response is associated with the treatment but may not be caused by the treatment.

Obviously, if possible we want to use controlled experiments instead of observational studies, therefore reducing the effects of bias and confounding.

Example 5

An agriculturist has developed a new growth enhancer (fertilizer) for plants, and states that it is better than any previously marketed fertilizer. Design a controlled experiment that will allow a comparison among the growth enhancer, today's leading brand of fertilizer, and no fertilization.

Example 6

It is proposed that smoking marijuana reduces a person's ambition to go to college. We randomly sample 1000 high school students as they enter their senior year and give to each an anonymous questionnaire on which we ask (among other questions) if they have smoked marijuana and if they are applying to college. Since the questionnaire is anonymous, we believe that the responses received are correct. The goal of the survey is to determine if a higher proportion of students who say they do not smoke marijuana are applying to college than the proportion of students who say they do smoke marijuana.

(a). Is this a controlled experiment or an observational study?

(b) What is the "treatment"? What is the "response"?

(c). What (if anything) is wrong with this procedure that prevents us from being able to answer our question?

(d). How can we improve the procedure?

Additional Reading and Examples

1. A controlled experiment requires the imposition of the treatments (and placebo) on the experimental units and the ability to make a comparison. If there are multiple treatments and treatment groups then a control group with a placebo is not necessary. However, if a control group is used, then a placebo should be used to eliminate the psychological effects that could bias the results if the experimental units know that they are (or are not) receiving the treatment. The placebo keeps the experimental units blinded.

2. Smoking cigarettes is hazardous to your health and to those around you, but for someone addicted to smoking quitting is not easy. One promising technique to help people quit smoking is to apply a patch to the skin that dispenses nicotine into the blood, and these nicotine patches have become one of the most frequently prescribed medications in the United States. A study funded by a grant from Lederle Laboratories and published in the *Journal of the American Medical Association* was conducted to test the effectiveness of these patches on the cessation of smoking. 240 smokers between the ages of 20 and 65, who had an expired carbon monoxide level of 10 ppm or greater, were in good health, who had a history of smoking at least 20 cigarettes per day, and who were motivated to quit were involved in the study.

   The participants were randomly assigned to receive either 22-mg nicotine patches or placebo patches for eight weeks. They were also provided with an intervention program recommended by the National Cancer Institute, in which they received counseling before, during, and for many months after the 8-week period of wearing the patches. After the 8-week period of patch use, 46% of the nicotine group had quit smoking while only 20% of the placebo group had. This was defined as "self-reported abstinence since the last visit and an expired air carbon monoxide level of 8 ppm or less." After a year the rates in both groups had declined to 27.5% and 14.2%. This indicated that some people had not "quit," but merely stopped smoking for a while, but the group who received the nicotine patch still had a higher percentage who had successfully quit than did the placebo group.

   This study was double-blind since neither the participants nor the nurses taking the measurements knew who had received the active nicotine patches. Replication and randomization were involved, and obviously a comparison was made between two groups. This was a **controlled experiment**.

3. In the above study, suppose the 120 smokers assigned to the nicotine patch group lived in homes with other smokers, while the 120 smokers assigned to the placebo patch group were the only smoker in their homes. Then the two groups differ in terms of something other than the treatment, and the results would likely be **biased**. In this case the treatment is **confounded** with whether or not there were other smokers at home.

4. To study the effectiveness of vitamin C for preventing colds a researcher recruited 200 volunteers. 100 were randomly assigned to take vitamin C for ten weeks, while the remaining 100 took nothing. The 200 participants recorded whether they had a cold during the ten weeks. The two groups were compared, and the researcher announced that taking vitamin C reduces the occurrence of colds.

This is a **controlled experiment** because a treatment (vitamin C or nothing) was randomly imposed on the subjects. However, it is not blind and hence the results may not be trustworthy. Giving the control group a fake vitamin capsule (placebo) would increase the reliability of the results (and possibly change the conclusions).

5. A local high school graduating class consisted of 127 students, of which 48 had an overall scholastic average of more than 85. A school administrator is interested in comparing the satisfaction with life of the 48 high scholastic average students to the satisfaction with life of the other 79 students. One year after graduation each of the 127 students was asked their satisfaction with life, and the data used to compare the two groups.

This is an **observational study** because the graduates were not randomly assigned to the two groups but instead were observed as they are. There is no imposition of a treatment. Hence there are likely some confounding factors present that would cause someone to do well in school and be satisfied with their life, such as a good financial and family situation. The conclusions from the above study are not reliable.

Practice Problems:

II. I.   In November 2000 a Florida newspaper asked the following question:

Should the 2000 Presidential election results be ignored and a new election take place? Express your opinion in a special call-in poll tonight. If yes, call 1-900-527-4300. If no, call 1-900-527-4400. Charge is 50 cents for the first minute.

Explain why this call-in poll is almost certainly biased.

II. 2.   A chemistry professor wants to understand the opinions of her students regarding a particular laboratory instructor. Below is a list of all the students who are in the two laboratories directed by this particular laboratory instructor. Use the Table of Random Digits on page 337 beginning at line 139 to choose a simple random sample of 6 students to be interviewed in detail regarding their opinion of the laboratory instructor.

Althouse	Green	Metelus	Rolfe
Bland	Harrison	Mitchell	Sears
Busch	Haroon	Myers	Shaykh-Nasir
Clemens	Hylton	Parent	Stanley
Cunningham	Jallow	Powell	Taylor
Graham, Em.	Jean-Richard	Pride	Wetzel
Graham, Ev.	Mendoza	Reese	Yuan

II. 3.   Accountants often use stratified random samples during audits to verify a company's records of such things as accounts receivable. The stratification is based on the dollar amount of the item. One company reports 5,000 accounts receivable. Of these, 100 are in amounts over $50,000; 500 are in amounts between $1,000 and $50,000; and the remaining 4,400 are in amounts under $1,000. Explain how stratified random sampling can be used to obtain a representative sample of 100 accounts receivable. Then use the Table of Random Digits on page 337, beginning at lines 115, 125, and 135, respectively, to identify all large and midsize accounts to be included in the sample and the first 5 small accounts to be included in the sample.

II. 4.   The 2008 Summer Olympic Games took place in Beijing, China from August 8 until August 24. Of the 195 countries in the world, 192 of them participated, with only Brunei, Kosovo and Vatican City not participating. Additionally, 12 territories participated (including American Samoa, Aruba, Bermuda, British Virgin Islands, Cayman Islands, Cook Islands, Guam, Hong Kong, Netherlands Antilles, Palestine, Puerto Rico and U. S. Virgin Islands). Hence there were a total of 204 countries and territories that were competing and eligible to win Olympic medals, and it is of interest to gather information about these 204 competing countries and territories. Certain things, such as the numbers of gold, silver and bronze medals won and the number of athletes participating in the Olympic games, were easy to determine for each country or territory, but other information could not be collected for all countries and territories.

It is of interest to select a sample of 20 of the competing countries or territories for further analysis. Three methods for selecting the sample were proposed, as described below. For each identify the type of sampling procedure described.

(a). The 20 countries and territories that won the most medals were selected, with a tie (if necessary) broken by choosing the country or territory involved in the tie that won the most gold medals.

(b). From Africa, South America, Europe and Asia, the four continents with the most competing countries or territories, 4 countries or territories were randomly selected from each. From North America 3 countries or territories were randomly selected, and from Australia 1 country or territory was randomly selected. [Note: the seventh continent, Antarctica, has no countries and hence is of no relevance to this question].

(c). The 204 competing countries and territories were listed in alphabetical order, and a random sample of 20 were selected.

II. 5.   On February 24, 2009, about one month after his inauguration, President Barack Obama made the following statement:

> "I suffer no illusions that this will be an easy process. It will be hard. But I also know that nearly a century after Teddy Roosevelt first called for reform, the cost of our health care has weighed down our economy and the conscience of our nation long enough. So let there be no doubt: health care reform cannot wait, it must not wait, and it will not wait another year."

President Obama developed a health care reform package that was heavily debated across the country during the rest of 2009. At a rally in Miami, Florida 838 people joined together in a crowded high school gym to debate the plan with local politicians. From these 838 people, 46 were randomly selected to answer further questions. To select the sample of 46 attendees of which additional questions were asked the following three methods were proposed. For each identify the type of sampling procedure described.

(a). 46 of the attendees have physical ailments that prevented them from walking without assistance. These 46 people were placed in a special area in the gym and were the ones asked the additional questions.

(b). The people in attendance were divided into two groups, those receiving Social Security and on Medicare and those who were not. From these two groups, 18 people who were receiving Social Security and on Medicare were randomly chosen and 28 people who were not receiving Social Security and not on Medicare were randomly chosen.

(c). As the people entered the gymnasium they were given numbered tickets with seat locations. 46 of the 838 seat locations were randomly selected and these 46 people were asked the additional questions.

II. 6. On January 4, 2010 Virginia Commonwealth University (VCU) opened the new Cary Street Gym that features many new amenities. Since it opened the facility has been heavily used by students, faculty and staff. Of interest is to determine the amount of use, and the items being used, by all current VCU students, faculty and staff. 100 current VCU students, faculty and staff were contacted and each completed a brief survey. To select the sample of 100 people who completed the survey the following three methods were proposed. For each identify the type of sampling procedure described.

(a). The identification or V-numbers of all currently enrolled students and all currently employed faculty and staff were compiled in a spreadsheet, and then 100 of these V-numbers were randomly selected. The student, faculty member or staff member associated with each randomly selected V-number was contacted and completed the survey.

(b). Surveys were handed out to 100 students, faculty and staff who were donating blood at the VCU Homecoming Blood Drive on January 27, 2010, and each of those 100 people completed the survey.

(c). A list of all currently enrolled students was acquired, and 72 students were randomly selected from this list. Similarly, a list of all currently employed faculty was acquired, and 13 faculty were randomly selected from this list. Finally, a list of all currently employed staff was acquired, and 15 staff members were randomly selected from this list. Each of the randomly selected people then completed the survey.

II. 7. A manufacturer of food products uses package liners that are sealed at the top by applying heated jaws after the package is filled. The customer peels the sealed pieces apart to open the package. What effect does the temperature of the jaws have on the force needed to peel the liner? To answer this question, engineers obtain 20 pairs of pieces of package liner. They seal five pairs of each at 250° F, 275° F, 300° F, and 325°F. Then they measure the force needed to peel each seal.

(a). What are the experimental units?

(b). There is one treatment factor. What is it, and what are its levels?

(c). What is the response variable?

(d). In addition to the information given, what would be required to make this a controlled experiment?

II. 8. A pharmaceutical company has developed a new path-relief medication. Sixty patients suffering from arthritis and needing pain relief are available. Each patient will be treated and asked an hour later, "About what percentage of pain relief did you experience?"

(a). Why should the pharmaceutical company not simply administer the new drug and record the patients' responses?

(b). Outline the design of an experiment to compare the drug's effectiveness with that of aspirin and of a placebo.

(c). Should the patients be told which drug they are receiving? How could this knowledge probably affect theft reactions? If patients are not told which treatment they are receiving, the experiment is single-blind. Should this experiment also be double-blind? Explain.

II. 9.   Some medical researchers suspect that added calcium in the diet reduces blood pressure. You have available 40 men with high blood pressure who are willing to serve as subjects.

(a). Outline an appropriate design for the experiment, taking the placebo effect into account.

(b). The names of the subjects appear below. Use the Table of Random Digits on page 337, beginning at line 119, to do the randomization required by your design, and list the subjects to whom you will give the drug.

Alomar	Denman	Han	Liang	Rosen
Asihiro	Durr	Howard	Maldonado	Solomon
Bennett	Edwards	Hruska	Marsden	Tompkins
Bikalis	Farouk	Imrani	Moore	Townsend
Chen	Fratianna	James	O'Brian	Tullock
Clement	George	Kaplan	Ogle	Underwood
Cranston	Green	Krushchev	Plochman	Willis
Curtis	Guillen	Lawless	Rodriguez	Zhang

II. 10.   For each of the following identify the treatment, identify the response, and identify whether it is a controlled experiment or an observational study.

(a). An agriculturalist is interested in determining the type of fertilizer that is preferred for use in growing a particular type of tomato. There are four fertilizer types that he is trying to choose from, and he has 40 plots of land on which the tomatoes are being grown. To determine which fertilizer is preferred, he randomly assign each fertilizer to 10 of the 40 plots and at the end of the growing season determines the yield of tomatoes in terms of the number of tomatoes produced per plot and the average weight of the tomatoes per plot.

(b). Mathematicians are interested in comparing the quality of the mathematical education acquired by students at the University of Richmond (UR), Virginia Commonwealth University (VCU), and Virginia Union University (VUU). In June of 2009 they contacted random samples of 50 recent (May) graduates from each university and gave each student an identical 40-question mathematics test with questions ranging from basic arithmetic to calculus Each of the 150 students who participated received a $25 gift certificate from Barnes and Noble, and as an incentive to do his or her best the student who performed the best on the test received a $500 gift certificate from Barnes and Noble. Mathematicians who did not know from which college the student graduated evaluated the tests, and the results were compared.

(c). Political analysts are interested in comparing the opinions of three groups of people on a new abortion law: those who usually vote for the Democratic Party, those who usually vote for the Republican Party, and those without a strong party preference. The analysts randomly sampled a "large" number of people from each group, gave each person a copy of the proposed abortion law, and then asked them to answer some questions that address their support or opposition to the law.

(d). A physician is interested in comparing three different methods of treating poison ivy. One is a patch treated with a lotion that the person wears over the infected area. A second is a spray that is used on other types of itches, such as mosquito bites. The third is a substance that is spread over the infected area that then hardens on the skin and in essence dries the infected area. To compare the three methods, the physician contacted 54 people with a case of poison ivy. Each person was then randomly assigned to use one of the three treatment methods, and the number of days until the poison ivy was cleared up recorded. The results were then compared to determine the effect of the three treatment methods.

(e). A study was conducted to determine the effects of two written statements on the opinions of U.S. citizens about the confirmation of Judge Samual A. Alito, Jr. to the U.S. Supreme Court. 300 U.S. citizens without a prior opinion were randomly selected to participate. 150 were randomly selected to read a statement prepared by the Republican party, and the other 150 read a statement prepared by the Democratic party. The opinions of the citizens regarding the confirmation of Judge Alito were then determined and compared.

(f). El Spadino, a Mexican restaurant, is interested in comparing a new method for preparing burritos with the current method. They decided to conduct a study, as described below, to determine which method they will use. The study took place over a two-week period and involved all customers who ordered burritos during that time. With each order, a coin is flipped. If the coin lands heads, the burrito is prepared using the new method; if the coin land tails, the burrito is prepared using the current method. After the meal, the customers are given a short, anonymous questionnaire in which they are asked to rate the quality of the burrito on a scale of 1 to 10 (with larger numbers reflecting higher satisfaction). At the end of two weeks the data are analyzed and the results compared.

(g). A local university is interested in determining the effect that two new statistics preparation short courses have on student performance. One course is a two-day course of teacher-led instruction on basic mathematics topics required in statistics, while the other course is a two-day course in which students are given a set of representative problems to work on and seek help from an instructor when the need arises. A group of 120 students who have signed up for the university's introductory level statistics class are randomly selected to participate in the study. After controlling for such demographics as race, sex, age, and the like, 40 students are randomly assigned to the teacher-led course, 40 students are randomly assigned to the representative problems course, and the third set of 40 randomly chosen students participate in neither course. Grades at the end of the introductory statistics class are compared to determine the effect of the short courses.

II. 11. Consider the study described in part (f) of problem II. 10. Suppose some customers refuse to complete the questionnaire at the end of the meal. What type of bias can this potentially cause?

III. Graphically Displaying Distributions

In Moore: Read Chapter 1 (pages 6 – 22)

Once data has been generated, it then becomes necessary to analyze and describe the data. Descriptive statistics involves both graphical and numerical methods of analyzing and describing data. **When describing a distribution it is necessary to describe four things: (1) the center of the distribution, (2) the spread of the distribution, (3) the shape of the distribution, and (4) any unusual features in the distribution, such as extreme values (outliers), ranges of values not represented, and concentrations of data.** The goal of this chapter is to introduce several methods for graphically displaying data. These methods should simplify the data and hence make it easy to make inferences about a population based on the data obtained from a sample. We then discuss how the graphical displays can be used to describe the distributions. In the next chapter we will discuss some specific numerical measures of center and spread.

Recall that qualitative or categorical variables are variables whose measurements vary in kind or name but not in degree, meaning that the measurements cannot be arranged in order of magnitude. For qualitative variables the most often used methods for graphically displaying the data are pie charts and bar graphs. These methods display the percentages of observations falling in each category of the qualitative variable in such a way that the user can visually determine which categories are most likely to occur. We will not discuss these two methods further (information can be found on pages 6 – 11 in Moore), but instead will restrict our study to methods for displaying quantitative variables.

Quantitative variables are variables whose measurements vary in magnitude from trial to trial, meaning some order or ranking can be applied. Quantitative variables can be discrete (countable) or continuous (measured or calculated), for the purposes of this section it does not matter whether the quantitative variable is discrete or continuous. To display quantitative data we must divide the possible measurements into intervals. These intervals are called <u>class intervals</u> and are chosen so that <u>every</u> measurement falls in <u>exactly one</u> interval. Details on how these intervals are chosen are given when the specific graphical procedures are described.

Example: Suppose one is interested in a person's age rounded to nearest full year, which can be treated as a discrete quantitative variable, and suppose the ages of the people in the sample range from 0 to 80. In the BAD set of intervals below, some numbers (such as 19) fall in two intervals, while other numbers (such as 31, 32, and 33) do not fall in any interval. The GOOD set of intervals below corrects this problem.

BAD	GOOD
0 – 10	0 – 10
11 – 16	11 – 15
15 – 20	16 – 20
18 – 30	21 – 30
34 – 34	31 – 50
51 – 80	51 – 80

The two graphical procedures for quantitative data discussed in this chapter are the stem-and-leaf plot and the histogram. For the stem-and-leaf plot the procedure automatically chooses the class intervals, while the procedure for histograms includes a few steps that determine the class intervals. In the next chapter a third graphical method for displaying quantitative data, the boxplot, is introduced. The boxplot uses some of the numerical measures of center and spread introduced in the next chapter.

Video Game Example:

As we go through this chapter, this example will be used to connect the concepts back to previous chapters and to connect the concepts to each other. Many college students enjoy playing video games, and a study was created to estimate what percentage of all students at this university who include playing video games on their list of top three things to do. For those who play video games, it is also of interest to estimate the typical cost of the video games, and to describe the distribution of video game costs.

As described, what is the population of interest for this example?

What type of characteristic is percentage of all students at this university who include playing video games on their list of top three things to do?

What type of characteristic is cost of video games, to the nearest dollar and cent (for example, $40.95)?

In a sample of 130 students at this university, 20 included video games on their list of top three things to do. Hence 20/130 = 15.4% of the students in this sample included video games on their list.

Is 15.4% an example of a parameter or a statistic?

The cost of the last video game that was purchased by each of the 20 students is given below. This data will be used in later sections of this chapter.

| 59.95 | 35.99 | 41.29 | 38.99 | 45.39 | 24.95 | 29.59 | 32.95 | 40.50 | 47.85 |
| 30.99 | 52.95 | 25.50 | 44.45 | 47.99 | 34.85 | 32.00 | 26.99 | 48.59 | 53.29 |

A. Stem-and-Leaf Plot (Stemplot)

A stem-and-leaf plot is a graphical procedure that can be used to display quantitative date, either discrete or continuous. It has as an advantage over the other graphical procedures the fact that it retains the actual data values, which can then be used for further analysis. Once constructed, a stem-and-leaf plot can be used to sort a large list of data, and to describe the distribution of the data, to include the center of the distribution, the spread (or range) of the distribution, the shape of the distribution, and any unusual features such as any range of values not represented, any concentration of data, and any extreme values (outliers).

When constructing a stem-and-leaf plot, it is important that all data have the same number of digits. If, for example, the data ranges from 23 to 78, then all values have two digits and the process is relatively simple. However, if the data ranges from 7 to 87, where 7 is a one-digit number while 87 is a two-digit number, the procedure requires a minor modification. In a situation like this, all values would be converted to two-digit numbers by inserting a 0 in front of all single digit numbers. Hence 7 would become 07 for the purpose of constructing the stem-and-leaf plot. As another example, if the data ranges from 23 to 4320, the two-digit number 23 would become 0023, the three-digit number 567 would become 0567, and four-digit numbers like 4320 would remain unchanged.

1. Standard Stem-and-Leaf Plot

A **standard stem-and-leaf plot** involves dividing each number in a data list into two parts - a "stem" and a "leaf" and in the procedure described below simply listing the stems in consecutive order. The procedure for constructing a stem-and-leaf plot involves five steps, we introduce them with the simplest of cases and that involves two-digit numbers. With two-digit numbers such as 95, the digit in the ten's place (the 9 in 95) is the stem and the digit in the one's place (the 5 in 95) is the leaf.

(1)   Determine the smallest and largest observations in the data set (and hence the data range) and determine the options for the stems and which is preferred. With two-digit numbers there is only one option, as we continue the number of options will increase.

(2)   Once the data range has been determined and the preferred range of stems determined, list them consecutively without skipping any values. The stems are listed vertically with a vertical line drawn to the right of the stems, and usually the smallest stem is listed at the top with the largest stem at the bottom (although it is not incorrect to list the largest stem at the top and then go down). For example, if the data ranges from 30 to 95, then the possible stems are 3, 4, 5, 6, 7, 8 and 9 and these values will be listed as follows.

3 |
4 |
5 |
6 |
7 |
8 |
9 |

(3)   For each number in the data list, write the leaf next to its corresponding stem (for 95, write 5 next to 9). If a number repeats in the data list, a separate leaf value is written for each occurrence of that number. Hence if the number 67 occurs three times in the data set, there should be three 7's beside the stem of 6. For example, if the first six numbers in a data list are 95, 67, 32, 67, 48 and 88, then we would have the following (note there are two 7 leaves next to the 6 stem).

Stem	Leaf
3	2
4	8
5	
6	7, 7
7	
8	8
9	5

(4)   State a defining rule which indicates how the stem-and-leaf plot should be interpreted. The number used does <u>not</u> matter, but the defining rule is <u>required</u>.

For example, writing "where 9|5 = 95" tells the user that a stem of 9 and a leaf of 5 represents the number 95, as opposed to 9.5. If you have data with decimal places, the defining rule can be used to indicate this without recording the decimal with each leaf. Such a defining rule allows the user to retain the actual data and allows this process to be applied to both discrete and continuous data.

(5)   If the goal is to sort the data from smallest to largest, then for each stem the leaves can be ordered from smallest to largest. This is really not required if the goal is to describe the distribution, which is our primary goal, and hence this is an <u>optional</u> step for the remainder of this chapter.

Example 7

A statistics class consisted of 37 students, and the data below reflect the grades that they earned on the final exam. Construct a standard stem-and-leaf plot.

92	82	80	68	91	77	94	79	88	77	80	85	*95*	91
84	43	85	85	83	*8*	92	83	76	44	86	84	88	87
75	74	86	83	37	78	93	48	89					

When the numbers in the data set have more than two digits, then a decision for how the split the data into stems and leaves must be made. For example, with three digit numbers, each number can be split into a two-digit stem and a one-digit leaf, or each number can be split into a one-digit stem and a two-digit leaf. For example, the number 436 could be written 4|36 or it could be written 43|6. Which should we choose? This decision depends on the number of observations and on the range of the observations.

Our goal is to have enough stems to adequately display the distribution, while at the same time not so many stems that many of the stems have no leaf values actually written beside them. Hence we define the following rule that is should be followed during the first two construction steps when the stems are being chosen. **For moderate size data sets less than 6 stems is too few and more than 20 stems is too many; <u>between 10 and 15 stems is often considered ideal</u>**.

As the number of digits in the numbers increases, the number of choices for stems and leaves also increases. For example, with four-digit numbers there are actually three choices, such that the number 5385 could be written 5|385, 53|85, or 538|5. It is essential that all options be considered so that the best possible stem-and-leaf plot is constructed.

Example 8

The following data give the violence tendency scores (maximum score is 100) for a simple random sample of 20 teenagers. A high score indicates a higher tendency for violent behavior. Construct an appropriate stem-and-leaf plot for this data.

| 12.7 | 87.9 | 15.9 | 35.9 | 77.9 | 68.0 | 24.8 | 33.8 | 90.1 | 26.8 |
| 25.6 | 74.3 | 50.3 | *93.6* | 84.2 | 45.0 | *9.5* | 80.5 | 89.4 | 45.2 |

2. Extended Stem-and-Leaf Plot

As mentioned above, for moderate size data sets less than 6 stems is too few and more than 20 stems is too many; <u>between 10 and 15 stems is often considered ideal</u>. However, occasionally there are situations when constructing a standard stem-and-leaf plot to accomplish this is not possible. If we have a data set with a large number of observations that cover a relatively small range, this would produce a standard stem-and-leaf plot with only a few stems and many leaves per stem. For example, a statistics class has 200 students and each student takes a quiz worth 25 points. If a standard stem-and-leaf plot is constructed, the possible stem values are 0, 1 and 2. This causes a problem because the stem-and-leaf plot is so compact that it is difficult to describe the distribution. This problem can be solved if we <u>split the stems</u> to produce an **extended stem-and-leaf plot**.

An extended stem-and-leaf plot is constructed like a standard stem-and-leaf plot, except each stem value is repeated. Though not required, symbols are often written next to the stem values to make it easier to record the leaves, such as the commonly used symbols ● and *. Leaf digits beginning with 0 through 4 correspond to the stems with ●, and leaf digits beginning with 5 through 9 correspond to the stems with *. For example, if the data range from 33 to 67, possible stem values are 3, 4, 5 and 6. Each of these can be split, such that data values between 30 and 34 would be recorded next to 3●, data values between 35 and 39 would be recorded next to 3*, data values between 40 and 44 would be recorded next to 4●, data values between 45 and 49 would be recorded next to 4*, data values between 50 and 54 would be recorded next to 5●, data values between 55 and 59 would be recorded next to 5*, data values between 60 and 64 would be recorded next to 6● and data values between 65 and 69 would be recorded next to 6*. This would produce a stem-and-leaf plot with eight stems instead of just four.

Similarly, with three-digit numbers between 310 and 590, if one went with one-digit stems and two-digit leaves, stems would be 3, 4 and 5, which is too few. If one went with two-digit stems and one-digit leaves, stems would be 31, 32, 33, ..., 59, which is 29 stems and is too many. But if the one-digit stems were split into 3●, 3*, 4●, 4*, 5● and 5*, then the six stems would be fine. Leaf values 00 through 49 would go next to ●, and leaf values 50 through 99 would go next to *.

Extended stem-and-leaf plots can be constructed where each stem is split into five parts, with leaf digits 0 and 1 next to the first stem, leaf digits 2 and 3 next to the second stem, leaf digits 4 and 5 next to the third stem, leaf digits 6 and 7 next to the fourth stem, and leaf digits 8 and 9 next to the fifth stem. See the Additional Reading and Examples section for an example.

Example 9

A flight from Hawaii to the mainland United States is carrying 40 passengers returning from vacation. The data below reflect the checked luggage weights (in pounds) for each of the 40 passengers on the flight. Construct an appropriate stem-and-leaf plot for this data.

30 27 12 42 35 47 38 36 27 35 22 17 29 3   21 *0* 38 32 41 33

26 45 18 43 18 32 31 32 19 21 33 31 28 29 *51* 12 32 18 21 26

Advantages of stem-and-leaf plots:

(1) They graphically display the distribution of the data.

(2) They can be used to determine the center, spread, and shape of the distribution, plus any unusual features such as outliers, gaps in the distribution, and data concentrations.

(3) They retain the actual data values for potential further analysis.

(4) They are easy to construct.

(5) They make the sorting of a data set easier.

Disadvantages of stem-and-leaf plots include:

(1) They are not very effective for large data sets.

(2) The choice of the stems depends on the data type and data range.

Video Game Example:

Many college students enjoy playing video games, and a study was created to estimate the typical cost of the video games, and to describe the distribution of video game costs. The cost of the last video game that was purchased by each of the 20 students who listed that they enjoy video games is given below. Construct an appropriate stem-and-leaf plot to graphically display this data.

| 59.95 | 35.99 | 41.29 | 38.99 | 45.39 | 24.95 | 29.59 | 32.95 | 40.50 | 47.85 |
| 30.99 | 52.95 | 25.50 | 44.45 | 47.99 | 34.85 | 32.00 | 26.99 | 48.59 | 53.29 |

3. Back-to-Back Stem-and-Leaf Plots

When we have two sets of data, both measured in the same units, that we wish to compare, the distributions can be displayed using a **back-to-back stem-and-leaf plot**. A back-to-back stem-and-leaf plot will allow the description of each distribution, and a comparison of the two distributions. To construct a back-to-back stem-and-leaf plot the two sets of data are combined and a <u>common</u> list of stems is determined using the same rules described previously. This should be done such that each stem-and-leaf plot has between 6 and 20 stems, with between 10 and 15 stems preferred. Now that the common set of stems is determined, the leaves for one set of data are displayed to the right of the stems, as done for the previous examples, and the leaves for the other set of data are displayed to the left of the stems. There is one defining rule that allows the user to interpret the stem-and-leaf plot.

Example 10

The U. S. Department of Agriculture compiles information on acreage, production, and value of potatoes and publishes its findings in *Agricultural Statistics*. Potato yield is measured in hundreds of pounds (cwt) per acre. Independent simple random samples of forty 1-acre plots of potatoes from Idaho and thirty-two 1-acre plots of potatoes from Nevada gave the following yields. Construct a back-to-back stem-and-leaf plot.

Idaho:	299	337	396	379	301	414	380	328	386	311	288	354	381	399
	324	287	369	336	334	334	360	368	375	314	373	369	378	
	330	*274*	361	312	385	316	392	363	353	351	337	382	355	

Nevada:	353	324	398	362	385	406	448	384	382	398	342	377	418
	303	424	*470*	411	383	379	378	410	370	386	338	329	346
	341	432	410	409	370	403							

B.   Histograms

A histogram is a second graphical method for displaying quantitative data. Like a stem-and-leaf plot a histogram breaks the range of values of a variable into class intervals, but unlike a stem-and-leaf plot that displays the actual data values, a histogram displays either the number of or percentage of the observations in each interval (not the actual data values). The histograms can then be used to describe the distribution of the data. The description involves the same things as for the stem-and-leaf plot, except we cannot be as specific because the actual data is not retained. For large data sets the histogram is usually easier to construct than a stem-and-leaf plot because instead of recording every actual data value, only the number of values or percentage of values for each interval is recorded.

There are many methods for constructing histograms. The method described below produces histograms with an **equal class width**, along with enough intervals to adequately describe the distribution. To construct a histogram, proceed as follows:

1.   Determine the number of class intervals to use. This number is occasionally stated in the problem. If not, for moderate to large data sets an appropriate number of intervals can be found by taking the square root of the sample size, and rounding up.

       Example: Suppose we have 210 observations, with a low value of 202 and high value of 496. Then, $\sqrt{210} = 14.5$ and we round up to 15 intervals.

2.   Determine the range of the data, where range = largest observation – smallest observation.

       Example: Suppose we have 210 observations, with a low value of 202 and high value of 496.
               Range 496 – 202 = 294.

3.   Divide the range by the number of class intervals and round the result to a convenient class width.

       Example: Suppose we have 210 observations, with a low value of 202 and high value of 496.

$$\text{Class width} = \frac{\text{range}}{\text{number of intervals}} = \frac{294}{15} = 19.6, \text{ rounding up use an equal class width of 20.}$$

4.   Determine what the intervals should be. To do so, two rules should be followed. First, the endpoints of each interval should be multiples of the class width, and second, the smallest value in the data set should fall in the first interval. Hence the lower limit of the first interval should be chosen to be a multiple of the class width (possibly 0) that would create an interval that would contain the smallest

53

observation. The remaining intervals are found by adding the class width to this original lower limit until an interval that contains the largest observation is created.

Example: From step 3, the multiples of the class width (20) are 0, 20, 40, 60, 80, 100, 120, 140, 160, 180, 200, 220, 240, and so forth. The smallest observation is 202, so we choose the lower limit of the first interval to be 200. The intervals would be 200 – 220, 220 – 240, 240 – 260, 260 – 280, 280 – 300, 300 – 320, 320 – 340, 340 – 360, 360 – 380, 380 – 400, 400 – 420, 420 – 440, 440 – 460, 460 – 480 and 480 – 500. We stop at 500 because the largest observation, 496, would fall in the interval 480 – 500.

Note: Due to the rounding in step 3, this procedure often produces one (and occasionally two) less or one (and occasionally two) more class interval(s) than specified in step 1. If this happens do **not** worry about it.

5. Determine the **frequency** (or **class frequency**) for each interval. The frequencies (or class frequencies) are the <u>numbers</u> (<u>counts</u>) of observations falling in each interval. Since each observation should fall in <u>exactly</u> one class interval, an observation is counted in an interval if it matches the lower endpoint but not if it matches the upper endpoint. The class frequencies should sum to the number of observations.

Example: With class intervals 200 – 220, 220 – 240, 240 – 260, and so forth, an observation of 220 will be counted in the 220 – 240 interval, not the 200 – 220 interval.

6. Determine the **relative frequencies** of each class interval by dividing the frequencies by the total number of observations and multiplying by 100. The relative frequencies are the <u>percentages</u> of observations in each interval. The relative frequencies should sum to 100%.

Example: If the frequency for the interval 200 – 220 is 3, then the relative frequency would be as follows: 3/210 * 100% = 1.4%.

It is often the case that the class intervals, class frequencies and relative frequencies are displayed together in three columns, creating what is called a **frequency table**.

7. Construct the histogram. On the horizontal axis mark and label the class intervals. On the vertical axis, mark and label either the frequencies or relative frequencies. Over each class interval, draw a rectangle whose height equals the appropriate frequency or relative frequency.

Notes: 1. If we mark the frequencies on the vertical axis we create a **frequency histogram**; if we mark the relative frequencies on the vertical axis we create a **relative frequency histogram**. If given a choice, a relative frequency histogram is often preferred to a frequency histogram because it more easily allows for a comparison between two or more distributions (sets of data).

2. For a given data set and the same set of class intervals, a frequency histogram and a relative frequency histogram will look the same. The only difference is the labeling of the vertical axis. For this reason you <u>must always label both axes.</u>

Example 11

A youth U12 soccer tournament has four teams, each with 15 players. The data below reflect the weights of these 60 players. Construct a relative frequency histogram for this data. For ease, the data has been ordered from smallest to largest.

52 57 58 61 61 64 65 65 66 67 68 68 69 71 71 71 72 73 74 74
74 75 75 77 78 80 80 80 81 83 83 84 85 86 86 87 88 90 91 91
91 92 93 96 96 97 99 100 100 101 103 105 107 107 108 110 112 115 118 140

Many college students enjoy playing video games, and a study was created to estimate the typical cost of the video games, and to describe the distribution of video game costs. The cost of the last video game that was purchased by each of the 20 students who listed that they enjoy video games is given below. Construct a histogram to graphically display this data.

| 59.95 | 35.99 | 41.29 | 38.99 | 45.39 | 24.95 | 29.59 | 32.95 | 40.50 | 47.85 |
| 30.99 | 52.95 | 25.50 | 44.45 | 47.99 | 34.85 | 32.00 | 26.99 | 48.59 | 53.29 |

C. Describing a Distribution

To completely describe a distribution, we describe the center, spread and shape of the distribution, and any unusual features in the distribution, such as outliers, concentrations of data, or significant gaps in the distribution without data. Numerical methods of calculating measures of center and spread are discussed in the next chapter. For now we can estimate the <u>center</u> of the distribution to be the balance point of the stem-and-leaf plot or histogram, and we can estimate the <u>spread</u> of the distribution by describing the range of the data. The terms below describe the <u>shape</u> of the distribution. When actually describing the shape of a distribution, a combination of the following terms can be used.

1. A distribution is called **symmetric** if the left and right sides of the distribution are mirror images of each other. Each of the following are examples of symmetric distributions.

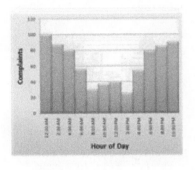 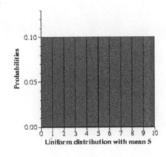 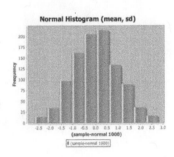

2. A special symmetric distribution is the **normal** distribution. The normal curve is a symmetric, bell-shaped curve with a single peak in the middle of the distribution. It is the most commonly used type of distribution, will be the basis for many of the statistical inferences to be made in later chapters, and chapter VI is dedicated entirely to the normal distributions. The third example above (most to the right) is an example of a normal distribution.

3. A distribution is said to be **skewed** if one "tail" of the distribution is longer than the other. Therefore, a distribution is <u>skewed to the left</u> if the left side of the graph extends much farther out than the right side (see histogram on the left below), and a distribution is <u>skewed to the right</u> if the right side of the graph extends much farther out than the left side (see histogram on the right below).

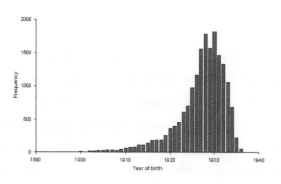 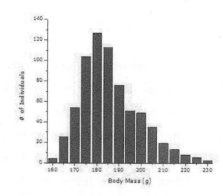

4. A distribution with multiple peaks is said to be multimodal. If the distribution has <u>two</u> significant peaks it is called **bimodal**, and if it has <u>three</u> significant peaks it is called **trimodal**. The histogram to the left below is bimodal (two peaks, one at each end) and the histogram to the right is trimodal.

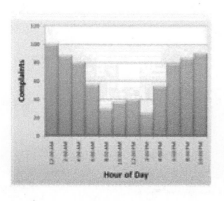 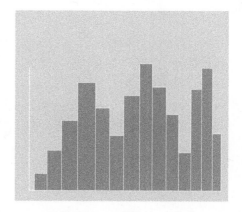

<u>Unusual features</u> in a distribution imply things that create a distribution that is not symmetric (or more specifically, not normal). Unusual features can include a heavy concentration of values, a range of values not represented (a gap in the distribution), or extreme values at the ends of the distributions called outliers. An **outlier** is an observation that stands out from the other observations (an extreme value) and that often creates a skewed distribution. For example, if the data reflects ages of students in a college class, and the ages are 17, 18, 18, 20, 21, 21, 23, 24 and 78, the age of 78 would be considered an outlier.

Example 12

Use the stem-and-leaf plots and histograms constructed in examples 7 through 11 to <u>completely</u> describe the distributions from which the data was sampled.

Stem-and-leaf plot of example 7

Stem-and-leaf plot of example 8

Stem-and-leaf plot of example 9

Back-to-back stem-and-leaf plot of example 10

Relative frequency histogram of example 11

Many college students enjoy playing video games, and a study was created to estimate the typical cost of the video games, and to describe the distribution of video game costs. The cost of the last video game that was purchased by each of the 20 students who listed that they enjoy video games is given below. Use the stem-and-leaf plot and histogram constructed earlier in this chapter to completely describe the distribution of video game costs.

| 59.95 | 35.99 | 41.29 | 38.99 | 45.39 | 24.95 | 29.59 | 32.95 | 40.50 | 47.85 |
| 30.99 | 52.95 | 25.50 | 44.45 | 47.99 | 34.85 | 32.00 | 26.99 | 48.59 | 53.29 |

Additional Reading and Examples

1. To completely describe a distribution one must specify the center of the distribution, the spread of the distribution, the shape of the distribution, and any unusual features in the distribution, such as outliers, concentrations of data, and gaps. Most of the inference procedures that will be performed will assume that the distribution has an approximate normal shape, and stem-and-leaf plots and histograms can be used to determine if this assumption is valid or not.

2. On January 28, 1986 the U.S. space shuttle Challenger exploded shortly after liftoff. The Presidential Commission that investigated the accident concluded that the disaster was caused by the failure of an O-ring, which resulted in a combustion gas leak through a field joint on the rocket booster. It was determined that the O-rings did not seal properly at low temperatures. The temperature on January 28, 1986 was 31 degrees, and the following are the recorded temperatures on the 24 launches of the shuttle prior to the accident.

| 66 | 70 | 69 | 80 | 68 | 67 | 72 | 73 | 70 | 57 | 63 | 70 |
| 78 | 67 | 53 | 67 | 75 | 70 | 81 | 76 | 79 | 75 | 76 | 58 |

To describe the data (including the fatal launch temperature of 31), a stem-and-leaf plot will be constructed. The data ranges from 31 to 81, suggesting stem values of 3, 4, 5, 6, 7, and 8. To better display the data each of these stems will be split to create an extended stem-and-leaf plot.

```
3●  │ 1
3*  │
4●  │
4*  │
5●  │ 3
5*  │ 7, 8
6●  │ 3
6*  │ 6, 7, 7, 7, 8, 9
7●  │ 0, 0, 0, 0, 2, 3
7*  │ 5, 5, 6, 6, 8, 9
8●  │ 0, 1
8*  │                        where 6|3=63 degrees
```

Obviously the 31 degrees temperature on the day of the fatal launch is an outlier, which skews the distribution heavily to the left. Without the outlier the distribution is much more symmetric, while still slightly skewed to the left. The center of the distribution is 70 degrees, and the data ranges from 53 to 81 degrees without the outlier and from 31 to 81 degrees if all data is considered. A majority of the data is concentrated between 66 and 81 degrees (80% of the observations), with the coolest successful launch temperature being 53 degrees. This type of analysis prior to the launch probably would have delayed the launch and prevented the catastrophe.

3. A lab instructor teaches three lab sections of introductory statistics, each with 20 students. She gives a quiz each week that is graded out of 25 points. The data below reflect the quiz grades for her 60 students on the first quiz given in the semester.

14 25 25 20 21 25 25 21 23 23 21 25 25 25 21 25 10 25 21 23
18 25 21 25 23 22 20 25 15 18 25 19 23 25 11 25 17 22 20 0
17 25 25 21 23 20 16 12 25 25 21 20 7 17 21 22 25 23 12 0

A standard stem-and-leaf plot for this data would involve only three stems, 0, 1 and 2, and this is not sufficient. Using an extended stem-and-leaf plot with each stem split into two parts would generate six stems, which would be better and would likely make it possible to describe the distribution. However, if an extended stem-and plot with each stem split into five parts is used, then there will be a total of 15 stems (13 of which will be used), which will make it easier to describe the distribution and hence is the preferred procedure. The resulting extended stem-and-leaf plot is as follows (the symbols are not required, t is used to represent two and three, f is used to represent four and five, s is used to represent six and seven).

Stem	Leaves
0•	0, 0
0t	
0f	
0s	7
0*	
1•	0, 1, 2
1t	2
1f	4, 5
1s	7, 7, 6, 7
1*	8, 8, 9
2•	0, 1, 1, 1, 1, 1, 1, 1, 0, 0, 1, 0, 1, 0, 1
2t	3, 3, 3, 3, 2, 3, 2, 3, 2, 3
2f	5, 5, 5, 5, 5, 5, 5, 5, 5, 5, 5, 5, 5, 5, 5, 5, 5, 5, 5, 5, 5
2s	
2*	

where 1 | 2 = 12

The distribution is clearly skewed fairly heavily to the left, with two scores of 0 representing outliers. The score of 7 is also a potential outlier. The center of the distribution is around 20, and the data ranges from 0 to 25. Note also most students did extremely well on this quiz, as a third of the students (20 out of 60) scored a perfect score of 25.

4.   A medical study is interested in the blood cholesterol levels of patients. A random sample of 43 persons was obtained and the blood cholesterol levels were as follows.

239 212 249 227 218 310 281 330 226 233 223 161 195 233 249 284

245 174 154 256 196 299 210 301 199 258 205 195 227 244 355 234

195 179 357 282 265 286 286 176 195 163 297

Suppose we want to display this distribution using an equal class width frequency histogram. The square root of 43 is 6.557, so 7 intervals will be appropriate. The data ranges from 154 to 357, a range of 357 − 154 = 203. Then the class width should be 203/7 = 29. For convenience an equal class width of 30 will be used. Multiples of 30 are 0, 30, 60, 90, 120, **150**, **180**, 210 and so forth, and since the smallest observation is 154, the lower limit of the first interval is 150. Then the class intervals, frequencies, and relative frequencies are as follows.

Class Intervals	Frequencies	Relative Frequencies
150 – 180	6	13.95%
180 – 210	7	16.28%
210 – 240	11	25.58%
240 – 270	7	16.28%
270 – 300	7	16.28%
300 – 330	2	4.65%
330 – 360	3	6.98%
	43	100.00%

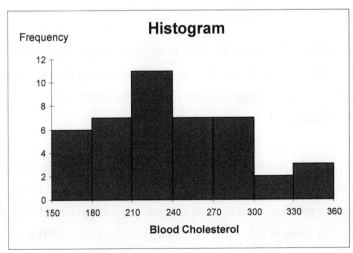

The distribution is skewed slightly to the right, with a center around 240. The data ranges from roughly 150 to 360. There are no apparent outliers, nor gaps in the distribution.

TI-83/84 Calculator

Suppose a set of data has been collected and entered into list L1 of the TI-83/84 calculator. See page 8 for details on entering data into a list. The following provides detailed steps for generating a frequency histogram on the TI-83/84 calculator.

1. Begin by making sure your plotting area is clear. To do so, press **Y=** and be sure that all ten (Y1 through Y0) of your functions are clear (empty). If a function is not clear, use the up-arrow and down-arrow buttons to move the cursor to that function and press **CLEAR** to clear it out.

2. Be sure that no other statistical plots are activated. To do so, choose **STAT PLOT** by pressing the **2nd** button followed by the **Y=** button, then select option **4: PlotsOff**, and then press **ENTER** twice. Now all plots should be off.

3. To activate a statistics plot, choose **STAT PLOT** by pressing the **2nd** button followed by the **Y=** button, then select option **1: Plot...Off**, and then press **ENTER**. Your screen should look like the picture below.

The cursor should be blinking over the word **On**; press **ENTER** to activate this plot. Use the down-arrow button to move the cursor down to the **Type:** of graph setting. Use the left-arrow and right-arrow buttons to move the cursor to the desired graph, which for a histogram is the option in the upper right corner. Once that graph is highlighted, press **ENTER** to select it.

4. Assuming that your data is in list L1, press the down-arrow button to move the cursor to **Xlist:**, Note that your cursor is in ALPHA mode, and to choose list L1 you would press the **2nd** button followed by the **1** button. Now press the down-arrow button to move to **Freq:**, and since all the data is in one list, enter **1** here. Note that while in ALPHA mode, to leave ALPHA mode in order to enter a numerical value the **ALPHA** button needs to be pressed.

5. Now you must set the window size so that you can see the graph properly. To do so, press **WINDOW**. Now you must enter the dimensions of your graph. For **Xmin**=, enter the lower limit of the first class. For **Xmax**=, enter a value slightly larger than the upper limit of the last class. For **Xscl**=, enter the class width. For **Ymin**=, enter **-1**. For **Ymax**=, enter a value slightly larger than the highest frequency. For **Yscl**=, enter **1**. For **Xres**=, enter **1**.

6. To view the resulting frequency histogram, simply press **GRAPH**. To determine the actual class limits and frequencies, just press **TRACE** and use the right-arrow and left-arrow buttons to move the cursor across each bar. The values in the upper left corner indicate the plot number (**P1**) and which list is plotted (**L1**). The values in the lower left corner indicate the lower class limit and the upper class limit for the selected bar (the bar under the cursor). Finally, the frequency of the selected bar/class is indicated in the lower right corner.

Practice Problems:

III.1. The weights (in pounds) of a sample of 35 people who attended the 2009 American Music Awards show are given below.

207 153 187 114 123 243 221 132 141 201 179 129 218 167 198 143 96 173
225 204 118 183 105 134 121 189 178 192 123 137 122 195 190 184 193

Make a stem-and-leaf plot for this data and use the stem-and-leaf plot to completely describe the distribution of weights from which the sample was selected.

III.2. Babe Ruth is recognized as one of the greatest home run hitters of all-time, and Mark McGwire was considered the best home run hitter of the late 1990's. In fact, Ruth held the single season home run record of 60 home runs for many years, until Roger Maris broke the record with 61 home runs in 1961. Maris held the record until 1998, when McGwire broke the record with 70 home runs. The current single season record holder is Barry Bonds, who hit 73 home runs in 2001. The data below give the number of home runs that Babe Ruth hit in his 15 years with the New York Yankees (1920 to 1934) and the number of home runs that Mark McGwire has hit in his first 14 years in the major leagues.

Babe Ruth: 54 59 35 41 46 25 47 60 54 46 49 46 41 34 22
Mark McGwire: 49 32 33 39 22 42   9   9 39 52 58 70 65 32

(a). Construct a back-to-back stem-and-leaf plot for this data and use it to describe the distributions.
(b). Use the back-to-back stem-and-leaf plot to compare the two distributions. Is Ruth's 1927 high of 60 home runs an outlier? What about McGwire's record 70 home runs? Based on this data, which player was a more consistent home run hitter?

III.3. A national advertising agency is interested in determining the optimal length of a television commercial. For the same product, commercials of lengths 15 seconds, 30 seconds, 45 seconds, and 60 seconds were created. 200 consumers were then randomly selected, and each was randomly assigned to watch one of the four commercials. After watching the commercial, the consumer was asked a short list of questions, such as the product being advertised, quality of the commercial, and degree of humor in the commercial. For each consumer the responses were converted to numerical values and a "knowledge and satisfaction score" ranging from 0 (bad) to 10 (good) determined. The "knowledge and satisfaction scores" for the sample of 30 consumers who watched the 45-second commercial are given below.

5.0 4.2 3.0 2.0 5.8 4.8 3.7 2.6 1.3 5.3 5.0 4.0 4.4 3.3 5.2

4.6 4.4 3.5 3.1 2.9 5.5 5.1 4.9 3.7 2.7 5.4 4.6 3.9 5.3 5.0

(a). For the situation described above, what is the "treatment"? What is the "response"? As described is this a controlled experiment or observational study?

(b). Make an appropriate stem-and-leaf plot to graphically display this data.

(c). Use the stem-and-leaf plot to completely describe the distribution.

III.4. Upward, the world's largest Christian sports program for children, was created with a vision to provide the best sports experience possible for every child. Each year some 1 million people around the world play, coach, referee, or volunteer in Upward sports leagues and camps hosted by more than 2,600 churches. Anyone – children and volunteers of any faith or no faith – can participate in Upward sports. Specifically designed for children in K5- sixth grade, Upward aims to bring out "the winner" in every child – regardless of the game's score. The data below gives the total number of points scored in a random sample of 33 Upward basketball games. Construct an appropriate stem-and-leaf plot to graphically display this data, and use the stem-and-leaf plot to completely describe the distribution.

30 45 51 63 72 35 41 33 67 48 36 56 31 54 60 98 45
64 43 50 47 53 55 66 76 23 37 40 54 46 39 47 59

III.5. The Virginia Department of Game and Inland Fisheries is interested in determining the health of "farm ponds" throughout Virginia. It is estimated that 80,000 farm ponds exist in Virginia. On a recent trip to a farm pond in Goochland County the researchers captured and released 26 large mouth bass. The weights in pounds for the 26 bass are given below. Construct an appropriate stem-and-leaf plot to graphically display this data, and use the stem-and-leaf plot to describe the distribution.

3.78 2.24 1.23 0.32 3.21 1.27 2.08 5.23 1.99 2.12 1.08 1.54 0.99

2.76 1.63 0.71 0.45 0.82 2.83 1.72 2.89 1.10 1.81 2.24 1.88 3.42

III.6. The excursion fares (in dollars) from Richmond International Airport to airports in 30 randomly chosen cities are given below. Construct an appropriate stem-and-leaf plot for this data, and use the stem-and- leaf plot to describe the distribution.

214 213 198 295 172 252 233 238 252 254 307 352 523 340 210
317 352 329 241 210 198 250 462 487 238 350 519 523 290 193

III.7. An advertisement was randomly selected from each of the top 30 selling magazines and the number of sentences per advertisement determined. The data is given below. Construct an appropriate stem-and-leaf plot to graphically display the data, and use the stem-and-leaf plot to describe the distribution.

11 20 9 9 4 18 9 13 5 25 16 6 12 10 6
16 22 14 4 16 48 16 5 14 6 24 9 18 6 13

III.8. A medical experiment was conducted in which 72 guinea pigs were injected with tubercle bacilli. The data below are the survival times in days following the injections. Construct a frequency histogram for this data and use it to completely describe the distribution.

43 45 53 56 56 57 58 66 67 73 74 79 80 80 81 81 81 82 83 83
84 88 89 91 91 92 92 97 99 99 100 100 101 102 102 102 103 104 107 108
109 113 114 118 121 123 126 128 137 138 139 144 145 147 156 162 174 178 179 184
191 198 211 214 243 249 329 380 403 511 522 598

III.9. The VCU Honors College conducts the Berglund Seminar Series that "aims to generate stimulating discussions and debates on topical, and sometimes controversial, subjects. Discussions are led by guests from the university faculty and administration, as well as leaders representing a variety of fields from across the Richmond community." The data below reflect the number of students in attendance at a random sample of 25 Berglund Seminar Series seminars. Construct a histogram to graphically display this data, and then completely describe the distribution.

14 16 18 19 21 22 22 24 26 28 30 31 31 33 35 38 38 39 40 42 43 45 48 50 92

III.10. Recreational skiing is big business in some of the western and New England states. Many recreational skiers are beyond the beginning level and want intermediate or "more difficult" terrain. The data below give the percentage of skiing terrain that is at the more difficult level for 35 top-rated ski areas. Construct a relative frequency histogram for this data and use it to completely describe the distribution.

36 54 51 49 30 43 40 46 35 40 52 28 57 51 40 40 45 40
60 20 25 50 40 65 58 43 59 49 55 30 33 60 30 46 65

III.11. The number of miles that a random sample of 40 countries had to travel to reach the 2004 Summer Olympic Games in Athens, Greece is given below. The data is measured from the capital of each country to Athens.

1689	442	2790	3106	2107	1405	1683	1212	794	2650	7327	2665	4895	4337	1790
3678	6326	2238	1490	2053	5125	5688	2354	1129	3489	4285	2970	8002	2100	3560
3456	6101	5337	3575	4103	3875	979	1945	2857	3344					

Construct a graph to display this data, and use your graph to completely describe the distribution of travel distances to Athens.

III.12. Twenty-five batteries for hand calculators from a particular manufacturer were tested. Each battery was tested in a calculator that was programmed to do a continuous "loop" of typical calculations. The time in hours to failure of each battery is recorded below.

| 13.26 | 10.66 | 11.24 | 13.62 | 12.12 | 12.68 | 10.25 | 11.76 | 10.94 | 11.33 | 10.92 | 10.85 | 11.62 |
| 12.49 | 10.84 | 11.53 | 11.36 | 11.12 | 12.55 | 11.55 | 12.12 | 11.45 | 14.99 | 11.54 | 11.24 | |

Construct a graph to display this data, and use your graph to completely describe the distribution of time to failure for the batteries.

III.13. Richmond Ford, located at 4600 West Broad Street in Richmond, Virginia, is one of the oldest automobile Dealerships in the country. A sample of 30 pre-owned vehicles was selected from the population of all pre-owned vehicles owned by Richmond Ford, and the mileage of each vehicle is recorded below.

16,354	12,682	31,818	55,284	70,971	5,225	20,859	36,934	62,495	15,761	68,414
42,695	74,910	45,899	34,067	65,794	10,884	57,994	13,833	40,293	12,046	26,677
36,997	63,280	49,303	22,190	26,286	14,076	19,984	94,208			

(a). Construct an appropriate stem-and-leaf plot for this data.

(b). Construct a relative frequency histogram for this data.

(c). Based on the stem-and-leaf plot and histogram, describe completely the distribution of mileages for this sample of 30 pre-owned vehicles.

Note that in practice problem IV.12 on page 97 a boxplot is constructed for this data, and it can also be used to help describe the distribution.

IV. Numerically Describing Distributions

In Moore: Read Chapter 2

In the previous chapter we discussed stem-and-leaf plots and histograms, two graphical procedures for displaying quantitative data, and then learned how to describe the distributions. This includes the description of the center, spread, shape and any unusual features (outliers) of the distribution. In this chapter we discuss some specific <u>numerical</u> summaries that can be used in describing the center and spread of a distribution of a quantitative variable.

Our goal is to determine the values of various <u>population parameters</u>, which will be designated using Greek letters in the remainder of the chapters. In this chapter there are two types of parameters that we are interested in:

1. A **central location parameter** that measures where the <u>center</u> of a distribution lies, and
2. A **dispersion parameter** measures the amount of <u>spread</u> or <u>variability</u> around this center.

We will discuss several location and dispersion parameters, and give the formulas of the appropriate <u>sample statistics</u> that are used to estimate these parameters. We must calculate the sample statistic and not the parameter itself because typically data for all subjects in the population is not available and instead we must obtain a sample of the population. These sample statistics will be denoted with symbols using regular English letters.

For notation purposes, suppose we have a sample of size n from the population and we denote the ith member of the sample by X_i along with its respective observed value x_i (i = 1,2,...,n). For example, suppose we take a sample of n = 10 students and record the age of each student. Then x_1 = observed age of the first student (say 23), x_2 = observed age of the second student (say 18), x_3 = observed age of the third student (say 25), and so forth until we get to x_{10} which is the observed age of the tenth (and last) student (say 19).

<u>Attendance at Statistics Review Sessions Example</u>:

As we go through this chapter, this example will be used to connect the concepts back to previous chapters and to connect the concepts of this chapter to each other. A statistics course at a large university provides free to students statistics review sessions that students can use to answer questions, with help solving problems, and with help studying for tests. The course instructor is interested in the number of students who attend each hour of review session, and selects a sample of 15 review session hours spread out over a month's time. The number of students who attended these 15 review session hours is as follows.

6   1   8   3   1   5   11   7   4   28   12   9   2   10   13

As described, what is the population of interest for this example?

What type of characteristic is the number of students who attend each hour of review session?

A. Measures of Central Location

   In Moore: Read pages 39 – 43

   Our goal is to locate (or estimate) the center of a distribution. In the last section we illustrated how the center of a distribution can be estimated from a graphical display of the distribution. In this section we discuss two numerical measures of the center of a distribution.

1. Mean (Average)

   The most commonly known and used measure of center is the **mean**, or **average**. The mean has nice mathematical properties that makes it the choice of a measure of center in many inference procedures that are done in statistics, including the inference procedures discussed in later chapters.

   The **population mean** is denoted by the Greek letter μ and is the sum of all the measurements in the population divided by how many measurements there are. This is a parameter and is usually unknown or not calculable because usually data for all subjects in the population is not known. Since we usually only have _sample_ data, then we can compute the **sample mean**, denoted by $\overline{X}$, and use $\overline{X}$ to make inferences about μ.

   The sample mean is calculated as: $\overline{X} = \dfrac{\sum X}{n} = \dfrac{X_1 + X_2 + \ldots + X_n}{n}$. Note that in this formula the symbol $\sum$ implies to sum (add) the data values.

Example 13

Of interest is to determine the typical weight of all entertainers. Hence the population is all entertainers, the characteristic of interest is the mean weight of all entertainers, and weight is a continuous quantitative variable. Since the weights of all entertainers are not known, this mean weight must be estimated using data from a sample. A sample of 8 entertainers is selected, and their weights are as follows. Calculate the mean weight of these 8 entertainers and identify whether you are calculating μ or $\overline{X}$.

128 150 183 222 113 154 201 150

As mentioned above the mean is the most commonly used measure of center, but one disadvantage of the mean is that it is highly influenced by extreme values (outliers). This creates a problem because in this situation the mean may not accurately measure the true center of a distribution, and a different measure of center may be preferable. The following example illustrates the effect that an outlier can have on the mean.

Example 14

Professional wrestling is now considered a form of entertainment instead of a sport. Suppose that in addition to the 8 entertainers in the sample in example 13, a professional wrestler who weighs 391 pounds is randomly selected for the sample. Find the mean weight of the following sample of 9 entertainers.

128 150 183 222 113 154 201 150 *391*

2. Median

In cases in which the distribution is heavily skewed due to outliers the mean may not be an accurate measure of center and something else may be preferred. A measure of central location that is more <u>resistant</u> to outliers is the **median**. The term **resistant** implies that the median may be slightly influenced by the outliers, but that the degree of influence is much less than the influence that outliers have on the mean. The median is the central value that is larger than half of the data and smaller than the other half of the data.

Denote the population median by the Greek letter η (read eta), and the sample median as M. In some cases the median is uniquely defined, and in other situations there are actually multiple definitions. For the purposes of this book the sample median M is calculated as follows.

1. Order the data from smallest to largest.
2. Determine where the median will be located in this ordered list of numbers. This median location can be determined by making the following calculation: $\dfrac{n+1}{2}$.
3. Calculate the median.

    i. If n is odd, then $\dfrac{n+1}{2}$ is a whole number and the median is the $\left(\dfrac{n+1}{2}\right)^{th}$ ordered observation.

    For example, if n = 19, then $\dfrac{n+1}{2} = \dfrac{19+1}{2} = 10$, and the median is the 10th ordered observation (count from either the left or right).

    ii. If n is even, then $\dfrac{n+1}{2}$ is a fraction of a whole number ending in .5 and the median is the <u>average</u> of the $\dfrac{n+1}{2} - .5$ and $\dfrac{n+1}{2} + .5$ ordered observations. For example, if n = 22, then $\dfrac{n+1}{2} = \dfrac{22+1}{2} = 11.5$ and the median is the average of the 11th and 12th ordered observations.

Example 15

The weights of the 8 entertainers of example 13 are repeated below. Calculate the median weight of this sample of 8 entertainers.

128   150   183   222   113   154   201   150

As indicated above, the median is resistant to outliers. As an illustration of this concept, consider the following example in which the outlier weight of the professional wrestler is added to the sample.

Example 16

Compute the median of the entertainers when the professional wrestler who weighs 391 pounds is added to the sample. The (ordered) data are: 113   128   150   150   154   183   201   222   391

Compare the results of examples 15 and 16 with those of examples 13 and 14. In examples 13 and 14 the mean changed from 162.625 pounds to 188 pounds, an increase of 25.375 pounds. Such a change is not a trivial increase. However, in examples 15 and 16 the median increased from 152 pounds to 154 pounds, a much smaller increase. The median is resistant to the outlier being added to the data set.

The sample mean $\overline{X}$ is the point at which the histogram balances. Since outliers influence the mean, for skewed distributions the mean is pulled in the direction of the long tail. Since the median is resistant to outliers, it is not affected as much by the skewness of a distribution. Hence for a symmetric distribution the mean and median will be nearly the same (see graph 1 below). For a skewed right distribution the mean ($\overline{X}$) will be significantly greater than the median (M) (see graph 2). Finally, for a skewed left distribution, the mean ($\overline{X}$) will be significantly less than the median (M) (see graph 3).

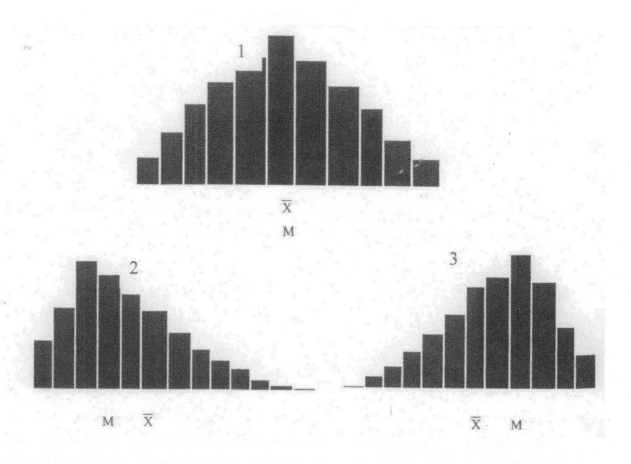

Attendance at Statistics Review Sessions Example:

A statistics course at a large university provides free to students statistics review sessions that students can use to answer questions, with help solving problems, and with help studying for tests. The course instructor is interested in the number of students who attend each hour of review session, and selects a sample of 15 review session hours spread out over a month's time. The number of students who attended these 15 review session hours is as follows.

6   1   8   3   1   5   11   7   4   28   12   9   2   10   13

Calculate the mean and median of this data.

What do the values suggest about the shape of the distribution?

28 is twice as large all the other observations and could be considered an outlier. If it were removed from the data set, which of the mean or the median would be affected more?

B. Measures of Spread (or Dispersion or Variation)

In Moore: Read pages 43 – 45 and 49 – 58 .

A constant was defined to be a characteristic in which the measurements of the characteristic do not change in repeated measurements over time. For a constant, the mean and median are both the constant value (for example, there are 31 days in January every year, so both the mean and median of the number of days in January is 31), and there is no spread (or dispersion or variation) in the data. However, when the measurement of the characteristic does change from measurement to measurement, the characteristic is called a variable and it becomes of interest to measure the amount of spread (or dispersion or variation) in the data. Our goal is to discuss ways of measuring the spread (or dispersion or variation), with particular interest in measuring the amount of spread around the central values, either the mean or the median. In what follows we discuss three measures of spread, how to calculate them, and characteristics of each.

1. Range

The **range** is the simplest measure of data variation, being the difference between the smallest (minimum) and largest (maximum) observations in the data set.

Range = maximum – minimum

Hence the range is a measure of overall spread, not variation about a central value. Since outliers are located at the tails of the distribution, outliers can heavily influence the range. This is illustrated in the following example.

Example 17
The weights of the 9 entertainers are repeated below. Calculate the range of the data both without and with the professional wrestler's weight of 391, and compare to see the impact of the outlier.

128   150   183   222   113   154   201   150   391

Without:

With:

2.   Standard Deviation

Since we want to describe the variability around the center of a distribution, it would better to discuss measures of variability around the mean and the median. A measure of variability about the mean is called the **standard deviation**. A **deviation** from the mean is the amount that a particular observation X is from the mean $\overline{X}$. So a deviation is $X - \overline{X}$.

For example, suppose in a sample of five students the ages of the students are 20, 21, 22, 25 and 32, such that the mean is $\overline{X} = 24$. Then the deviations from the mean are $20 - 24 = -4$, $21 - 24 = -3$, $22 - 24 = -2$, $25 - 24 = 1$ and $32 - 24 = 8$. The standard deviation is a measure of the "typical" deviation from the mean, similar to an average but calculated a little differently.

The **population standard deviation** is denoted by the Greek symbol σ (read sigma). Since all individuals of the population are usually not known, like the population mean μ the population standard deviation σ usually cannot be computed. Instead the population standard deviation is usually estimated by the **sample standard deviation**, denoted by S and calculated as:

$$S = \sqrt{\frac{\sum(X - \overline{X})^2}{n - 1}}$$

From the formula for the sample standard deviation one can see that the standard deviation is a measure of spread around the mean $\overline{X}$, and that the calculation of the individual deviations from the mean $X - \overline{X}$ are required to calculate the standard deviation. Once again the symbol Σ implies add or sum the values that follow.

The calculation of the sample standard deviation can be broken down into the following six steps.

1.   Calculate the sample mean $\overline{X}$. In the example above, the sample mean is $\overline{X} = 24$.

2.   Compute the n deviations from the mean by subtracting the sample mean $\overline{X}$ from each observation: $X - \overline{X}$. If these deviations are added the sum should always be 0 (or close to 0 if some rounding has occurred): $\sum(X - \overline{X}) = 0$. In the example above, the deviation are -4, -3, -2, 1 and 8, which sum to 0.

3.   For each of the n deviations, square each deviation: $(X - \overline{X})^2$. In the example above the squares of the deviations are $(-4)^2 = 16$, $(-3)^2 = 9$, $(-2)^2 = 4$, $(1)^2 = 1$ and $(8)^2 = 64$.

4.   Sum the squared deviations: $\sum(X - \overline{X})^2$. In the example above, this sum would be $16 + 9 + 4 + 1 + 64 = 94$.

5. Divide the sum of squared deviation by n – 1: $\dfrac{\sum(X-\overline{X})^2}{n-1}$. The divisor n – 1 is called the

degrees of freedom and will take on significance when we get to later chapters. In the example

above the sample size is n = 5, so this becomes $\dfrac{94}{5-1} = \dfrac{94}{4} = 23.5$.

6. Take the square root of the above number to determine the sample standard deviation:

$S = \sqrt{\dfrac{\sum(X-\overline{X})^2}{n-1}}$. In the example above, this means s = $\sqrt{23.5} = 4.85$.

For the example above with the ages of five students, the standard deviation of 4.85 implies that the "typical" deviation around the mean age of 24 is about 4.85 years.

Another measure of spread around that mean that is related to the standard deviation is the **variance**, which is the result one gets following step 5 (before taking the square root). The **population variance** is denoted by the Greek symbol σ^2 (read sigma squared) and since the population is usually unknown the population variance is estimated using the **sample variance** denoted by S^2 and calculated as $S^2 = \dfrac{\sum(X-\overline{X})^2}{n-1}$.

Note that in step 3 of the standard deviation calculation the deviations are squared, and a square root is not taken until step 6. Hence the standard deviation is measure in the units of the original data (the example above, the standard deviation is 4.85 years). However, for the variance the square root is not taken and hence the variance is measured in the units of the original data squared. In the example above, the variance is 23.5 years squared. Hence the standard deviation is much easier to interpret and use than the variance.

The standard deviation and the variance are measures of spread around the mean, and they will both always be greater than or equal to 0. They will equal 0 only if there is no variation in the data, meaning all the observations are the same (a constant).

Example 18

The weights of the sample of 8 entertainers are repeated below. Calculate the standard deviation of this data.

128   150   183   222   113   154   201   150

Being a measure of spread around the mean, the standard deviation is the most often used measure of spread and will be used in many of the inference problems that we consider in later chapters. However, the standard deviation and variance both have one big disadvantage. Since outliers affect the mean and the calculation of the standard deviation (and variance) requires the mean to be calculated, then the standard deviation (and variance) is also highly influenced by outliers. Therefore, the sample mean $\overline{X}$ best describes the <u>center</u> of a **symmetric** distribution, and the sample standard deviation S best describes the <u>spread</u> of a **symmetric** distribution. When considering heavily skewed distributions with outliers, the mean and standard deviation may not be the preferred measures of center and spread, respectively. To illustrate the effect that outliers have on the standard deviation, consider the following example.

Example 19

Calculate the standard deviation of the weights of the sample of entertainers when the professional wrestler who weighs 391 pounds is added to the data set.

128   150   183   222   113   154   201   150   391

3. Interquartile Range

As mentioned above the range is a measure of overall spread that is <u>not</u> resistant to outliers, and both the standard deviation and variance are measures of spread around the mean and hence both are also <u>not</u> resistant to outliers. To calculate a measure of spread that is resistant to outlier one should consider a measure of spread around the median. One measure of the spread around the median is the **interquartile range (IQR)** and, like the median, the interquartile range is resistant to outliers. Hence the IQR may be a better measure of spread than the range and standard deviation (or variance) when the distribution is skewed.

Recall that the median is the central measurement that is larger than 50% of the data and that is smaller than the other 50% of the data. Thus the median can also be thought of as the <u>middle quartile.</u> The **lower quartile**, denoted Q_1, is the measurement that is larger than 25% of the data and that is smaller than 75% of the data. The **upper quartile**, denoted Q_3, is the measurement that is larger than 75% of the data and that is smaller than the other 25%. Hence the lower quartile, median, and upper quartile divide the distribution into fourths (quarters). The lower and upper quartiles Q_1 and Q_3 enclose the middle 50% of the data, and the interquartile range, which is the difference between the lower and upper quartiles, $IQR = Q_3 - Q_1$, measures the <u>range</u> of the middle 50% of the data.

As an example, consider the following data set. The eight observations are divided into four sets of two observations each, and the IQR is the range of the middle 50% of the data.

$$
\begin{array}{c c | c c | c c | c c}
 & & Q_1 & & M & & Q_3 & \\
5 & 10 & 12 & 15 & 16 & 21 & 25 & 89 \\
\end{array}
$$

middle 50% of data

The procedure for calculating the IQR of a sample is as follows.

1. Arrange the data from smallest to largest.

2. Calculate the median location $\dfrac{n+1}{2}$ and median as described earlier.

3. Find the lower and upper quartiles.

   (i) If the sample size n is an **odd** number, then the median will be the middle ordered observation without having to average the middle two observations. The lower quartile Q_1 is the median of the ordered observations to the <u>left</u> of the median, and the upper quartile Q_3 is the median of the ordered observations to the <u>right</u> of the median.

For example, if n = 21, then $\frac{n+1}{2} = \frac{21+1}{2} = 11$ such that the median is the 11th ordered observation. Then Q_1 is the median of the 10 ordered observations to the left of the median, and Q_3 is the median of the 10 ordered observations to the right of the median.

(ii) If the sample size n is an **even** number, then the median will be the <u>average</u> of the middle two ordered observations. In this case the smaller of the middle two observations is considered as part of the ordered observations less than the median, and Q_1 is the median of the ordered observations to the left of the median. Also in this case the larger of the middle two observations is considered as part of the ordered observations greater than the median, and Q_3 is the median of the ordered observations to the right of the median.

For example, if n = 24, then $\frac{n+1}{2} = \frac{24+1}{2} = 12.5$ and the median is the average of the 12th and 13th ordered observations. The 12th ordered observation is considered to be less than the median, and Q_1 is the median of the smallest 12 ordered observations (those less than the median). The 13th ordered observation is considered to be greater than the median, and Q_3 is the median of the largest 12 ordered observations (those greater than the median).

In this example with n = 24, it is possible that the 12th and 13th ordered observations are the same number (say they are both 82). Then the median is the average of these two numbers (which is also 82). When the quartiles are calculated, one of the numbers is included with the data set less than the median, and the other is included with the data set greater than the median. Hence one of the 82's is in the lower data set, and the other 82 is in the upper data set.

4. Calculate the IQR = $Q_3 - Q_1$. The resulting number gives us the range of the middle 50% of the data and reflects a measure of spread around the median value.

The method described above is not a unique method for determining the interquartile range, but it is a very convenient procedure and it is the procedure used by the TI-83/84 calculator (see page 93 for details).

Example 20

The weights of the sample of 8 entertainers are repeated below. Calculate the IQR for this data.

128   150   183   222   113   154   201   150

Example 21

Calculate the IQR when the professional wrestler is added to the sample of entertainers.

128   150   183   222   113   154   201   150   391

Attendance at Statistics Review Sessions Example:

A statistics course at a large university provides free to students statistics review sessions that students can use to answer questions, with help solving problems, and with help studying for tests. The course instructor is interested in the number of students who attend each hour of review session, and selects a sample of 15 review session hours spread out over a month's time. The number of students who attended these 15 review session hours is as follows.

6   1   8   3   1   5   11   7   4   28   12   9   2   10   13

Calculate the range, standard deviation and interquartile range of this data.

28 is twice as large all the other observations and could be considered an outlier. If it were removed from the data set, which of the range, standard deviation and interquartile range would be affected the least?

The last observation in the data set is 13, and it is the second largest number in the data set (only 28 is larger). If the 13 were changed to 23, which of the measures of spread (range, standard deviation, interquartile range) would be affected by this change and which would not?

C.   Boxplots

In Moore: Read pages 45 – 49

In the last chapter we discussed the stem-and-leaf plot and the histogram, both of which are graphical methods for displaying quantitative data. We then learned how to use the stem-and-leaf plot and/or histogram to describe the center, spread, shape and any unusual features in the distribution. Another graphical method of displaying quantitative data that uses several of the numerical measures learned in this chapter is the **boxplot**. Once constructed a boxplot can also be used to give information on the shape (symmetry or skewness) of a distribution, on the center and spread in a distribution, and on the concentrations of data values in the tails of a distribution (outliers).

The procedure for constructing a boxplot is as follows.

1.   Order the data from smallest to largest.

2.   Calculate the median and lower and upper quartiles as described earlier in the chapter, and display this information, together with the minimum and maximum measurements, in a **five-number summary.** A five-number summary divides the entire data set up into quarters (fourths), and each component of a five-number summary is displayed on the boxplot.

$$\text{minimum} \quad Q_1 \quad \text{median} \quad Q_3 \quad \text{maximum}$$

3.   Compute the interquartile range, $IQR = Q_3 - Q_1$.

4.   To provide a mathematical rule for identifying an observation as being an outlier, compute what are called the **fence values** and use these fence values to determine if any outliers exist and if so what they are. The fence values are not displayed on the boxplot, and they are calculated as follows:

lower fence $= Q_1 - 1.5(IQR)$ and   upper fence $= Q_3 + 1.5(IQR)$.

Any measurement in the data set <u>less than</u> the lower fence is considered an **outlier**, and any measurement in the data set <u>greater than</u> the upper fence is considered an **outlier**. A data set may have multiple outliers, on either end of the distribution (or both), and of course it is possible that a data set may not have any outliers.

5. Determine the lower and upper **adjacent values** (also called **whisker values**). After removing the outliers (if any), the **lower adjacent value** is the <u>smallest</u> observation that remains in the data set and the **upper adjacent value** is the <u>largest</u> observation that remains in the data set. Note that the minimum value will be identified as being either an outlier or the lower adjacent value, and similarly the maximum value will be identified to be either an outlier or the upper adjacent value.

6. Draw the boxplot by completing the following steps.
   (i). Draw and label an axis (can be either horizontal or vertical).
   (ii). Construct a box, where the ends of the box are Q_1 and Q_3.
   (iii). Draw a line through the box corresponding to the median.
   (iv). Mark an "x" at the lower and upper adjacent values, and draw a dashed line from each "x" to the end of the box.
   (v). Indicate all outliers with a circle.

Once a boxplot has been constructed it can be used to describe the four components of a distribution in more detail than when using a stem-and-leaf plot or a histogram.

(1) The center of the distribution can be described by stating the median.

(2) The spread of the distribution can be described using either the IQR (the length of the box itself) or the range (since both the minimum and maximum values are marked as either outliers or adjacent values).

(3) The shape of the distribution, in particular the symmetry or skewness of a distribution, can be described by observing if the median is in the middle of the box and if the adjacent values are equal distances from the box. Details for describing the shape of the distribution are provided after the next example.

(4) Any unusual observations in the tails of the distribution (outliers).

Example 22

The data below reflect the number of text messages received per month for a random sample of 50 college students. Construct a boxplot to graphically display this data. Note that the data is ordered from smallest to largest.

350	450	470	470	480	480	480	500	510	520	520	530	530	530
540	540	540	540	540	550	550	550	560	560	560	560	560	570
570	570	570	570	570	570	580	580	580	580	590	590	600	610
610	610	620	620	630	650	650	720

A boxplot can be used to describe the shape of the distribution. If the boxplot has the median near the middle of the box, and if the adjacent values are nearly the same distance from the ends of the box, then the distribution is <u>symmetric</u>. A symmetric boxplot that has outliers on **both** ends of the distribution is sometimes referred to as a <u>long-tailed</u> distribution.

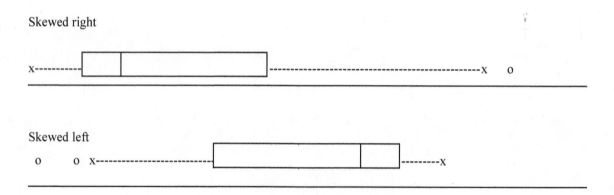

Symmetric

Long-tailed

A boxplot can also indicate that the distribution is skewed if any one (or more) of the following three conditions exist. First, looking at the box itself, if the median is not in the middle of the box but instead is closer to one end, the distribution could be skewed in the direction of the longer distance between the median and the end of the box. Second, looking at the adjacent values, if one is further from the end of the box than the other, the distribution could be skewed in the direction of the adjacent value that is further from the box. Finally, if there are outliers on **only one** end of the distribution, then the distribution could be skewed in that direction.

Skewed right

Skewed left

The boxplot in example 22 has approximately the symmetric shape, but the three outliers, two of which are on one end of the distribution and the third on the other end of the distribution, suggest a possible long-tailed distribution.

Side-by-side boxplots can be used to compare the distributions (center, spread, shape, outliers) of several distributions. To do so the five-number summaries and other statistics are computed for each distribution, and the boxplots drawn side-by-side using a common axis

88

<u>Attendance at Statistics Review Sessions Example</u>:

A statistics course at a large university provides free to students statistics review sessions that students can use to answer questions, with help solving problems, and with help studying for tests. The course instructor is interested in the number of students who attend each hour of review session, and selects a sample of 15 review session hours spread out over a month's time. The number of students who attended these 15 review session hours is as follows.

6   1   8   3   1   5   11   7   4   28   12   9   2   10   13

List the components of the five-number summary, and construct a boxplot to graphically display this data.

Describe the distribution of the number of students attending each hour of review session.

Additional Reading and Examples

1. A primary goal of statistics is to describe population distributions. As discussed in the previous section, this involves describing the center of the distribution, the spread (or dispersion or variation) of the distribution, the shape of the distribution, and any unusual features. The characteristics discussed in this section allow for a more specific description of the center and spread of a distribution, and when combined with the graphical procedures allow for the most complete specification.

2. The goal is to describe the center and spread of a <u>population</u> distribution. However, in most problems data for the entire population is not known, and the formulas and calculations illustrated in this section primarily involve statistics computed from sample data. The calculation of these statistics is descriptive statistics, and using these sample statistics to make statements about population parameters will be the primary focus of the statistical inference chapters to come later.

3. As a matter of convenience, Greek letters or symbols (such as μ, η, σ^2 or σ) are used to denote population parameters and alpha letters (such as $\overline{X}$, M, S or S^2) are used to denote sample statistics. This is a generally accepted method for distinguishing between parameters and statistics and will remain consistent for the rest of the book.

4. In most practical problems the mean and standard deviation are the measures used to describe the center and spread of the distribution. These statistics are used because they have nice mathematical properties that allow for easier derivations of other statistics. However, because outliers affect both the mean and standard deviation, these other statistics and the inference procedures associated with them require the assumption of near normal (or symmetric) distributions. If the distribution is not normal, then procedures based on the median and interquartile range may be better. In these cases, the five-number summary does a better job of describing the distribution than does the mean and standard deviation.

5. Earthquakes occur worldwide and are one of the most catastrophic natural disasters. The data below reveal the number of deaths caused by 15 of the largest earthquakes in the last 30 years (these earthquakes all measured 5.5 or greater on the Richter scale). Year 2010 earthquakes in Haiti and Chile are not included in this sample.

250   81   1300   146   4200   4000   1000   1000   55000   62   114   8   40000   1621   1200

Of interest is to describe the distribution of the deaths in these earthquakes. A stem-and-leaf plot shows that the distribution is heavily skewed to the right due to the earthquakes in Armenia and Iran that killed (respectively) 55,000 and 40,000 people.

Due to the skewness of the distribution the median may be a more reliable measure of central location than the mean. The mean of this data is

$$\bar{x} = \frac{250+81+1300+146+4200+4000+1000+1000+55000+62+114+8+40000+1621+1200}{15} = \frac{109982}{15} = 7332.13$$

When the two extreme values are removed, the mean becomes

$$\bar{x} = \frac{250+81+1300+146+4200+4000+1000+1000+62+114+8+1621+1200}{13} = \frac{14982}{13} = 1152.46 \text{, a big}$$

difference (the mean drops from 7332.13 to 1152.46).

To calculate the median we must first order the data from smallest to largest:

8 62 81 114 146 250 1000 1000 1200 1300 1621 4000 4200 *40000* *55000*

The median is located at the $\frac{n+1}{2} = \frac{15+1}{2} = 8^{th}$ ordered observation, and hence the median is 1000. When the two outliers are removed, the median is located at the $\frac{n+1}{2} = \frac{13+1}{2} = 7^{th}$ ordered observation and the median remains **unchanged** at 1000.

In terms of the spread in the distribution, the above discussion indicates that the interquartile range is likely a better measure of spread for this skewed distribution than the standard deviation. Using all of the data, the lower quartile is the median of the smallest 7 ordered observations, which is $Q_1 = 114$, while the upper quartile is the median of the largest 7 ordered observations, which is $Q_3 = 4000$. Hence the interquartile range is IQR = $Q_3 - Q_1$ = 4000 – 114 = 3886.

When the two outliers are removed, the lower quartile is the median of the smallest 6 ordered observations, which is $Q_1 = \frac{81+114}{2} = 97.5$, while the upper quartile is the median of the largest 6 ordered observations, which is $Q_3 = \frac{1300+1621}{2} = 1460.5$ (recall that 40000 and 55000 have been removed). Hence the interquartile range is IQR = $Q_3 - Q_1 = 1460.5 - 97.5 = 1363$.

The chart below contains the calculations required to compute the standard deviation.

$x - \bar{x}$	$(x - \bar{x})^2$
250-7332.13=-7082.13	50156612.55
81-7332.13 =-7251.13	52578934.62
1300-7332.13 = -6032.13	36386632.55
146-7332.13=7186.13	51640512.28
4200-7332.13= -3132.13	9810259.22
4000-7332.13=-3332.13	11103112.55
1000-7332.l3=-6332.13	40095912.55
1000-7332.13=-6332.13	40095912.55
55000-7332.13 = 47667.87	2272225513
62-7332.13 =-7270.13	52854838.68
114- 7332.13= -7218.13	52101448.82
8-7332.13 =-7324.13	53642929.08
40000-7332.13 = 32667.87	1067189513
1621-7332.13=-5711.13	32617043.95
1200-7332.13 = 6132.13	37603059.22
	3860102235

So the standard deviation is s = $\sqrt{\dfrac{\sum (x-\bar{x})^2}{n-1}} = \sqrt{\dfrac{3860102235}{15-1}} = \sqrt{275,721,588.2} = 16,604.87$ deaths. Note that

with all the data the mean and standard deviation indicate that the typical number of deaths per earthquake is 7,332 (a value that is not close to any of the observed values) with a standard deviation of 16,605 deaths, which is also not reasonable. If the two outliers are removed the standard deviation becomes s = 1,421.23. Reporting that the typical number of deaths is 1,152 with a standard deviation of 1,421.23 is much more reasonable and much closer to the median and interquartile range values.

To display the data using a boxplot, the five-number summary is: 8   114   1000   4000   55000.

With an IQR of 4000 − 114 = 3886, the lower and upper fence values are:

Lower fence= Q_1 − 1.5(IQR) = 114 − 1.5 (3886) = -5715

Upper fence = Q_3 + 1.5(IQR) = 4000 + 1.5(3886) = 9829

Then the lower adjacent value is 8 and the upper adjacent value is 4200, with both 40000 and 55000 being outliers. The skewed to the right boxplot is then

6. For symmetrical/normal distributions, often it is possible to estimate the standard deviation by calculating the range and dividing by 4. For example, with the example above the range is 55000 − 8 = 54992, dividing by 4 gives an estimated standard deviation of 13,748. This is close to the calculated value of 16,604.87. When the two outliers are removed the range becomes 4200 − 8 = 4192, dividing by 4 gives an estimated standard deviation of

1,048. This is even closer to the calculated value of 1,421.23, which is expected since once the outliers are removed the distribution is closer to symmetric.

TI-83/84 Calculator

Suppose a set of data has been collected and entered into list L1 of the TI-83/84 calculator. See page 8 for details on entering data into a list. The following provides detailed steps for calculating the numerical summaries discussed in this chapter, and for generating a boxplot on the TI-83/84 calculator.

1. To get the numerical summaries, press **STAT** and use the right-arrow button to move the cursor to the **CALC** menu and press **ENTER**. Select the first option, **1:1-Var Stats**. Now enter the name of the list that contains the data (for example, list L1) and press **ENTER**. You can now use the up-arrow and down-arrow buttons to scroll up and down to get the following values.

   $\overline{x}$ is the sample mean

   $\sum x$ is the sum of the data values

   $\sum x^2$ is the sum of the squared data values

   S_x is the sample standard deviation

   σ_x is the population standard deviation

   n is the sample size

   minX is the minimum value

   Q_1 is the lower quartile

   Med is the median

   Q_3 is the upper quartile

   maxX is the maximum value

   Note that the last five items on the above list are the five-number summary, and since we usually have sample data (as opposed to data for the entire population) we generally us Sx (instead of σ_x) for the standard deviation.

2. To generate a boxplot, begin by implementing the first three steps given on page 64 to prepare the calculator to generate a plot. For a boxplot with outliers, for the **Type:** of graph setting choose the option in the bottom left corner. Once that graph is highlighted, press **ENTER** to select it. Assuming that your data is in list L1, press the down-arrow button to move the cursor to **Xlist:**. Note that your cursor is in ALPHA mode, and to choose list L1 you would press the **2nd** button followed by the 1 button. Now press the down-arrow button to move to **Freq:**, and since all the data is in one list, enter **1** here. Note that while in ALPHA mode, to leave ALPHA mode in order to enter a numerical value the **ALPHA** button needs to be pressed. Now use the down-arrow button to

move to **Mark:** and choose a symbol to indicate outliers. Now you must set the window size, so you can see the graph properly. To do so, press **ZOOM**. To select appropriate dimensions, simply select **9: ZoomStat** (you will need to use the down-arrow button to scroll down to this option) to view the boxplot. You can press **TRACE** and move the cursor across the plot to see the values for the plot and any outliers.

Practice Problems:

IV. 1. The scores of 18 first-year college women on the Survey of Study Habits and Attitudes (SSHA) test are as follows.

154   109   137   115   152   140   154   178   101   103   126   126   137   165   165   129   200   148

(a). Find the mean score on the test for all 18 first-year college women.

(b). A stem-and-leaf plot suggests that the score of 200 is an outlier. Recompute the mean score on the test after dropping the score of 200. Briefly describe how the outlier changes the mean.

(c). Calculate the median score on the test, first for all 18 scores and then for the 17 scores that remain when the outlier is removed. Briefly describe how the outlier changes the median.

IV. 2. (a). The <u>median</u> amount of time that it took 7 students to take a statistics test was 38 minutes. If the times that it took two additional students to take the test were 30 and 43 minutes, what would be the <u>median</u> amount of time that it took the 9 students to take the statistics test?

(b). The <u>mean</u> amount of time that it took 7 students to take a statistics test was 38 minutes. If the times that it took two additional students to take the test were 30 and 43 minutes, what would be the <u>mean</u> amount of time that it took the 9 students to take the statistics test?

IV. 3. A local church congregation is concerned with how they will pay to put a new roof on their church building. They decide to create a special roof repair fund, to which congregation members are asked to pledge their contribution to the project. A random sample of 18 of the pledge cards currently received contained the following pledge amounts (in dollars).

720 1200 1800 850 775 700 825 1125 1000 500 685 950 800 640 750 900 650 725

A stem-and-leaf plot of this data suggests that 1800 is an outlier. Compute measures of central location and spread that will be resistant to this outlier value.

IV. 4. The National Science Foundation, Division of Science Resources Studies, collects data on the ages of recipients of science and engineering doctoral degrees. Results are published in *Survey of Earned Doctorates*. A simple random sample of one year's recipients yields the following ages.

37   28   36   33   37   43   41   28   24   44   27   24

Calculate the range, standard deviation, and interquartile range for this data. Which do you feel is the best measure of dispersion in this data?

IV. 5. Exercise is fundamental to a healthy life. The following data are the maximum number of sit-ups completed by a random sample of 19 participants in an exercise class after one month in the program.

24   31   54   62   28   37   55   18   27   58   32   37   41   55   39   56   42   35   40

Construct a graph to display this fitness data, then compute appropriate numerical summaries. Write a brief description of the important features of the distribution.

IV. 6. Universal properties in Orlando, Florida have well-kept lawns and vegetation that are very attractive to small lizards. A random sample of 14 people were asked to count the number of lizards they saw over one 24-hour period during their vacation at Universal. The data is as follows.

42   64   70   87   90   100   69   7   52   94   79   105   96   39

(a).   Construct a stem-and-leaf plot for this data and use the stem-and-leaf plot to describe the distribution.

(b).   Calculate the mean and median of this data. Based on the shape of the distribution described in part (a), which would you prefer to use to describe the center of the distribution?

(c).   Calculate the range, standard deviation, and interquartile range of this data. Based on the shape of the distribution described in part (a), which would you prefer to use to describe the spread of the distribution?

IV. 7. The rejuvenation of an older region of a local city will involve the destruction of 13 buildings and the renovation of 17 other buildings. The ages of these 30 buildings are displayed in the boxplot below. Use this boxplot to completely describe the distribution of the ages of the buildings.

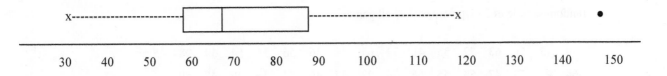

IV. 8. The distribution of the ages of the 535 members of Congress in 2002 is displayed in the boxplot below. Use this boxplot to completely describe the distribution of the ages of the members of Congress.

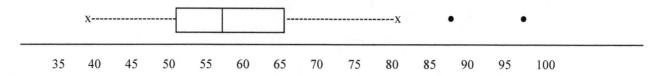

35	40	45	50	55	60	65	70	75	80	85	90	95	100

IV. 9. Babe Ruth is recognized as one of the greatest home run hitters of all-time, Roger Maris held the single season home run record for 37 years, and Mark McGwire was considered the best home run hitters of the late 1990's. The data below give the number of home runs that Ruth hit in his 15 years with the New York Yankees, the number of home runs that Maris hit in his 10 years in the American League, and the number of home runs that McGwire has hit in his first 14 years in the major leagues.

Babe Ruth: 54   59 35 41   46 25   47   60   54 46   49 46   41 34   22

Roger Maris: 13   23 26 16   33 61   28   39   14   8

Mark McGwire: 49   32 33 39   22 42   9   9   39 52   58 70   65 32

Compute the five-number summary for each player and make side-by-side boxplots of the home run distributions. What does your graph show about Ruth, Maris, and McGwire as home run hitters?

IV. 10. The number of miles that a random sample of 40 countries had to travel to reach the 2004 Summer Olympic Games in Athens, Greece is given below. The data is measured from the capital of each country to Athens.

1689   442   2790 3106 2107 1405 1683 1212   794 2650 7327 2665 4895 4337 1790
3678 6326 2238 1490 2053 5125 5688 2354 1129 3489 4285 2970 8002 2100 3560
3456 6101 5337 3575 4103 3875   979 1945 2857 3344

Compute the five-number summary, and construct and interpret a boxplot for this data.

IV. 11. Upward, the world's largest Christian sports program for children, was created with a vision to provide the best sports experience possible for every child. Each year some 1 million people around the world play, coach, referee, or volunteer in Upward sports leagues and camps hosted by more than 2,600 churches. Anyone – children and volunteers of any faith or no faith – can participate in Upward sports. Specifically designed for children in K5 through sixth grade, Upward aims to bring out "the winner" in every child – regardless of the game's score. The data below gives the total number of points scored in a random sample of 33 Upward basketball games.

30   45   51   63   72   35   41   33   67   48   36   56   31   54   60   98   45
64   43   50   47   53   55   66   76   23   37   40   54   46   39   47   59

(a). Construct a boxplot for this data.

(b). Based on the boxplot, describe completely the distribution of the number of points scored for this sample of 33 Upward basketball games.

(c). Compute the mean and standard deviation of this data.

IV. 12. Richmond Ford, located at 4600 West Broad Street in Richmond, Virginia, is one of the oldest automobile Dealerships in the country. A sample of 30 pre-owned vehicles was selected from the population of all pre-owned vehicles owned by Richmond Ford, and the mileage of each vehicle is recorded below.

16,354 12,682 31,818 55,284 70,971 5,225 20,859 36,934 62,495 15,761 68,414

42,695 74,910 45,899 34,067 65,794 10,884 57,994 13,833 40,293 12,046 26,677

36,997 63,280 49,303 22,190 26,286 14,076 19,984 94,208

(a). Construct a boxplot for this data.

(b). Based on the boxplot, describe completely the distribution of mileages for this sample of 30 pre-owned vehicles.

(c). This same data was analyzed in practice problem III.13 on page 68, and a stem-and-leaf plot and histogram were constructed. How does the description of the distribution based on the boxplot compare to the description of the distribution based on the stem-and-leaf plot and histogram constructed in practice problem III.13?

V. Describing Relationships Between Variables

A. Introduction

In Moore: Read Chapter 4 (pages 95 – 97) and Chapter 5 (pages 142 – 143)

Up to this point we have learned several graphical and numerical methods for describing the distribution of a single variable. However, in many processes we have more than one variable and may be interested in describing the relationship between any two of the variables. The primary goal is to describe a **causal relationship** between the two variables, implying that changes in one of the variables are thought to explain or cause changes in the second variable. However, all relationships are not causal – in some cases we would only be interested in the **association** between the variables.

As an example, with younger children, as they get older they tend to gain weight and grow taller. Hence if the two variables are age of the child and weight of the child (or age of the child and height of the child) there would be a causal relationship because as a child gets older this <u>causes</u> the child's weight (or height) to increase.

Contrast this with this example. Suppose there exists a group of college students, all of whom are in the same math and chemistry classes. It is noticed that those students who did well on the first chemistry test also did well on the first math test. Doing well on the chemistry test did <u>not cause</u> the student to do well on the math test, but it is <u>associated</u> with this fact. There are other factors, such as the overall ability of the student or the amount of effort toward studying, that may be causing the relationship that is being observed.

We will begin by looking at relationships between two quantitative variables, and will conclude the section by analyzing relationships between qualitative or categorical variables.

Suppose we have two <u>quantitative</u> (discrete or continuous) variables X and Y. If there is a causal relationship between X and Y, then this relationship can be described by writing Y as a function of X. This function (or mathematical equation) can then be used to <u>predict</u> Y values for specified values of X.

In this setting, the variable X is called the independent or explanatory variable. The **independent** or **explanatory** variable is the quantitative variable that has no restraints placed on it and that attempts to explain the observed outcomes of another variable. The other variable, Y, is called the **dependent** or **response variable**, and is the quantitative variable that measures an outcome of a process that is the effect or consequence of the independent variable. Note that actual observed values of X and Y are denoted by x and y, respectively.

For example, above, the age of the child would be the independent or explanatory variable X, and the weight of the child (or height of the child) would be the dependent or response variable Y.

Example 23

In an effort to sell more cars, a car dealership has been running ads on a local television station advertising the different models and price ranges of the cars on the lot that week. The car dealership is of moderate size, having between 100 and 125 on the lot each week. The goal is determine how well the number of television ads run in a particular week predicts the number of cars that will be sold that week. During a ten week period the dealer kept a weekly record of the number of television ads run versus the number of cars sold. In this situation identify the independent and dependent variables.

When describing relationships between two variables we would like to show a causal relationship between the independent and dependent variables – the fact that changes in X cause changes in Y. However, occasionally we observe an association between X and Y but there is no evidence that one variable is causing changes in another. This often results due to the existence of one or more **lurking variables**. A lurking variable is a variable that has an important effect on the relationship between the two variables X and Y but which is not included in the list of variables being studied.

In the example above with the college students enrolled in the same math and chemistry classes, the overall ability of the student and the amount of effort toward studying would both be examples of lurking variables.

When the effect of the explanatory variable X on the response variable Y interacts with the effect of a lurking variable on Y, then we say that X is **confounded** with the effect of the lurking variable.

We now turn our attention to describing the relationship between the independent variable X and the dependent variable Y. A complete description of this relationship includes specifying the direction, form and strength of the relationship, and to accurately describe these three things we need both a graph and a numerical descriptor. In the two sections that follow we learn about the scatterplot (a graph) and the correlation coefficient (a numerical descriptor).

B. Scatterplots

In Moore: Read Chapter 4 (pages 97 – 104)

The relationship between the independent or explanatory variable X and the dependent or response variable Y can be displayed graphically by plotting the data in a **scatterplot**. In a scatterplot we label the independent variable X along the horizontal axis, label the dependent variable Y along the vertical axis, and then we plot each (x, y) observation on the plot. The labeling of the axes can affect the appearance of the relationship as depicted by the scatterplot, so it is important to use equal increments on the axes that cover the range of the data.

Example 24

The data below are the observed number of ads run and the observed number of cars sold by a dealer in a ten week period. Construct a scatterplot to display the relationship between these two variables.

Number of Ads Run	Number of Cars Sold
6	15
20	31
0	10
14	16
25	28
16	20
28	40
18	25
10	12
8	15

Once the scatterplot has been constructed it can be used to specify the <u>direction</u>, <u>form</u> and <u>strength</u> of the relationship between the independent variable X and the dependent variable Y.

1. The **direction** determines the <u>type of association</u> between X and Y.

   (i) Two variables are **positively associated** if small values of X are associated with small values of Y and if large values of X are associated with large values of Y. A scatterplot where the general trend slopes <u>upward</u> from left to right indicates a positive association.

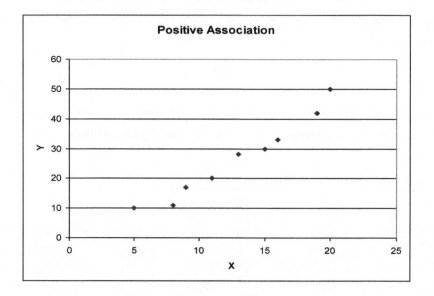

   (ii) Two variables are **negatively associated** if small values of X are associated with large values of Y, and large values of X are associated with small values of Y. A scatterplot where the general trend slopes <u>downward</u> from left to right indicates a negative association.

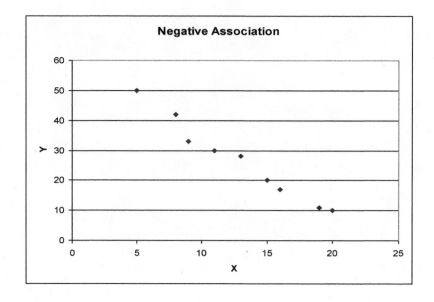

2. The **form** of the relationship describes the type of trend in the data. We typically look for a **linear** relationship, in which the data is scattered along a straight line. Not all relationships are linear, and two common types of **nonlinear** trends include quadratic relationships and exponential growth (or exponential decay).

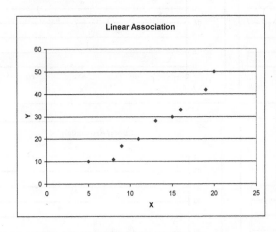

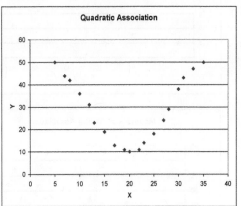

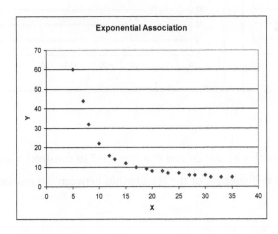

3. The **strength** of the relationship measures the amount of scatter around the general trend. Since we primarily are interested in determining linear relationships, when we speak of strength we are usually measuring scatter around some line. The more scatter revealed in the scatterplot, the weaker the relationship between the two variables. One method of numerically measuring the strength of the linear relationship between X and Y is to calculate the correlation coefficient. This will be discussed in the next section. In the scatterplots that follow the strength increases as we move from the top left to the bottom right scatterplot.

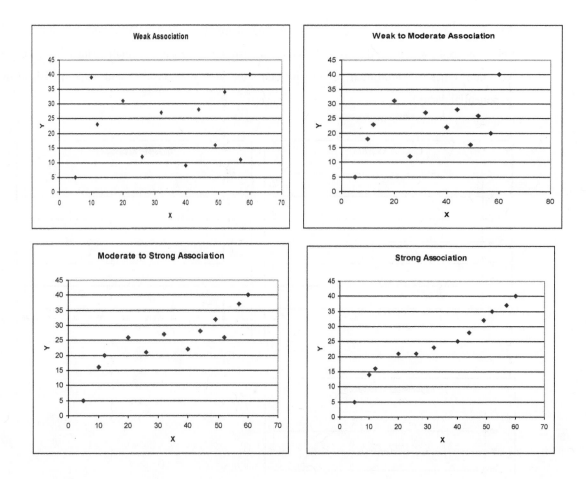

Example 25

For the car dealership data described in examples 23 and 24 and that was used to construct a scatterplot in example 24, describe the direction, form and strength of the relationship between the number of ads run and the number of cars sold.

C. Correlation

In Moore: Read Chapter 4 (pages 104 – 112)

The scatterplot is a graphical method for displaying the relationship between two variables, and for that reason is a useful tool. However, to accurately describe the relationship between the two variables, in addition to the scatterplot a numerical measure of the relationship is also needed. The **correlation coefficient** is a numerical measure of the direction and strength of the linear relationship between two variables. The correlation coefficient is related to the regression line (the regression line will be discussed in the next section), and measures the direction of the relationship and the amount of scatter of the observations around the regression line.

The **population correlation coefficient** is denoted by the Greek letter ρ (read rho). Since the entire population is usually unknown, the population correlation coefficient ρ is usually estimated using the **sample correlation coefficient**, denoted by r. The sample correlation coefficient r has the following properties.

1. The sample correlation coefficient r always falls between -1 and +1: $-1 \le r \le +1$, and is unitless.
2   A negative r indicates a negative association between the two variables.
3. A positive r indicates a positive association between the two variables.
4. A correlation near 0 implies that there is a very weak linear relationship. Since r measures the strength of a linear relationship, an r near 0 could result either from a strong nonlinear relationship (the graph on the right) or from no relationship at all (the graph on the left).

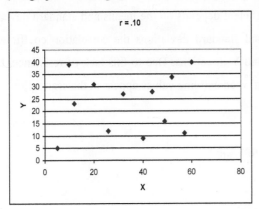 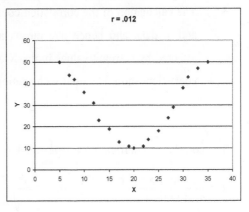

5. The strength of the linear relationship increases as r moves away from 0 toward -1 or +1. A correlation r near -1 or +1 indicates a strong linear relationship between X and Y, and if r is equal to exactly -1 or +1 there is a perfect linear relationship, meaning all the points fall exactly on a line.

Note that on the four scatterplots that follow the trend is positive and the correlation coefficient increases as the amount of scatter decreases.

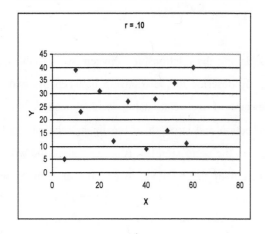

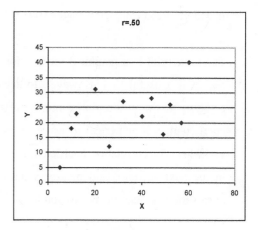

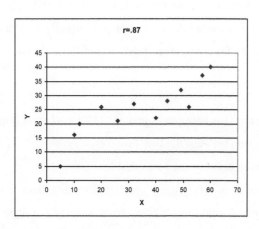

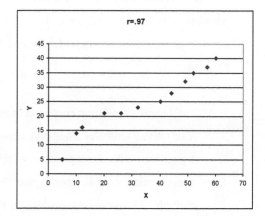

6. The calculation of the correlation coefficient depends on the means and standard deviations of the X and Y data, and hence like means and standard deviations the correlation coefficient is strongly affected by extreme values in the X and Y directions. Due to this lack of resistance, the correlation coefficient should be used with caution when extreme values appear in the scatterplot.

The correlation coefficient r is calculated as follows:

$$r = \frac{1}{n-1} \sum \left(\frac{x - \bar{x}}{s_x} \right) \left(\frac{y - \bar{y}}{s_y} \right) \quad \text{or} \quad r = \frac{S_{xy}}{\sqrt{S_{xx}S_{yy}}}$$

where $\bar{x}$ and s_x are the mean and standard deviation of the X variable values

$\bar{y}$ and s_y are the mean and standard deviation of the Y variable values

$$S_{xx} = \sum x^2 - \frac{\left(\sum x \right)^2}{n}$$

$$S_{yy} = \sum y^2 - \frac{\left(\sum y\right)^2}{n}$$

$$S_{xy} = \sum xy - \frac{\left(\sum x\right)\left(\sum y\right)}{n}$$

Above S_{xx} and S_{yy} are sum of squares terms that measure the amount of variation (or spread or dispersion) in the X and Y data, respectively. In fact, if you take both S_{xx} and S_{yy}, divide each by $n - 1$ and then take the square root, you have the standard deviations s_x and s_y. Since these are measures of spread, both S_{xx} and S_{yy} must <u>always</u> be non-negative, and will be positive unless all the values for a particular variable are the same, at which point the value will be 0.

S_{xy} is called a cross-project term, and it is the measure of how the X and Y variables move together. S_{xy} can be either positive or negative, and hence the sign of the correlation coefficient depends entirely on the sign of S_{xy}.

Example 26

The car dealer data that gives the observed number of ads run and the observed number of cars sold over a ten week period is repeated below (first two columns). The last three columns were calculated from the observed data, as follows. To get the column labeled x^2 the data in the first column was squared (for example, $6^2 = 36$). To get the column labeled y^2 the data in the second column was squared (for example, $15^2 = 225$). To get the column labeled xy the data in the first two columns were multiplied (for example, $6 \times 15 = 90$). Calculate and interpret the correlation coefficient.

Number of Ads Run (x)	Number of Cars Sold (y)	x^2	y^2	xy
6	15	36	225	90
20	31	400	961	620
0	10	0	100	0
14	16	196	256	224
25	28	625	784	700
16	20	256	400	320
28	40	784	1600	1120
18	25	324	625	450
10	12	100	144	120
8	15	64	225	120

Additional Reading and Examples

1. To completely determine the relationship between two variables, it is usually necessary to both construct a scatterplot and to compute the correlation coefficient r. Only computing and trying to interpret the correlation coefficient is occasionally misleading and may not describe the relationship that actually exists. See the activity on page 111.

2. The correlation coefficient is always between -1 and +1, and is unitless. When describing the relationship, it is necessary to describe the direction, form, and strength of the relationship. For some nonlinear relationships (such as quadratic relationships) it may not be possible to describe the direction because the trend is increasing over one range of data and decreasing over another.

3. Women made significant gains in the 1970's in terms of their acceptance into professions that had been traditionally populated by men. To measure just how big these gains were, the percentage of professional degrees awarded to women in 1973 – 1974 (X) will be compared to the percentage of professional degrees awarded to women in 1978 – 1979 (Y) for selected fields of study. The data is as follows:

Field	x = % degrees to women in 1973-1974	y = % degrees to women in 1978-1979
Dentistry	2.0%	11.9%
Law	11.5%	28.5%
Medicine	11.2%	23.1%
Optometry	4.2%	13.0%
Osteopathic medicine	2.8%	15.7%
Podiatry	1.1%	7.2%
Theology	5.5%	13.1%
Veterinary Medicine	11.2%	28.9%

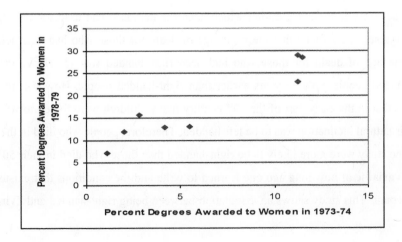

109

The scatterplot above shows a strong, positive, linear relationship between the two variables. This, together with the obvious increases in each field, illustrates the advancement made by women in the 1970's.

To calculate the correlation coefficient we must first calculate the summary statistics.

x	y	x^2	y^2	xy
2.0	11.9	4.00	141.61	23.80
11.5	28.5	132.25	812.25	327.75
11.2	23.1	125.44	533.61	258.72
4.2	13.0	17.64	169.00	54.60
2.8	15.7	7.84	246.49	43.96
1.1	7.2	1.21	51.84	7.92
5.5	13.1	30.25	171.61	72.05
11.2	28.9	125.44	835.21	323.68
49.5	141.4	444.07	2961.62	1112.48

$$S_{xx} = \sum x^2 - \frac{(\sum x)^2}{n} = 444.07 - \frac{(49.5)^2}{8} = 137.78875$$

$$S_{yy} = \sum y^2 - \frac{(\sum y)^2}{n} = 2961.62 - \frac{(141.4)^2}{8} = 462.375$$

$$S_{xy} = \sum xy - \frac{(\sum x)(\sum y)}{n} = 112.48 - \frac{(49.5)(141.4)}{8} = 237.5675$$

So the correlation coefficient is $r = \dfrac{S_{xy}}{\sqrt{(S_{xx})(S_{yy})}} = \dfrac{237.5675}{\sqrt{(137.78875)(462.375)}} = .9412$. This corresponds with the strong, positive, linear relationship illustrated in the scatterplot.

5. A highly publicized study by Coren and Halpern (1991, *Psychological Bulletin* 109, no. 1, PP. 90 – 106) stated that left-handed people do not live as long as right-handed people. The researchers sent letters to the next of kin for a random sample of recently deceased individuals, asking which hand the deceased had used for writing, drawing, and throwing a ball. The researchers found that the mean age of death for those who had been left-handed was 66, whereas the mean age of death for those who had been right-handed was 75. Hence they concluded that on average left-handed people die nine years earlier than right-handed people. However, they failed to take into account the fact that in the early part of the 20th century many children were forced to write with their right hands, even if their natural inclination was to be left-handed. Therefore, people who died in their 70's and 80's during the time of the study were more likely to be right-handed than those who died in their 50's and 60's. Therefore, the **lurking variable** of how long ago one learned to write and the conditions that existed at that time was not taken into account. This study shows an association between being right-handed and living longer, but not causation.

Review Activity - Anscombe Data

Students will be divided into four groups, and each group will be assigned one of the four data sets below. Each group is to compute the correlation coefficient for their data set (keep at least three decimal places). When all groups have completed their calculations, scatterplots will be constructed and students will compare the scatterplots and correlation coefficients, therefore illustrating the need to both construct a scatterplot and calculate the correlation coefficient. (Frank Anscombe (1973), "Graphs in Statistical Analysis," *American Statistician*, 27: 17 – 21.)

Data Set 1		Data Set 2		Data Set 3		Data Set 4	
x	y	x	y	x	y	x	y
10	8.04	10	9.14	10	7.46	8	6.58
8	6.95	8	8.14	8	6.77	8	5.76
13	7.58	13	8.74	13	12.74	8	7.71
9	8.81	9	8.77	9	7.11	8	8.84
11	8.33	11	9.26	11	7.81	8	8.47
14	9.96	14	8.10	14	8.84	8	7.04
6	7.24	6	6.13	6	6.08	8	5.25
4	4.26	4	3.10	4	5.39	19	12.50
12	10.84	12	9.13	12	8.15	8	5.56
7	4.82	7	7.26	7	6.42	8	7.91
5	5.68	5	4.74	5	5.73	8	6.89

D. Regression Line

In Moore: Read Chapter 5 (pages 125 – 147)

As mentioned earlier in this chapter, to completely describe the relationship between two variables we need to describe the direction, form and strength of the relationship. The scatterplot is a graphical tool to assist in describing the relationship, and the correlation coefficient quantifies the direction and strength of the linear relationship between the two variables. For the purposes of this section we are going to assume that there is a linear relationship between the independent and dependent variables, and our goal is to numerically describe this relationship. To do so we will construct a **regression line** that will model (explain) the linear dependence of the dependent variable Y on the independent variable X.

Recall that the equation of a line is Y= intercept + slope (X).

(NOTE: other mathematical expressions for the equation of a line are Y = a + bX or Y = mX + b. In the first expression a is the intercept and b is the slope, and in the second expression m is the slope and b is the intercept. We use the terms intercept and slope without attaching a letter to represent them.)

The **intercept** is the predicted value of Y when x = 0 (location where the line crosses the Y-axis). Hence when x = 0, the predicted y is the intercept value.

The **slope** is the amount that Y changes (increases if positive, decreases if negative) when X is increased by one unit. Hence if x increases by one unit, then the predicted y increases/decreases by slope units.

For example, suppose we want to use a child's age (X) to predict a child's weight (Y). The regression line is predicted weight = 6 + 10(age). The intercept is 6 and the slope is 10. The intercept of 6 implies that if a child is 0 years old (x = 0) then the predicted weight of the child is 6 pounds. The slope of 10 implies that as a child's age increases by 1 year, his or her predicted weight increases by 10 pounds.

Once the regression line is determined, we can use it to predict values of Y for specified values of X. The **prediction equation** is $\hat{Y}$ = intercept + slope (X), and our goal is to determine values for the intercept and slope such that the predicted values, $\hat{Y}$'s, are as close as possible to the observed values, the Y's.

Then y = an observed value of the dependent variable (a value in the data set) and

    $\hat{y}$ = the corresponding predicted value of the dependent variable.

The difference between these two values, $y - \hat{y}$, is defined to be a **residual**. The method we will use to determine values for the intercept and slope is called the **method of least squares** and involves minimizing the sum of the squared residuals. Hence the method of least squares makes $\sum \left(Y - \hat{Y} \right)^2$ as <u>small</u> as possible.

The least squares formulas for the intercept and slope are

$$\text{slope} = \frac{S_{xy}}{S_{xx}} \quad \text{or equivalently} \quad \text{slope} = r\left(\frac{s_y}{s_x} \right) \quad \text{and} \quad \text{int ercept} = \overline{y} - \text{slope}(\overline{x})$$

where $\overline{x}$ and $\overline{y}$ are the sample means of the X and Y data, respectively, and s_x and s_y are the sample standard deviations of the X and Y data. As defined in the previous section, $r = \dfrac{S_{xy}}{\sqrt{S_{xx}S_{yy}}}$ is the sample correlation coefficient, and S_{xx}, S_{yy} and S_{xy}, are as defined on pages 106 and 107.

These constants are used to define the regression line $\hat{Y} = \textbf{intercept} + \textbf{slope(X)}$, which can then be used to predict values of Y for specified values of X simply by substituting the given X values into the equation.

Example 27

For the car dealership data of examples 23 – 26, determine the equation of the regression line that can be used to predict number of cars sold (Y) from number of ads run (X) and interpret the slope and intercept values.

To predict Y values for specified X values, we simply substitute the X value into the prediction equation $\hat{Y}$ = intercept + slope(X) and solve for $\hat{Y}$. This prediction can (mathematically) be made for any value of X. However, when predicting, it is important that the value of the independent variable X falls in the range of the original data. The regression line describes the linear relationship between X and Y only for the range of data that we have. Predicting Y values for X values outside the range of the original values is called **extrapolation** and in most cases <u>should be avoided.</u>

For example, suppose we want to use a child's age (X) to predict a child's weight (Y). The regression line is predicted weight = 6 + 10(age). For a four-year old child, the prediction is predicted weight = 6 + 10(4) = 46 pounds, which is a logical weight for a 4 year old. However, if the prediction is done for a 45 year old, the predicted weight = 6 + 10(45) = 456 pounds, which is possible but very unlikely; and likewise for a 90 year old, predicted weight = 6 +10(90) = 906 pounds.

Once the regression line is determined it can be drawn on the scatterplot. To do so simply choose two values of X and substitute them into the regression equation to obtain predicted Y values. These two points can then be placed on the scatterplot and the line that connects them is the regression line. It is usually the case that choosing one of the two points to be the intercept (in other words, choose X = 0) minimizes the work required to draw the regression line.

Example 28
For the car dealership data of examples 23 – 27, predict Y = number of cars sold when the dealership runs X = 10, 20, and 200 ads. Use the intercept and predictions for x = 10 and x = 20 to draw the regression line on the scatterplot. The scatterplot constructed in example 24 on page 101 is repeated below.

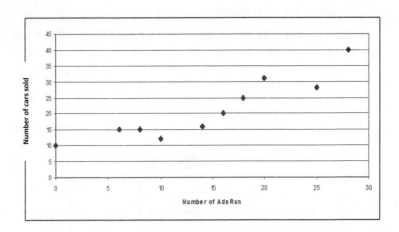

As mentioned earlier, the difference between an observed Y value (Y) and a predicted Y value ($\hat{Y}$) is called a residual. Hence a **residual** is the <u>vertical</u> deviation of a data point from the regression line. For example, when x = 20 ads were run, it is observed that y = 31 cars were sold (see data in example 26 on page 108). From the regression line we predict that $\hat{y}$ = 26.760 cars will be sold (see example 28 on page 115). Hence the residual is y - $\hat{y}$ = 31- 26.760 = 4.240. A similar calculation can be done for every observation in the original data set, with the results appearing in example 29 on the next page.

One property of residuals is that the sum of <u>all</u> residuals is <u>always</u> equal to 0 ($\sum (Y-\hat{Y})=0$). Also, the method of least squares implies that the sum of the squared residuals, $\sum (Y-\hat{Y})^2$ will be minimized.

The scatterplot can be used to describe the relationship between the two variables, and in particular to determine if there is a strong linear relationship between the variables. The residuals can be used to further analyze the quality and usefulness of the regression line. To do so, calculate the residual for each data point by substituting the x value into the regression equation and then subtracting the resulting predicted value from the observed y value. Then make a type of scatterplot called a **residual plot** by plotting the independent variable X values along the horizontal axis and the <u>residuals</u> along the vertical axis.

The ideal residual plot will have residuals that are close to 0, with an equal amount of variability (scatter) for each range of X values. A residual is "small" (close to 0) if the absolute value of the residual is small in comparison to the Y values. For example, if the Y data ranges from 20 to 40, then residuals between -5 and 5 are small. However, if the Y data ranges from 2 to 10, then residuals between -5 and 5 are fairly large.

A residual plot that reveals some type of pattern or which has different variability for different ranges of X values indicates that the linear regression procedure performed was <u>not</u> appropriate.

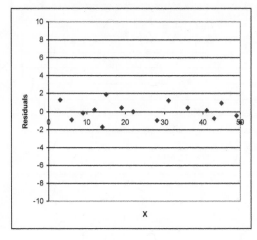

Random scatter – good

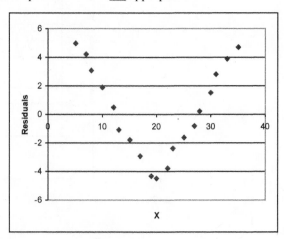

Quadratic trend - bad

116

Example 29

The car dealership data from examples 23 – 28 is repeated below, together with the predicted values and the residuals. Construct a residual plot, and use it to analyze the quality of the regression.

Ads Run (x)	Cars Sold (y)	$\hat{y} = 6.54 + 1.011(x)$	Residual = $y - \hat{y}$
6	15	12.606	2.394
20	31	26.760	4.240
0	10	6.540	3.460
14	16	20.694	-4.694
25	28	31.815	-3.815
16	20	22.716	-2.716
28	40	34.848	5.152
18	25	24.738	0.262
10	12	16.650	-4.650
8	15	14.628	0.372

As mentioned earlier, extreme values in terms of either the independent (X) or dependent (Y) variable can affect the correlation coefficient and the calculations of the slope and intercept. Hence being able to identify potential observations that may affect these statistics is important.

Recall that with a single variable an <u>outlier</u> is an observation that is significantly smaller or larger than the majority of the data. For example, if the ages of ten students are 18, 19, 19, 20, 22, 22, 23, 25, 27, and 70, then 70 would be an outlier.

With <u>two</u> variables, an **outlier** is an observation that falls within the range of the other X values but which lies far above or below the regression line and hence produces a large residual. Hence an outlier stands out in the Y (vertical) direction.

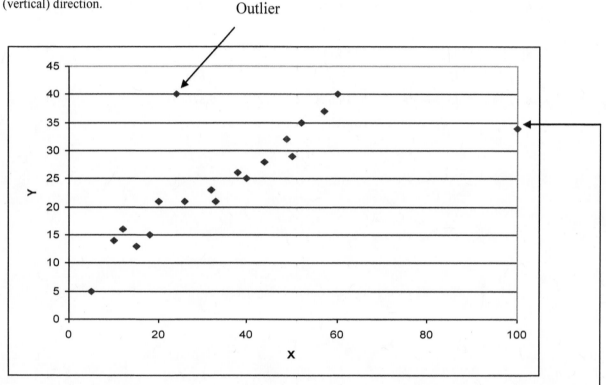

Observations that are separated in the X (horizontal) direction from the other observations are called **influential observations** because they have unusually large influence on the position of the regression line. When influential observations are found, you should proceed with caution, and in some cases should compute the correlation and regression line with the influential observation omitted.

Influential observation

118

The residual plot provides a graphical measure of the quality and usefulness of the regression line. To get a numerical measure of the quality and usefulness of a regression line one can compute the **coefficient of determination**. The coefficient of determination, denoted r^2, is simply the square of the correlation coefficient:

$$r^2 = \frac{(S_{xy})^2}{S_{xx}S_{yy}}$$, and will always take a value between 0 and 1. The coefficient of determination represents the

proportion or fraction of the total variation in Y values that is explained by the X variable (or by the linear relationship when Y is regressed versus X).

For example, if the correlation coefficient between two variables is computed to be 0.6, then the coefficient of determination is $r^2 = (0.6)^2 = .36$, implying that the X variable explains approximately 36% of the variation in the Y variable values.

Obviously, we want r^2 as large as possible (close to 1) because that would indicate that the regression line does a good job of predicting Y values for specified X values. r^2 close to 0 indicates that the regression line is rather useless for predicting purposes.

Example 30
For the car dealership data, calculate and interpret the coefficient of determination between the number of ads run and the number of cars sold.

Additional Reading and Examples

1. The regression <u>line</u> explains the linear relationship between the independent and dependent variable only for the range of X values in the data set from which the regression line was computed. Trying to predict for X values outside the range of the original data is **extrapolation** and in most cases should be avoided. Also, since the regression line describes the <u>linear</u> relationship between the two variables, it is not very useful for prediction purposes if the correlation coefficient r (and hence the coefficient of determination r^2) is near 0. There are methods of determining the equations of nonlinear relationships, but they are not discussed here.

2. Consider the data on pages 109 and 110 dealing with the increase in the 1970's in the percentage of women receiving degrees. In that example we computed $S_{xx} = 137.78875$, $S_{yy} = 462.375$, and $S_{xy} = 237.5675$. The correlation coefficient was calculated to be r = .9412.

    Then we have the following calculations for the slope and intercept:

    $$\text{slope} = \frac{S_{xy}}{S_{xx}} = \frac{237.5675}{137.78875} = 1.724$$

    $$\text{intercept} = \bar{y} - \text{slope}(\bar{x}) = 17.675 - 1.724(6.1875) = 7.008$$

    So the prediction equation is $\hat{Y} = 7.008 + 1.724(X)$. With such a high correlation coefficient, this equation will be useful for predicting the percentage of degrees awarded in 1978 – 1979 using X = degrees awarded in 1973 – 1974 between 1.1 and 11.5. The intercept means that if no degrees were awarded to women in 1973 – 1974, we predict that 7.008% of all degrees would be awarded to women in 1978 – 1979. Similarly, the slope of 1.724 means that for every one percent increase in the degrees awarded to women in 1973 – 1974 there is a predicted 1.724% increase in the degrees awarded to women in 1978 – 1979. The coefficient of determination is $r^2 = (.9412)^2 = .8859$, implying that the percent of women receiving degrees in 1973 – 1974 explains approximately 88.59% of the variation in the percent of women receiving degrees in 1978 – 1979.

3. The United Way is interested in the relationship between the age of a contributor and the amount of the contribution to their fundraising campaign. Data for 48 contributors is available and is displayed in the scatterplot on the following page. Using this data the regression line is calculated to be:

    Predicted contribution (in dollars) = 1.37 + 1.20 × age of contributor (in years)

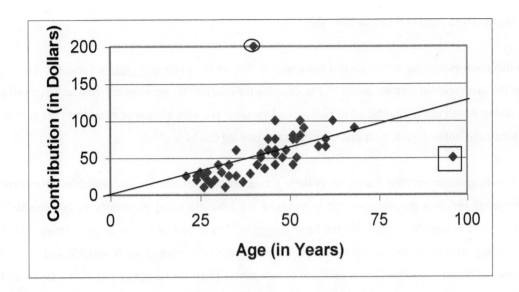

The intercept of 1.37 implies that if the age of a contributor is 0 years (at birth) the contributor is predicted to contribute $1.37. The slope of 1.20 means that for every one year increase in a contributor's age, his or her predicted contribution will increase by $1.20. The intercept can also be used to draw the regression line on the scatterplot. At x = 100, the predicted contribution is $\hat{y}=1.37+1.20(100)=121.37$, so we can draw the regression line by connecting the points (0, 1.37) and (100, 121.37). The point that is circled (40, 200) is an outlier because it has a large vertical deviation from the regression line (a large residual). The point that is inside the box (96, 50) is an influential observation that has a large impact on the regression line.

There is a moderate, positive, linear relationship between the two variables. The correlation coefficient is r = .509, with the resulting coefficient of determination being $r^2 = (.509)^2 = .2591$. Therefore, the ages of the contributors explain approximately 25.91% of the variation in the amount that the contributors give. Both the correlation coefficient and the coefficient of determination are higher if the influential observation (96, 50) is removed: the correlation becomes r =.619 and the coefficient of determination becomes $r^2 = .3833$.

E. Categorical Data

In Moore: Read Chapter 6 (pages 161 – 170)

To this point everything in this chapter has assumed that we have two <u>quantitative</u> variables. Now suppose that the two variables that we would like to describe the relationship between are qualitative or categorical variables. Recall that a **qualitative** or **categorical variable** is a variable whose measurements vary in name or kind only, not in degree, such that no ordering or ranking can be applied.

The main question remains the same: is there a relationship between the two variables? However, with categorical variables the concepts and expressions we have discussed previously in this chapter are no longer valid because we usually do not have <u>numerical</u> data to plot or to use in our formulas. Therefore, with categorical variables we are restricted to naming the categories of each variable and counting the number of observations that falls in each pair of categories. These counts are displayed in a **two-way table**.

For example, suppose one wants to determine if there is a relationship between academic status (variable 1, with categories Warning, Probation and Good Standing) and academic year (variable 2, with categories Freshman, Sophomore, Junior and Senior). In the table below there are 15 subjects who are on warning (variable 1, category 1) and who are juniors (variable 2, category 3). Similar interpretations can be made for the other 11 cells.

Variable 2 = Academic Year

		Freshman	Sophomore	Junior	Senior
Variable 1	Warning	48	36	15	23
= Academic	Probation	29	42	12	14
Status	Good standing	71	37	18	62

To determine if there is an association between two categorical variables we construct <u>marginal</u> and <u>conditional</u> distributions of the two variables. A **marginal distribution** for a variable lists the categories of the variable together with either the frequency (count) or relative frequency (percentage) of observations in each category. The name marginal results because these are the totals in the margins of a two-way table. A marginal distribution based on <u>frequencies</u> (counts) is usually most beneficial.

Variable 2 = Academic Year

		Freshman	Sophomore	Junior	Senior	
Variable 1	Warning	48	36	15	23	122
= Academic	Probation	29	42	12	14	97
Status	Good standing	71	37	18	62	188
		148	115	45	99	407 = total

Example 31

Our goal is to determine if there is a relationship between smoking status and cough status of high school students. A study was initiated that involved 200 high school students in a particular school district. Each student was given a survey on which they answered many questions, including whether they were a regular smoker or not and if they would claim to experience persistent coughing or not. Of the 200 students, 43 were regular smokers who reported persistent coughing, 43 were regular smokers who did not report persistent coughing, 19 were nonsmokers who reported persistent coughing, and 95 were nonsmokers who did not report persistent coughing. Use this data to construct a two-way table and determine the marginal distributions for smoking status and cough status.

The marginal distributions do not clearly show the association between the two variables. To better see the association, we construct a set of **conditional distributions** by presenting the distribution of one variable given each category (individually) of the second variable. It does not matter which of the two variables we condition on, and we use the conditional distributions to determine if there is an association between the two variables, as follows. The conditional distributions can be displayed using either frequencies (counts) or relative frequencies (percentages), and it is usually more beneficial to display them using relative frequencies (percentages).

For example, with the academic status and academic year data, separate conditional distributions could be determined for students on warning, probation and good standing. Using percentages, these conditional distributions would be as follows.

Warning		Probation		Good Standing	
Freshman	39%	Freshman	30%	Freshman	38%
Sophomore	30%	Sophomore	43%	Sophomore	20%
Junior	12%	Junior	12%	Junior	10%
Senior	19%	Senior	15%	Senior	33%

If the conditional distributions are <u>similar</u> then there is <u>not</u> an association between the two variables, but if there are significant <u>differences</u> in the conditional distributions then there <u>is</u> an association between the two variables.

In the example above, the good standing conditional distribution is different from the other two: a much lower percentage of good standing students are sophomores than other classifications, and there is a higher percentage of seniors. Hence there is a relationship between academic status and academic year.

Example 32

For the smoking study data of example 31, determine the conditional distribution of coughing status conditioned on the student being a smoker, and then determine the conditional distribution of coughing status conditioned on the student being a nonsmoker. Use these two conditional distributions to state whether there is an association between smoking status and coughing status.

With categorical variables, the existence of a lurking variable can create a phenomenon known as **Simpson's paradox**. Simpson's paradox refers to a scenario in which there is a reversal of the direction of the relationship (association) between two categorical variables when data from several groups are combined to form a single group. The lurking variable creates the subgroups, and failure to take the lurking variable into account can lead to misleading conclusions regarding the association between the variables.

Example 33

A local college consists of two schools: a business school and an art school. One year 560 students applied to the college, with the applications and acceptances into the two schools as follows.

120 men applied to the business school of this college and 18 were accepted.

240 men applied to the art school of this college and 180 were accepted.

120 women applied to the business school of this college and 24 were accepted.

80 women applied to the art school of this college and 64 were accepted.

By combining the first two statements, 120 + 240 = 360 men applied to this college, 18 + 180 = 198 were accepted; and from the last two statements, 120 + 80 = 200 women applied to this college, 24 + 64 = 88 were accepted. Upon seeing these numbers a local women's group claims that the college discriminates against women. College officials say this claim is nonsense, that higher percentages of women are accepted. These are contradiction claims, and numerically both are correct. How is this possible?

Additional Reading and Examples

1. The row totals and column totals in a two-way table give the **marginal distributions** of the two variables separately. The marginal distributions give little information about the relationship between the two variables. To find the **conditional distribution** of the row variable for one specific value of the column variable, look only at that one column in the table. Find each entry in the column as a percent of the column total. Such a conditional distribution of the row variable can be determined for each column in the table. If the conditional distributions are nearly the same, then there is not a significant relationship between the two variables. However, if the conditional distributions are significantly different, then there is a relationship between the two variables. Similar statements hold if the rows and columns are interchanged in the description above.

2. The data in the two-way table below give the undergraduate college enrollment by age of student and type of institution for students enrolled in the fall 1991 semester (data in thousands of students).

Type of Institution

AGE	2-year full-time	2-year part-time	4-year full-time	4-year part-time
15-17	44	4	79	0
18-21	1345	456	3869	159
22-29	489	690	1358	494
30-44	287	704	289	627
≥45	49	209	62	160

Of interest is to determine if there is a relationship between type of institution and age. We begin by determining the marginal distributions for age and type of institution.

Age:			Type of institution:	
15 – 17	127		2-year full-time	2214
18 – 21	5829		2-year part-time	2063
22 – 29	3031		4-year full-time	5657
30 – 44	1907		4-year part-time	1440
≥ 45	480			

To answer the question above, we need to determine the conditional distribution of age given each type of institution category. The marginal distribution for type of institution is useful in doing this.

127

	2-year full-time	
15 – 17	44/2214=	1.99%
18 – 21	1345/2214=	**60.75%**
22 – 29	489/2214=	22.09%
30 - 44	287/2214=	12.96%
≥45	49/2214=	2.21%

	2-year part-time	
15 – 17	4/2063=	0.19%
18 – 21	456/2063=	22.10%
22 – 29	690/2063 =	**33.45%**
30 – 44	704/2063 =	**34.13%**
≥45	209/2063 =	10.13%

	4-year full-time	
15 – 17	79/5657=	1.40%
18 – 21	3869/5657=	**68.39%**
22 – 29	1358/5657 =	24.01%
30 – 44	289/5657 =	5.11%
≥45	62/5657=	1.10%

	4-year part-time	
15 – 17	0/1440=	0%
18 – 21	159/1440=	11.04%
22 – 29	494/1440 =	**34.31%**
30 – 44	627/1440 =	**43.54%**
≥45	160/1440=	11.11%

The conditional distributions for the 2-year and 4-year <u>full-time</u> institutions are very similar, and likewise the conditional distributions for the 2-year and 4-year <u>part-time</u> institutions are very similar. However, when all four conditional distributions are compared obvious differences are apparent We see that in the full-time institutions a majority of the students are between the ages of 18 and 21, while in the part-time institutions the students tend to be older (22 – 29 or 30 – 44). Hence there is a relationship between age and type of institution because there are differences in the four conditional distributions.

3. To help consumers make informed decisions about health care, the government releases data about patient outcomes in hospitals. One community is served by hospitals A and B. The following is a two-way table of the survival of patients after surgery in these two hospitals. All patients undergoing surgery in a recent time period are included. "Survived" means that the patient lived at least 6 weeks following surgery.

	Hospital A	Hospital B
Died	63	16
Survived	2037	784

In Hospital A, 2037 out of 2100 patients or 97% survived, while in Hospital B 784 out of 800 or 98% survived. Therefore, it appears Hospital B has the better survival rate and hence if you need surgery you may want to choose Hospital B.

The above analysis overlooks two important observations. First, not all surgery cases are equally serious (for example, open-heart surgery is much more serious than arthroscopic knee surgery), and the survival rate for serious surgeries is likely lower than for less serious surgeries. Second, the condition of the patient prior to

128

surgery can affect the result (and this of course may be related to the severity of the surgery case). Suppose that in addition to the outcome of the surgery, patients are also classified by their condition ("good" or "poor") prior to the surgery. The tables below provide this information.

	Good Condition			Poor Condition	
	Hospital A	Hospital B		Hospital A	Hospital B
Died	6	8	Died	57	8
Survived	594	592	Survived	1443	192

Now for patients in good condition, the survival rate in Hospital A was 594/600 = 99% and the survival rate in Hospital B was 592/600 = 98.67%. Good condition patients are better off in Hospital A.

For patients in poor condition, the survival rate in Hospital A was 1443/1500 = 96.2% and the survival rate in Hospital B was 192/200 = 96%. Poor condition patients are better off in Hospital A.

This is an illustration of **Simpson's Paradox**. The patient's condition is a **lurking variable**. When we ignore the lurking variable, Hospital B seems to be safer, even though Hospital A does better for both classes of patients. The reason for this is most of the patients in poor condition (1500 out of 1700) have their surgery performed at Hospital A, which deflates the overall success rate of Hospital A. Half of the patients in good condition use Hospital A and the other half use Hospital B.

TI-83/84 Calculator

Suppose you have data for two quantitative variables and you desire to construct a scatterplot and compute the statistics discussed in this chapter, including the correlation coefficient, the coefficient of determination, the intercept and the slope.

1. Begin by entering your data into two columns. For the purpose of what follows, suppose the independent variable X is entered into column L1 and the dependent variable Y is entered in column L2.

2. To construct a scatterplot, make sure your plotting area is clear. To do so, press the **Y=** button and be sure that all ten of the functions are clear (empty). If a function is not clear, use the arrow keys to move the cursor to that function and press **CLEAR** to clear it out. Also make sure that you have no other statistical plots activated. To do so, press **STATPLOT (2nd Y=)**, select option **4: PlotsOff** and then press **ENTER** twice. Now all plots are off.

To activate a statistics plot, press **STATPLOT**, select option **1: Plot1...Off**, and press **ENTER**. Your cursor should be blinking over the word **On**; press **ENTER** to activate the plot. Use the down-arrow button to move the cursor down to the **Type:** of graph setting, and use the left-arrow and right-arrow buttons to move the cursor to the desired scatterplot graph, which is the top left of the six choices. For **Xlist:** enter the list that contains the independent variable (X) data (L1 as described above). For **Ylist:** enter the list that contains the dependent variable (Y) data (L2 as described above). Now choose your plotting **Mark:** (the middle plus sign selection is usually the best one to use). To see your scatterplot, press **ZOOM** then select option **9: ZoomStat**.

3. To compute the correlation coefficient, coefficient of determination, and the intercept and slope of the regression line, begin by making sure the TI-83/84 diagnostics are turned on. To turn on the diagnostics, first press **CATALOG** (which involves pressing the **2nd button** followed by **0**) to get a listing of all of the TI-83/84 commands. Note that the **A** symbol is in the upper-right corner, indicating that the calculator is in ALPHA mode and you can press one of the keys with a green letter above to jump directly to the section of the list of commands that begin with that letter. Press **D** (the x^{-1} button) to jump to the commands that begin with the letter "D", and use the down arrow button to scroll down to **DiagnosticOn**. Press **ENTER** twice and you should see the word **Done** under **DiagnosticOn**.

To calculate the statistics, press **STAT** and then press the right-arrow button to get to the **CALC** menu. Select option **8: LinReg (a+bx)**. Note: choosing option **4: LinReg (ax+b)** is also a regression function, but this has the independent and dependent variables defined differently. Now enter the name of the list that contains the independent variable (X) data (L1 as described above), followed by the **,** button (directly above the 7 button), and then enter the name of the list that contains the dependent variable (Y) data (L2 as described above). Press ENTER. You then get (in order) the intercept (denoted a), the slope (denoted b), the coefficient of determination (denoted r^2) and the correlation coefficient (denoted r).

Practice Problems:

V. 1. How well does a child's height at age 6 predict height at age 16? To find out, a simple random sample of 6-year olds are selected and their heights are measured. Then 10 years later when they reach the age of 16, their heights are measured again. In this situation, what is the explanatory variable? What is the response variable? Are these variables qualitative or quantitative?

V. 2. We are interested in the relationship between how much money states spend on education (in dollars per pupil) and how much they pay their teachers (median teacher salaries, in thousands of dollars). The data (including the District of Columbia) are given below.

State	Dollars per pupil	Pay	State	Dollars per pupil	Pay	State	Dollars per pupil	Pay
Alabama	3648	27.3	Louisiana	4012	26.2	Ohio	5639	32.6
Alaska	7887	43.4	Maine	5894	28.5	Oklahoma	3742	24.3
Arizona	4231	30.8	Maryland	6164	38.4	Oregon	5291	32.3
Arkansas	3334	23.0	Massachusetts	6351	36.1	Pennsylvania	6534	36.1
California	4826	39.8	Michigan	5257	38.3	Rhode Island	6989	37.7
Colorado	4809	31.8	Minnesota	5260	33.1	S. Carolina	4327	28.3
Connecticut	7914	43.8	Mississippi	3322	24.4	S. Dakota	3730	22.4
Delaware	6016	35.2	Missouri	4415	28.5	Tennessee	3707	28.2
Florida	5154	30.6	Montana	5184	26.7	Texas	4238	28.3
Georgia	4860	29.2	Nebraska	4381	26.6	Utah	2993	25.0
Hawaii	5008	32.5	Nevada	4564	32.2	Vermont	5740	31.0
Idaho	3200	25.5	N. Hampshire	5504	31.3	Virginia	5360	32.4
Illinois	5062	34.6	N. Jersey	9159	38.4	Washington	5045	33.1
Indiana	5051	32.0	N. Mexico	4446	26.2	W. Virginia	5046	26.0
Iowa	4839	28.0	New York	8500	42.1	Wisconsin	5946	33.1
Kansas	5009	29.8	N. Carolina	4802	29.2	Wyoming	5255	29.0
Kentucky	4390	29.1	N. Dakota	3685	23.6	D.C.	8210	39.6

(a). If the goal is to use the education spending (dollars per pupil) to predict the median teacher salary (pay), identify the independent and dependent variables.

(b). Construct a scatterplot for this data.

(c). Use your scatterplot to completely describe the relationship between the two variables. Explain why observing a positive association between these variables makes sense.

(d). On the plot, identify a state where teacher salaries are unusually high relative to the state's education spending. This state is an outlier – which state is this?

V.3. (a). An automobile manufacturer claims that there is a very weak relationship between the length of a car trip and the miles per gallon of gasoline on the trip. Asked to quantify what he means, the automobile manufacturer says that the correlation coefficient is around -0.93. Do the opinions of the automobile manufacturer in the previous two sentences make sense (both logically and statistically)? Briefly explain.

(b). Upon checking his calculations, the automobile manufacturer determines that the correlation coefficient is actually r = -0.093. Based on this, calculate the coefficient of determination and interpret what the coefficient of determination value says in regards to using length of the car trip to predict miles per gallon of gasoline on the trip.

(c). The automobile manufacturer based his figures on a random sample of 40 car trips. The lengths of the car trips ranged from 65 miles to 589 miles, and the miles per gallon of gasoline ranged from 12.5 to

29.8. The data was also used to calculate the following regression line to describe the relationship between the two variables.

Predicted miles per gallon of gasoline = 31.2 -0.03 (length of trip)

Explain what an intercept value of 31.2 and a slope value of -0.03 say about the relationship between the length of a car trip and the miles per gallon of gasoline on the trip.

(d). Should the regression line given in part (c) be used to predict the miles per gallon of gasoline for a 200-mile car trip? What about for a 1200-mile car trip? Briefly explain your reasoning.

V. 4. Good runners take more steps per second as they speed up. Here are the average numbers of steps per second for a group of top female runners at different speeds. The speeds are in feet per second.

Speed	15.86	16.88	17.50	18.62	19.97	21.06	22.11
Steps/second	3.05	3.12	3.17	3.25	3.36	3.46	3.55

(a). You want to predict steps per second from running speed. Make a scatterplot of the data with this goal in mind.

(b). Calculate the correlation coefficient. Does this value correspond to the relationship observed from the scatterplot?

(c). Calculate the regression line that could be used to predict steps per second from running speed. Draw this line on your scatterplot.

(d). Does running speed explain most of the variation in the number of steps that a runner takes per second? Calculate the coefficient of determination r^2 and use it to answer this question.

(e). If you wanted to predict running speed from a runner's steps per second, would you use the same regression line? Explain your answer. Would r^2 stay the same?

V. 5. A statistics instructor is interested in predicting Y = the amount of time it takes a student to complete a statistics final exam. She believes there are four variables that could help predict the amount of time it takes a student to complete the statistics final exam: X_1 = the number of hours that the student studies; X_2 = the student's age; X_3 = the number of hours of sleep the student got the night before the exam; and X_4 = the student's score on the midterm exam.

Data was collected on 100 students who took the statistics final exam, and the correlation coefficient was calculated between the amount of time it took each student to complete the statistics final exam and each of the four X variables.

X_1 = the number of hours that the student studies, r = 0.48

X_2 = the student's age, r = –0.75

X_3 = the number of hours of sleep the student got the night before the exam, r = 0.57

X_4 = the student's score on the midterm exam, r = –0.14

(a). Which of the variables has the <u>strongest linear association</u> with the amount of time it takes a student to complete the statistics final exam?

(b). Which of the variables has the <u>weakest linear association</u> with the time it takes a student to complete the statistics final exam?

V. 6.   It is of interest to use X, the speed of a car, to predict Y, the fuel consumption of a car. Fuel consumption is measured in liters of gasoline per 100 kilometers driven and speed is measured in kilometers per hour. The data for 15 trips in a Ford Escort are as follows.

Speed (km/h)	Fuel Consumption (liters / 100 km)	Speed (km/h)	Fuel Consumption (liters / 100 km)
10	21.00	90	7.57
20	13.00	100	8.27
30	10.00	110	9.03
40	8.00	120	9.87
50	7.00	130	10.79
60	5.90	140	11.77
70	6.30	150	12.83
80	6.95		

The regression line for this data is $\hat{Y}=11.058-0.01466X$

(a). Make a scatterplot of the observations and draw the regression line on your plot.

(b). Should you use the regression line to predict Y from X? Explain.

(c). Use the regression line to calculate predicted values and residuals for each observation. Verify that the residuals sum to 0.

(d). Make a residual plot and comment on the pattern that you see. How does the pattern shown in the residual plot compare with pattern of data around the regression line drawn in part (a)?

V. 7.   Political campaigns are expensive to run, with advertising, trips, supporters to pay, and many other expenses. For this reason raising money to cover the cost of the campaign is a high priority for most politicians. The scatterplot below gives the number of campaign dollars raised (in millions) and the percent of the total vote received for a simple random sample of 48 politicians.

(a). The regression line is *predicted percent of votes received 47.5 + 1.48(campaign dollars raised)*. Draw this regression line on the scatterplot.

(b). Explain what an intercept value of 47.5 and a slope value of 1.48 imply about the relationship between campaign dollars raised and predicted percent of votes received.

(c). Identify any points that could be considered outliers or influential observations. What impact do they have on the regression line?

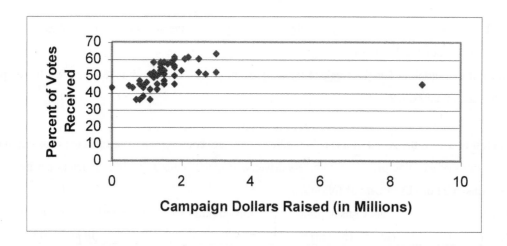

(d). A new candidate has raised $5 million for his political campaign. Use the regression line to predict the percent of votes that this candidate will receive. Is this value reasonable? Explain.

(e). Another candidate has raised $12 million for her political campaign. Use the regression line to predict the percent of votes that this candidate will receive. Is this value reasonable? Explain.

V. 8. A professor is interested in the relationship between the amount of time (in minutes) that it takes to complete an exam (maximum time is 4 hours = 240 minutes) and the score on the exam (maximum score is 200 points). A simple random sample of 42 students was selected, and the data displayed in the scatterplot below.

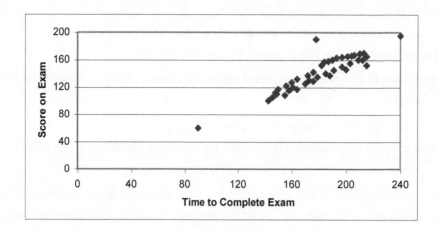

(a). Use the scatterplot to completely describe the relationship between amount of time to complete the exam and score on the exam.

(b). The regression line is: *predicted score on exam = -18.2445 + 0.8821(time)*. Draw this regression line on the scatterplot.

(c). On the scatterplot draw a circle around all points that you consider to be outliers and draw a box around all points that you consider to be influential observations.

134

V. 9.   A professor in interested in using the number of multiple-choice questions on a particular test to predict the average score on that test. An experiment was designed and 23 tests with varying number of multiple-choice questions were written. The data is presented in the scatterplot below.

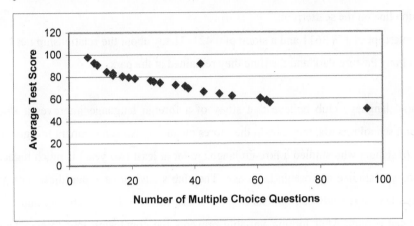

(a).   Use the scatterplot to completely describe the relationship between the number of multiple-choice questions on the test and the average test score.

(b).   The regression line is as follows. Draw this regression line on the scatterplot.

   Predicted average test score = 91- 0.49(number of multiple choice questions)

(c).   On the scatterplot draw a circle around all points that you consider to be outliers and draw a box around all points that you consider to be influential observations.

(d).   Explain what an intercept value of 91 and a slope value of -0.49 say about the relationship between number of multiple-choice questions on the test and average test score.

(e).   The above does not take into account the difficulty of the test or the subject matter being covered. Obviously these things can affect the average test score. In this scenario, difficulty of the test and the subject matter being covered would be considered examples of what?

V. 10. City planners in Richmond, Virginia are interested in the relationship between a visitor's age (in years) and the amount of time (in minutes) that they remain at Pony Pasture Park on the James River during a visit. A random sample of 40 visitors on August 5, 2001 (when the high temperature was 91 degree) was selected, and the age and amount of time they remained at Pony Pasture Park recorded for each. The following scatterplot graphically displays the data.

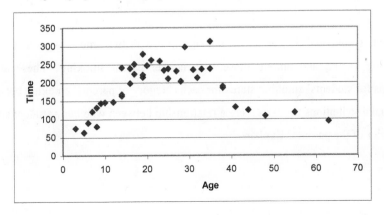

(a). Use the scatterplot to describe completely the relationship between age and time.

(b). The regression line is calculated to be:

Predicted time in minutes = 178.3611 + 0.421471 (age in years)

Draw the regression line on the scatterplot.

(c). Explain what an intercept of 178.3611 and a slope of 0.421471 say about the relationship between the age of a visitor to Pony Pasture Park and the time they remained at the park.

V. 11. Members of a high school language club believe that study of a foreign language improves a student's command of English. From school records, they obtain the scores on an English achievement test given to all seniors. The mean score of seniors who studied a foreign language for at least two years is much higher than the mean score of seniors who studied no foreign language. The club's advisor says that these data are not good evidence that foreign language study strengthens English skills. Identify the explanatory and response variables in the study. Then explain what lurking variable prevents the conclusion that foreign language study improves students' English skills.

V. 12. James and Charlie are the first two hitters for a softball team. During the regular season Charlie was second on the team in batting, going 30 for 43 for a .6977 average. James was the third leading regular season hitter, going 29 for 42 for a .6905 average. During the playoffs, Charlie batted 9 for 17 for a .5294 average. However, James missed two playoff games due to an ankle injury and only batted 4 for 8, for a .5000 average, during the two games he played. Since Charlie had the higher average in both the regular season and the playoffs, then obviously his overall average must be higher than James' overall average. Correct? Compute the overall avenge for both players and comment on the results. What is going on in this situation?

V. 13. Do the smoking habits of parents help explain whether or not their children smoke? The data below are from eight high schools and give a two-way table for smoking among students and the number of their parents that smoke.

	Student smokes	Student does not smoke
Both parents smoke	400	1380
One parent smokes	416	1823
Neither parent smokes	188	1168

(a). What percent of students smoke and do not smoke among those with two smoking parents, among those with one smoking parent, and among those with neither parent smoking? These are the conditional distributions for students' smoking status for each category of parents' smoking behavior.

(b). Based on the conditional distributions in (a), is there a relationship between whether a student smokes and the smoking behavior of the parents? Explain.

V. 14. Do child restraints and seat belts prevent injuries to young passengers in automobile accidents? The data below are for 26,971 passengers under the age of 15 in accidents reported in North Carolina during two years before the law required restraints.

	Restrained	Unrestrained
Injured	197	3,844
Uninjured	1,749	21,181

(a). What percent of these young passengers were restrained?

(b). Do the data provide evidence that young passengers are less likely to be injured in an accident if they wear restraints? Compute conditional distributions and compare in order to answer the question.

V. 15. Computer Magazine is interested in whether there is a relationship between type of computer (Dell, Gateway, other) and satisfaction with the computer (very satisfied, somewhat satisfied, not satisfied). The conditional distributions of satisfaction for each type of computer are as follows. Based on the conditional distributions, is there a significant relationship between type of computer and satisfaction with the computer? Briefly explain.

Dell		Gateway		Other	
Very satisfied	36%	Very satisfied	38%	Very satisfied	14%
Somewhat satisfied	58%	Somewhat satisfied	57%	Somewhat satisfied	59%
Not satisfied	6%	Not satisfied	5%	Not satisfied	27%

V. 16. The Gallup Organization is interested in people's opinions regarding what items the state of Florida should cut funding on in order to balance the state budget. Specifically, they want to determine if there is a relationship between age (18 – 30, 31 – 50, 51 and above) and opinion on the budget reduction items (road projects, education, medical/other social services). The conditional distributions of opinions for each age group are as follows.

	18-30	31-50	51 and above
Road projects	74%	72%	81%
Education	11%	25%	17%
Medical/other social services	15%	3%	2%

Does this information indicate that there is a significant association between age of person and opinion on the budget reduction items? Briefly explain.

VI. Distributions

As mentioned earlier, the ability to describe and use distributions is essential to the correct application of statistical procedures. When describing distributions one must describe the center, spread, shape and any unusual features in the distribution, and each distribution is unique in its description. Each distribution also has one or more parameters that must be specified in order for the distribution to be known.

In this chapter we learn in detail about two such distributions: the normal distributions and the Student's t-distributions. These are two of the most popular distributions used in statistics, and are the only two distributions used in the remainder of this book. Other distributions, such as the F-distribution and the chi-square distribution, are also often used in introductory statistics courses but this book does not use them.

Additionally, when one performs statistical inference you use statistics computed from sample data to make statements about unknown population parameters. The formulas used to make these inferences generally fall into one of two categories: either formulas for estimation (confidence interval formulas) or formulas for statistical tests (test statistics formulas). In either case the formulas are derived from the sampling distribution of the statistic being used to estimate the unknown parameter, and the last section of this chapter gives an overview of the concept of sampling distributions.

A.   Normal Distributions

In Moore: Read Chapter 3

1. Introduction

In Moore: Read pages 67 – 77

Many statistical inference procedures have as an assumption that the data comes from an approximately normal distribution. In this section we learn the properties of normal distributions, and how normal distributions can be used to solve probability problems and other applied problems.

The **normal curve** is a symmetric, bell-shaped curve as depicted on the following page. Data that is described by the normal curve is said to follow a **normal distribution**. A normal distribution is an example of a continuous distribution and hence a **normal variable** can assume any one of a countless number of possible outcomes. Additionally, at times one may have a discrete variable and say that the variable has an approximate normal distribution implying that while the discrete variable does not have an exact normal distribution, the normal curve is a good approximation for the actual distribution.

To describe a distribution we must describe the center, spread, shape and any unusual features of the distribution. We know that symmetric distributions are distributions where the left and right sides are mirror images of each other, and normal distributions are one type of symmetric distribution. To specify the center and spread of the distribution one must specify the population mean μ and the population standard deviation σ of the distribution. Finally, since "unusual features" are things that make a distribution not be normal (or symmetric), a normal distribution will have no unusual features.

If a variable X has a normal distribution with mean μ and standard deviation σ (μ and σ specified), then we write **X ~N (μ, σ)** and read this as "X is distributed normal with mean μ and standard deviation σ." For example, if X is the weight of students and the weights follow a normal distribution with mean 160 pounds and standard deviation 15 pounds, then we write X ~N(160, 15).

Both pictures above have the normal shape (symmetric, bell-shape) and they both have the same mean μ. However, the graph on the right has a larger standard deviation σ and hence is more spread out than the distribution on the left.

The normal distributions have the following properties:

1. The normal curve is bell-shaped.
2. The peak of the normal curve is the mean μ (the median is located at the same point).
3. The normal curve is <u>symmetric</u> about μ.
4. The center and spread of the normal curve depend entirely on the values of the population mean μ and the population standard deviation σ.
5. The total area under the normal curve is 1 (or 100%).
6. For any normal distribution the following 68-95-99.7% rule applies:
    (1). Approximately 68% of the measurements fall within one standard deviation of the mean μ: μ ± σ.
    (2). Approximately 95% of the measurements fall within two standard deviations of the mean μ: μ ±2σ.
    (3). Approximately 99.7% of the measurements fall within three standard deviations of the mean μ: μ ±3σ.

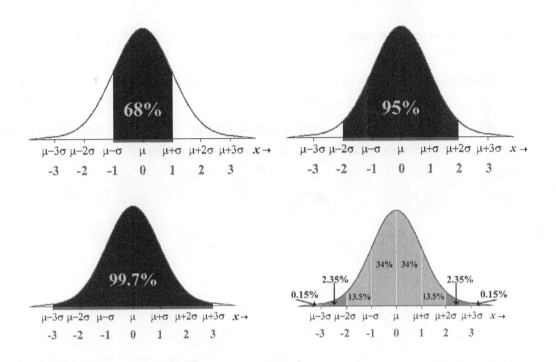

Normal distributions can be used to solve two types of problems.

(1) They can be used to determine the <u>probability</u> that a measurement of a normal random variable falls in a particular interval. This is equivalent to determining the <u>area</u> under the curve in a certain interval or the <u>proportion</u> (or <u>percentage</u>) of the measurements that fall in a certain interval. There are four types of <u>probability problems</u> that can be solved:

   (i) **Equal to** problems, such as find the probability that the normal variable X equals to some value x. Since normal distributions are continuous distributions, the probability that a normally distributed variable X (with any mean μ and any standard deviation σ) **equals** some specified value x is 0 for any value x. Hence $P(X = x) = 0$ for <u>all</u> x.

   (ii) **Less than** or **less than and equal to** problems; such as $P(X < x)$ or $P(X \le x)$.

   (iii) **Greater** than or **greater than and equal to** problems, such as $P(X > x)$ or $P(X \ge x)$.

   (iv) **Between** problems, where one wants to find the probability that X lies **between** two numbers x_1 and x_2; $P(x_1 < X < x_2)$ or $P(x_1 \le X \le x_2)$

(2) They can be used to determine the <u>value</u> of the normal random variable X to guarantee a given probability or percentage. There are three types of <u>value problems</u> that can be solved:

   (i) Find the value x of the normal variable X such that the probability of being **less than** or **less than and equal to** the value is as stated.

   (ii) Find the value x of the normal variable X such that the probability of being **greater than** or **greater than and equal to** the value is as stated.

   (iii) Find the two values x_1 and x_2 of the normal variable X such that the probability of being **between** the two values is as stated.

141

2. Standard Normal Distribution

In Moore: Read pages 74 - 84

A special normal distribution is the **standard normal distribution**, usually denoted by Z, and specified by a mean $\mu = \mathbf{0}$ and standard deviation $\sigma = \mathbf{1}$. So $\mathbf{Z{\sim}N\ (0,\ 1)}$

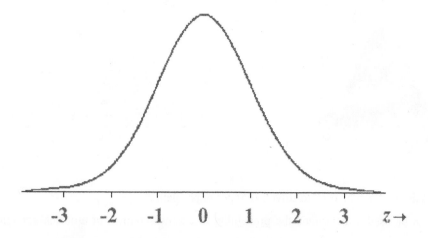

The standard normal distribution is important because probabilities (or proportions or percentages) are tabled and hence are easy to calculate. The Table of Standard Normal Probabilities on pages 338 – 339 gives the probability that Z falls <u>below</u> some specified value z. i.e. $P(Z < z)$.

The Table of Standard Normal Probabilities is used as follows. The table allows one to specify Z values to two decimal places, and you can read the Z values down the left column and the top row. For a Z number, such as $z = 1.58$, find 1.5 down the left column and .08 across the top row. Negative values of Z are on page 338 and positive values of Z are on page 339. The numbers in the body (or center) of the table are the probabilities, accurate to four decimal places. These values give the probability that Z is **<u>less than</u>** (or **<u>less than or equal to</u>**) to value of z specified.

As mentioned earlier there are two types of problems: first those in which you are given a value or values of Z and asked to find a probability, and then those in which you are given a probability and asked to find the corresponding value or values of Z. <u>We begin by using the table to determine probabilities</u>.

(i) **Equal to** problems: to find the probability that Z is equal to any specific value, by definition the probability is always 0. $P(Z = z) = 0$ for any value z.

142

Example 34

Find P(Z = 1.41)

Example 35:

Find P(Z = -2.64)

(ii) **Less than** or **less than and equal to** problems: these problems are looked up directly in the table, with the answer being the probability read from the table. Since the probability that Z equals a specific value is 0, then the equal to part does not affect the probability. This implies that for any value of z, P(Z < z) = P(Z ≤ z).

Example 36

Find P (Z < -2.00)

Example 37

Find P (Z ≤ 1.34)

(iii) **Greater** than or **greater than and equal to** problems: these problems <u>cannot</u> be looked up directly, but from the properties of normal distributions are easy to determine. Since the total area (or probability) under the normal curve is 1 (property #5), then we can use the table to look up the less than probability, and then this less than probability is subtracted from 1 to give the greater than probability. Since P(-∞ < Z < +∞) = 1, then to find P(Z > z), find P(Z < z) and subtract from 1.

So P(Z > z) = 1 – P(Z < z)

Example 38

Find P (Z > 0.52)

Example 39

Find P (Z > -1.85)

(iv) **Between** problems, where one wants to find the probability that Z lies **between** two numbers a and b; P(a < Z < b) or P(a ≤ Z ≤ b). It is also <u>not</u> possible to look these values up directly in the table, but these problems can be solved by converting the problem into two less than problems and subtracting the smaller probability from the larger probability. Note that probabilities cannot be negative nor can they exceed 1, so it is important to subtract the smaller probability from the larger probability.

So P(a < Z < b) = P(Z < b) – P(Z < a)

Example 40

Find P (1.00 < Z < 2.00)

Example 41

Find P (-0.49 < Z < 2.03)

In summary, with problems when you are finding a probability, for <u>equal to</u> problems the answer is always 0, for <u>less than</u> problems simply look the probability up in the table, for <u>greater than</u> problems look the probability up in the table and subtract the probability from 1, and for <u>between</u> problems look up the two values and then subtract the smaller probability from the larger probability.

In each of Examples 34 – 41 we specified the value or values of z and used the standard normal table to find the probability (or area or proportion or percentage) of that interval occurring. Another way to use the table is to first specify the probability (or area or proportion or percentage) that we desire and then use the standard normal table to **find the appropriate Z value.** As mentioned above there are three types of problems, and they are solved as follows.

(i) If we want to find the value z of the standard normal variable Z such that the probability of being **less than** or **less than and equal to** the value is as stated, there is only one step. In the standard normal table, find the specified <u>less than</u> probability in the **body** of the table and then read across to the left and up to the top to find the appropriate z value. Note that in the table page 338 has probabilities between 0 and .50, and page 339 has probabilities between .5 and 1.

Example 42

Find the value of z such that the probability of being less than z is .8212.

Example 43

Find the value of z such that the probability of being less than z is .10.

(ii) If we want to find the value z of the standard normal variable Z such that the probability of being **greater than** or **greater than and equal to** the value is as stated, there is one additional step that must be done. Since in order to use the table we must have a less than problem, we begin by taking the greater than probability and <u>subtract from 1</u>. This creates a less than probability, which is then looked up in the **body** of the table as above.

Example 44

Find the value of z such that the probability of being greater than z is .33.

Example 45

Find the value of z such that the probability of being greater than z is .57.

(iii) To find the two values z_1 and z_2 of the standard normal variable Z such that the probability of being **between** the two values is as stated, we must use the fact that the total area under the curve is 1 and the fact that the curve is symmetric.

For example, suppose we want to find the two values that the probability of being between the two values is .60. Since there is .60 between the two values, then there is 1 - .60 = .40 combined less than and greater than the two values, and since the curve is symmetric this is split evenly. So there is .40/2 = .20 at the lower end and .40/2 = .20 at the upper end.

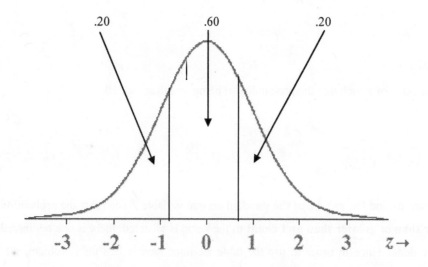

Since to use the table we must look up <u>less than</u> probabilities, in the **body** of the table we must first look up p = .20, which yields z_1 = -0.84, and then in the **body** of the table we must look up p = .20 + .60 = .80, which yields z_2 = +0.84. Since the curve is symmetric around a mean of 0, it will <u>always</u> be the case that the two numbers will be the same, one being positive and the other being negative.

The two numbers that we determine (-0.84 and +0.84 in the example above) enclose the middle 60% of the distribution.

Example 46:

Find the two values z_1 and z_2 such that the probability of being between the two values is .95.

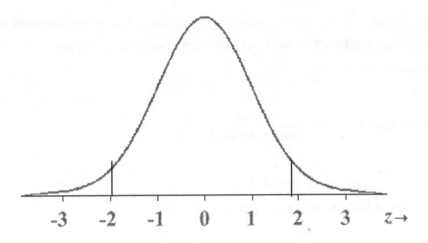

3. Z-Score Transformation

In Moore: Read pages 77 – 87

The previous section introduced the standard normal variable, $Z \sim N(0, 1)$, and we learned how to use the Table of Standard Normal Probabilities to solve problems that asked to find a probability given a value (or values) of Z, and problems in which a probability was given and we were asked to find the corresponding value (or values) of Z. Unfortunately, most real variables, even if they have a normal shape, do not have a mean of 0 and a standard deviation of 1. So suppose we have a normal variable X with some mean μ likely not equal to 0 and some standard deviation σ likely not equal to 1. Hence $X \sim N(\mu, \sigma)$.

Since there are an infinite number of possibilities for μ and σ, we <u>cannot</u> possibly table all cases. However, since all normal distributions have the same shape, if we can convert X to a standard normal variable (Z) then we can use the standard normal table. This can be done using the **Z-score transformation.**

The Z-score transformation formula takes two forms, one which allows us to transform from X to Z so that we can solve problems asking for a probability, and the other allows us to transform from Z to X so we can solve problems asking for a value (or values) of the variable.

For problems that ask us to determine a probability, to perform a Z-score transformation we take the value of the normal variable (X in this case), subtract the mean (μ in this case) and divide by the standard deviation (σ in this case).

Z-score transformation: $\qquad Z = \dfrac{X - \text{mean}}{\text{standard deviation}} = \dfrac{X - \mu}{\sigma}$

The subtraction of μ converts the mean to 0 ($\mu - \mu = 0$ for any value of μ), and the division by σ converts the standard deviation to 1 ($\sigma / \sigma = 1$ for any value of σ).

To find the probability that X is in some interval, say $P(X < a)$, $P(X > b)$, or $P(a < X < b)$, we first convert a and/or b to standard units by using the Z-score transformation and then we use the standard normal table on pages 338 and 339 (as in Examples 34 – 41) to **find the probability.**

$$P(a < X < b) = P\left(\frac{a - \mu}{\sigma} < \frac{X - \mu}{\sigma} < \frac{b - \mu}{\sigma}\right) = P\left(\frac{a - \mu}{\sigma} < Z < \frac{b - \mu}{\sigma}\right)$$

As with the standard normal distribution Z, the probability that a normal variable X equals a specific value is always 0, regardless of the value.

Example 47

Suppose X is normally distributed with mean $\mu = 10$ and standard deviation $\sigma = 5$. Find the probability that X is between 12 and 20.

Example 48

Suppose X is normally distributed with mean $\mu = 78$ and standard deviation $\sigma = 12$ Find the probability that X is greater than 84.

<u>For problems that ask to find a value of X</u>, we in essence reverse the steps from above. Suppose that we have a variable $X \sim N(\mu, \sigma)$. To find the value x of the variable X such that the probability of being in some interval is as specified, we begin by using the procedure described in the last section and the standard normal (Z) table to find the value of z to satisfy the probability. Examples 42 through 46 all involved doing this. Recall that to get the z value (or values) the problem must be converted to a <u>less than</u> problem and then the corresponding <u>less than</u> probability is looked up in the **body** of the table.

Once this is done, the Z-score transformation formula that converts from Z back to X is as follows.

$$X = \mu + Z\sigma$$

We substitute the value of z into this equation and solve for x.

Example 49

Suppose X is distributed normal with mean $\mu = 10$ and standard deviation $\sigma = 5$. Find the x value such that the probability that X is <u>greater than</u> x is .10.

Example 50:

Suppose X is distributed normal with mean $\mu = 30$ and standard deviation $\sigma = 8$. Find the two values of X such that the probability of being between those two values is .40.

4. Normal Distribution Applications

Now that we have learned all the tools for solving normal distribution problems, we can now apply these tools to real variables that follow normal distributions. To solve such normal distribution application problems, it is best to follow these five steps.

(i)   Identify the variable X that the problem involves.

(ii) Identify the distribution of the variable X, implying specify the mean μ and the standard deviation σ; $X \sim N(\mu, \sigma)$.

(iii) Read the problem closely and identify whether the problem involves finding a probability or finding a value (or values) of the variable X.

(iv) Work the problem, using the steps learned in the previous two sections.

(v) Make sure the answer makes sense! Probabilities cannot be negative, nor can they exceed 1. If the question asks for a value, make sure the value makes sense.

The following four examples involve actual applications of normal distributions.

Example 51

Through a study conducted at restaurants throughout the United States, it is known that the length of time that people stir sugar into their iced tea follows a normal distribution with a mean of 12.3 seconds and a standard deviation of 3.1 seconds. What is the probability that James Bond will take between 19.833 and 22.53 seconds to stir the sugar into his iced tea?

Example 52

Leatherbacks are the largest of all sea turtles, reaching lengths of 5.9 feet and weighing as much as 1,102 pounds. Scientists have found that the weights of all leatherback turtles follow a normal distribution with a mean of 760 pounds and standard deviation 98 pounds. Many captured turtles in recent field surveys are immature leatherback turtles whose weights fall in the bottom 20% of the distribution. How many pounds must a leatherback turtle weigh so that it falls in the bottom 20% of the distribution?

Example 53

The 19th season of The Oprah Winfrey Show debuted on Monday, September 13, 2004, and on the show Oprah gave new Pontiac G6 cars to everyone in the audience. Suppose that after the first month of driving, the miles per gallon for the new Pontiac G6's that Oprah gave away on her September 13 show have a <u>normal distribution</u> with mean 26.3 mpg and standard deviation 3.6 mpg. How many miles per gallon must a Pontiac G6 get to be in the top 20.19% of the distribution?

Example 54

Dental structure provides an effective criterion for classifying certain fossils. A number of years ago a baboon skull of unknown origin was discovered in a cave in Angola; the length of its third molar was 9.0 mm. Speculation arose that the baboon in question might be a "missing link" and belong to the genus *Papio*. Members of that genus have third molars whose length follows a <u>normal distribution</u> with mean 8.18 mm and a standard deviation of 0.47 mm. What is the probability of observing a baboon from this genus with the length of its third molar being 9.0 mm or more?

B. Student's t-Distributions

In Moore: Read pages 445 – 446

Another class of symmetric distributions that are similar to the normal distributions are the Student's t-distributions. To use the normal distributions as learned in the past section, one of the requirements was that the population standard deviation σ must be known. While in some cases this may be possible, in most cases the population standard deviation σ will not be known and hence the use of normal distributions is not appropriate (and not possible).

The Student's t-distributions relax the necessity that the population standard deviation σ must be known, and in its place they allow the use of the sample standard deviation s. Like the standard normal distribution Z the t-distributions are standardized, and the following comparisons can be made between the Z and t-distributions.

(1) Shape: both the Z-distribution and all the t-distributions have the same symmetric, bell-shape. See the picture below, where the curve for df = ∞ is the standard normal (Z) distribution.

(2) Center: both the Z-distribution and all the t-distributions have a mean of 0. From the picture below, you can see that all the curves are centered at a mean of 0.

(3) Spread: the standard deviation of the Z-distribution is 1, but the standard deviation of a t-distribution will be greater than or equal to 1 and depends on what is called the degrees of freedom (denoted df). As the degrees of freedom increases, the t-distribution gets closer and closer to the Z-distribution to the point that for df = ∞ the Z and t-distributions are the same and the standard deviation of the t-distribution with df = ∞ is 1 (the same as for Z). From the graph below you can see that the t-distributions are more spread out than the Z-distribution.

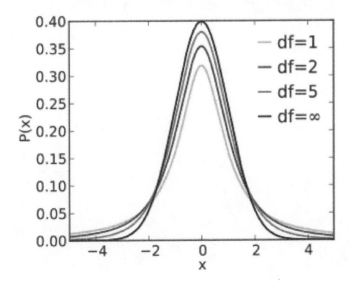

153

(4) Unusual features: because the t-distributions are symmetric with the same bell-shaped curve as the Z-distribution, then like the Z-distribution the t-distributions also will not have any unusual features.

Therefore, the only component of the distributions that is different is the spread: the t-distributions have a larger standard deviation than the Z-distribution. The shape, center and unusual features are all the same.

Probabilities associated with the Student's t-distributions are tabled on page 340. To use this table, the degrees of freedom are listed in the left-most column; the _upper-tail_ probabilities are listed in the top row; and the t-values are contained in the body of the table. Note that the degrees of freedom run from 1 to 30 without skipping, then skip to 40, 50, 60, 80, 100, and 1000. There is a t-distribution for every positive degrees of freedom, but it is not possible to list all in a table. If the problem has a degrees of freedom that is not listed in the table, you can use the closest degrees of freedom value given. The degrees of freedom is determined based on the inference problem being worked. The first type of inference problem that we will work that uses the t-distribution determines the degrees of freedom to be the sample size minus 1. Hence in those applications, $df = n - 1$.

Since the upper-tail probabilities are listed, this implies to use this table the problem must be set up as a **greater than problem**, the opposite of the less than problem required to use the Z-table.

Note that the last row of the table is labeled z*. This corresponds to a t-distribution with $df = \infty$, implying that as the degrees of freedom increases the t-distribution approaches the standard normal (Z) distribution.

Example 55
For each situation, find the critical value $t_{p,df}$ from the t-table (p is the upper tail probability).
(a). df = 11, p = .05

(b). df = 27, p = .01

(c). df = 68, p = .05

C. Sampling Distributions

Statistical <u>inference</u> involves using statistics computed from a sample to make statements about unknown population parameters. When these inferences are made formulas will be derived and used. These formulas will be derived from the <u>sampling distribution</u> of the statistic being used.

A **sampling distribution** of a statistic is the distribution of values taken by the statistic in a large number of simple random samples of the same size n from the same population. In the next chapter we will start statistical inference, and in each of the remaining chapters we will begin by stating the sampling distribution of the statistic being used. This will involve theoretically describing the shape, center, spread and any unusual features in the distribution.

However, in this chapter we just want to focus on the definition of a sampling distribution. So consider the following example.

Suppose the population consists of all students at this university. The parameter of interest is the mean age of all students at this university, which we will denote as μ. Now suppose each person in this class does the following.

The first person selects a simple random sample of n = 100 students at this university, and computes the mean age of the 100 students in the sample. Suppose this sample mean age is $\overline{X} = 23.8$.

The second person selects a simple random sample of n = 100 students at this university (which should be a different sample from the first student), and computes the mean age of the 100 students in the sample. Suppose the sample mean age is $\overline{X} = 24.3$.

The third person selects a simple random sample of n = 100 students at this university (again, this sample should be different from the first two), and computes the mean age of the 100 students in the sample. Suppose the sample mean age is $\overline{X} = 22.7$.

This process continues, so that every person has a sample and every person has a sample mean $\overline{X}$. These sample mean $\overline{X}$ values could be listed in a data set, as follows.

23.8   24.3   22.7   ...

If one were to construct a stem-and-leaf plot or histogram for this set of sample mean $\overline{X}$ values, this would be the sampling distribution of the sample mean $\overline{X}$.

Rectangle Activity

The grid on the following page displays a <u>population</u> of 84 rectangles. The characteristic of interest is the area of each rectangle, defined to be the number of small boxes making up the rectangle. For example, rectangle number 1 has an area of 1, while rectangle 14 has an area of 6. The parameter of interest is the mean area of all the rectangles.

Each student should use the Table of Random Digits on page 337 to select a simple random sample of 10 rectangles. Before turning to page 337, decide on the line number between 101 and 150 that you will use. Then write down the rectangle numbers of the first ten two-digit numbers that you get between 01 and 84 (if a number duplicates count it once but choose another two-number number to replace the duplicate). Then turn to the population of rectangles, record the area for each of your rectangles, and compute the sample mean $\overline{X}$ for your sample.

Simple Random Sample

<u>Rectangle Number</u>   <u>Area (number of boxes)</u>

1.

2.

3.

4.

5.

6.

7.

8.

9.

10.

          _____

    Sum of the Areas

    Mean = Sum ÷ 10

Rectangle Activity

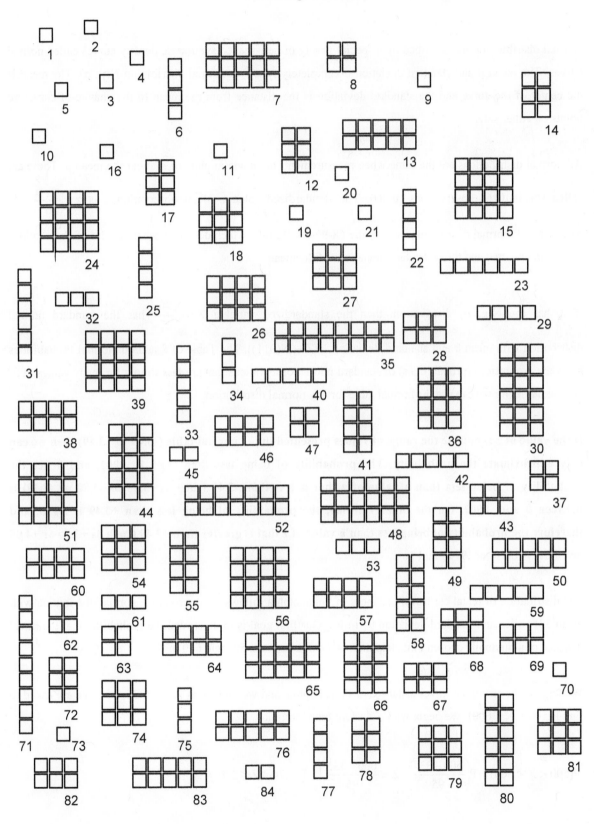

Additional Reading and Examples

1. Normal distributions are described by a special family of bell-shaped symmetric density curves called normal curves. The mean μ and standard deviation σ completely specify a normal distribution N(μ, σ). The mean is the center of the curve and the standard deviation is the distance from the mean to the change-of-curvature points on either side.

   All normal distributions are the same when measurements are made in units of σ about the mean μ. These are called standardized observations (units). The standardized value z of an observation x is $z = \dfrac{x - \mu}{\sigma}$. In particular, all normal distributions satisfy the 68-95-99.7% rule, which describes what percent of observations lie within one, two and three standard deviations of the mean.

   If X has the N(μ, σ) distribution, then the standardized variable $Z = \dfrac{X - \mu}{\sigma}$ has the standard normal distribution with mean 0 and standard deviation 1 (Z ~ N(0, 1)). The Table of Standard Normal Probabilities gives the proportions (probabilities) of standard normal observations that are **less than** z for many values of Z. By standardizing we can use the normal table for any normal distribution.

2. **If the value of z is outside the range of values presented in the normal table (-3.49 to +3.49) then we can only approximate the probability. The probability of being less than -3.49 is .0002, and hence the probability of being less than a value of z that is less than -3.49 (such as -3.50 or -4.00 or -8.39) is between 0 and .0002. On the other extreme, the probability of being less than +3.49 is .9998, and therefore the probability of being less than a value of z that is greater than +3.49 (such as +3.50 or +4.00 or +8.39) is between .9998 and 1.**

3. The distribution of rental car travel distances in Philadelphia follows an approximate normal distribution with mean 335 miles and standard deviation 95 miles. Our first goal is to determine the probability that the travel distance of a randomly chosen Philadelphia rental car is between 500 and 600 miles.

   We let X = the rental car travel distances in Philadelphia, and we know that X ~ N(335, 95). We are asked to find P(500 < X < 600). We begin with a Z-score transformation.

   $$P(500 < X < 600) = P\left(\frac{500 - 335}{95} < Z < \frac{600 - 335}{95}\right) = P(1.74 < Z < 2.79)$$

Now we must use the standard normal table to find the probability. We begin by converting the problem to two less than problems. We look up the probabilities in the table, and then subtract the smaller probability from the larger probability.

$$P(1.74 < Z < 2.79) = P(Z < 2.79) - P(Z < 1.74) = .9974 - .9591 = .0383$$

Hence the probability that the travel distance is between 500 and 600 miles is .0383.

Now suppose that the rental car company wants to determine the travel distance of a Philadelphia rental car such that it is in the top 16.67% (top 1/6) of the distribution.

We begin by determining the value of Z that satisfies the above requirement. Hence we need to find z such that $P(Z > z) = .1667$. To use the normal table we must have a less than problem, so we subtract the probability from 1 to yield $P(Z < z) = 1 - .1667 = .8333$. Now we look up .8333 in the body of the table, and read across and up to find z = 0.97.

To answer the question, we must convert this from z to x. Using $x = \mu + z\sigma$, we get x = 335 + 0.97(95) = 427.15 miles.

4. Suppose through a survey of all record labels it is known that the ages of all hip-hop/rap artists follow an approximate normal distribution with mean 23.5 years and standard deviation 3.7 years. Christian hip-hop/rapper VERBS was chronicled in the March 2005 volume of the Fellowship of Christian Athletes magazine *Sharing the Victory* (page 38). At that time VERBS was putting the finishing touches on THE TRAIN STATION, his Hip Hop Learnshop program for youth ages 12 to 18. Our first goal is to use the distribution described above to determine the probability that a hip-hop/rap artist will be less than 18 years old.

Let X = age of a hip-hop/rap artist, and we know that X ~ N(23.5, 3.7). We are asked to find P(X < 18). We begin with a Z-score transformation: $P(X < 18) = P\left(Z < \dfrac{18 - 23.5}{3.7}\right) = P(Z < -1.49)$. Since this is a less than problem we go directly to the table to determine $P(Z < -1.49) = .0681$.

Now suppose we want to determine the ages of hip-hop/rap artists that enclose the middle 50% of the distribution. For simplicity, let's call these ages A and B, such that A < B. If these two ages enclose the middle 50% of the distribution, then 25% of the ages will be less than A and 25% of the ages will be greater than B, implying that 75% of the ages are less than B.

To find A, since 25% of the ages are less than that value, we use the standard normal table and look up p = .25 in the <u>body</u> of the table. We find z = -0.67, and converting this to age units we have:

$$A = \mu + z\sigma = 23.5 - 0.67(3.7) = 21.021 \text{ years.}$$

To find B, since 75% of the ages are less than that value, we use the standard normal table and look up p = .75 in the <u>body</u> of the table. We find z = 0.67, and converting this to age units we have:

$$B = \mu + z\sigma = 23.5 + 0.67(3.7) = 25.979 \text{ years.}$$

Hence the middle 50% of the age distribution are between (approximately) 21 and 26 years of age.

5. The degrees of freedom specify which t distribution should be used. There is a t distribution for every positive degrees of freedom. The t-table on page 340 has degrees of freedom ranging from 1 to 30, then the degrees of freedom skip to 40, 50, 60, 80, 100, and 1000. If the degrees of freedom for a particular problem is not on this list, either use the closest degrees of freedom value or rely on the TI-83/84 calculator.

6. All t distributions are symmetric distributions similar in shape to the standard normal distribution, and the distributions approach the standard normal distribution as the degrees of freedom increases. Both the Z and t distributions have a mean of 0, but while the standard deviation of the Z distribution is 1, the standard deviation of a t distribution depends on the sample size and hence the degrees of freedom.

TI-83/84 Calculator

The TI-83/84 calculator can be used to give exact probability values for any normal distribution, and can be used to find exact values corresponding to given probabilities for any normal distribution. This uses the normal cumulative distribution function (cdf) which gives probabilities and values for less than problems (the same as the Table of Standard Normal Probabilities on pages 338 and 339).

1. To find normal probabilities, we use the normalcdf function on the calculator. To do so, use the **2nd** and **VARS** buttons to choose DISTR, and then use the down-arrow button to choose **2: normalcdf (**. Now four values need to be entered. The first two are the values of the variable that we want to find the probability of being between. The third is the value of the mean, and the fourth is the value of the standard deviation.

For example, suppose X has a normal distribution with mean 60 and standard deviation 8. There are three types of probability problems that can be solved: less than problems ($P(X < 50)$), greater than problems ($P(X > 72)$), and between problems ($P(64 < X < 74)$).

To solve a less than problem, for the first number use -1EE99 to represent negative infinity and for the second number use the value given (50 in the example). The EE can be entered by using 2nd and then the comma button. So to find $P(X < 50)$, we have **normalcdf (-1EE99, 50, 60, 8)**. The result is .105649839.

To solve a greater than problem, for the first number enter the value given (72 in the example) and for the second number use 1EE99 to represent positive infinity. So to find $P(X > 72)$, we have **normalcdf (72, 1EE99, 60, 8)**. The result is .0668072287.

To solve a between problem, enter the two numbers given, followed by the mean and the standard deviation. So to find $P(64 < X < 74)$ we have **normalcdf (64, 74, 60, 8).** The result is .2684784187.

2. To find values of the variable for a specified probability or area, we use the invNorm function on the calculator. To do so, use the **2nd** and **VARS** buttons to choose DISTR, and then use the down-arrow button to choose **3: invNorm(**. Now three values need to be entered. The first is the <u>less than</u> **probability**. For example, if you want to find the value of X such that the probability of being less than that value is .28, enter .28 for the first number. If the problem asks for the value of X such that the probability of being greater than that value is some number, such as .57, then first the probability must be subtracted from 1 (1 - .57 = .43) and we enter .43 for the first number. The second number is the mean, and the third number is the standard deviation (use 0 and 1 for the mean and standard deviation, respectively, if you desire a Z value instead of X).

For example, suppose X has a normal distribution with mean 60 and standard deviation 8. To find the value of X such that the probability of being less than that value is .28, we use the following: **invNorm (.28, 60, 8)**. The result is 55.33726798. To find the value of X such that the probability of being greater than that value is .57, we subtract .57 from 1 to get .43 and use the following: **invNorm (.43, 60, 8).** The result is 58.58900675.

Practice Problems:

VI. 1. The distribution of heights of adult men is approximately normal with mean 69 inches and standard deviation 2.5 inches. Draw a normal curve on which the mean and standard deviation are correctly located.

VI. 2. Scores on a standard IQ test for the 20 to 34 age group are approximately normally distributed with mean μ = 110 and standard deviation σ = 25. Use the properties of the normal distributions, including the 68-95-99.7% rule, to answer these questions.

    (a). About what percent of people in this age group have scores above 110?

    (b). In what range do the middle 95% of all IQ scores lie?

    (c). About what percent of people in this age group have scores above 160?

VI. 3. Each of the following involves a standard normal distribution. Use the normal table to find each of the following probabilities.

    (a). $P(Z < 2.85)$

    (b). $P(Z > 2.85)$

    (c). $P(Z > -1.66)$

    (d). $P(-1.66 < Z < 2.85)$

VI. 4. Each of the following involves a standard normal distribution.

    (a). Find the number z such that the probability of being less than z is 0.8.

    (b). Find the number z such that the probability of being greater than z is 0.35.

VI. 5. Three landmarks of baseball achievement are Ty Cobb's batting average of .420 in 1911, Ted Williams's .406 in 1941, and George Brett's .390 in 1980. These batting averages cannot be compared directly because the distribution of major league averages has changed over the years. The distributions are quite symmetric and (except for outliers such as Cobb, Williams, and Brett) reasonably normal. While the mean batting average has been held roughly constant by rule changes and the balance between hitting and pitching, the standard deviation has dropped over time. Here are the facts.

Decade	Mean	Standard Deviation
1910's	.266	.0371
1940's	.267	.0326
1980's	.261	.0317

Compute the standardized batting averages for Cobb, Williams, and Brett to compare how far each stood above his peers. In other words, compute Z-score transformations for each player. Relative to his peers, which of the three players did the best?

VI. 6. Xerox Corporation sells a copier maintenance agreement that provides same-day repairs of all problems with the copier and a set number of copies per month. Purchasers of the maintenance agreement have to pay extra for each additional copy above the agreed upon set number per month. Based on data over the past five years, Xerox Corporation knows that the number of copies made per month on all of its copiers serviced by a maintenance agreement follows an approximate normal distribution with mean 6582 copies and standard deviation 1732 copies.

    (a). What is the probability that a randomly selected Xerox copier serviced by a maintenance agreement would make 7244 copies or more?

    (b). Many small businesses own a Xerox copier and have purchased a maintenance agreement. These businesses usually make fewer copies per month than their larger competitors. How many copies must a copier make per month for it to fall in the bottom 16.16% of the distribution?

VI. 7. The distribution of heights of adult American men is approximately normal with mean 69 inches and standard deviation 2.5 inches.

    (a). What is the probability that an adult American man is at least 6 feet (72 inches) tall?

    (b). What is the probability that an adult American man is between 5 feet (60 inches) and 6 feet tall?

    (c). How tall must a man be to be in the tallest 10% of all adult men?

VI. 8. A professor believes that if a class is allowed to work on an examination as long as desired the time spent by the students would be approximately normal with a mean of 40 and a standard deviation of 6 minutes.

    (a). What percentage of students will finish within 45 minutes?

    (b). What percentage of students will finish within half an hour (30 minutes)?

    (c). What percentage of students will take longer than 1 hour (60 minutes)?

    (d). About how long should be allotted for the examination if the professor wants almost all (97.5 %) of the class to finish?

VI. 9. By law a box of cereal labeled as containing 16 ounces must contain at least 16 ounces of cereal. It is known that the machine filling the box produces a distribution of fill weights that is normal with mean equal to the setting on the machine and with a standard deviation equal to 0.03 ounces. To ensure that most of the boxes contain at least 16 ounces, the machine is set so that the mean fill per box is 16.09 ounces.

    (a). What is the probability that a box of cereal will contain less than 16 ounces?

    (b). What is the probability that a box of cereal will contain less than 16.05 ounces?

    (c). What is the probability that a box will contain more than 16.2 ounces?

    (d). What is the probability that a box will contain between 16.1 and 16.2 ounces?

VI. 10. A small computing center has found that the number of jobs submitted per day to its computers has a distribution that is approximately normal, with a mean of 83 jobs and a standard deviation of 10.

    (a). On about what percentage of days will the number of jobs submitted be less than 73?

    (b). On about what percentage of days will the number of jobs submitted be less than 93?

    (c). On about what percentage of days will the number of jobs be between 73 and 93?

VI. 11. The reading speed of students completing a speed-reading course follows a normal distribution with mean 450 words per minute (wpm) and standard deviation 70 wpm.

    (a). Find the probability that a student can read faster than 500 wpm.

    (b). Find the probability that a student reads slower than 375 wpm.

    (c). Find the probability that a student reads between 380 and 520 wpm.

    (d). To be in the slowest 10% what value would you have to read slower than?

    (e). To be in the fastest 5% what value would you have to read faster than?

VI. 12. A popular clothing manufacturer is interested in the number of minor imperfections in the fabric of their 100% cotton men's t-shirts. For t-shirts sized 40-42 the manufacturer has determined that the number of minor imperfections per shirt follows an approximate normal distribution with mean 38 imperfections and standard deviation 8 imperfections.

    (a). What is the probability that the number of imperfections in a size 40-42 t-shirt will be 60 or more?

    (b). The manufacturer is striving to reduce the number of imperfections per shirt. Based on the distribution described above, how many minor imperfections must a size 40-42 shirt have to fall in the bottom 11.2% of the distribution?

VI. 13. Scientists are interested in finding biological indicators of water quality. One such indicator is the Virginia freshwater snail Cone Vertigo (*Vertigo oralis*). After collecting data on hundreds of snails, biologist have determined that the width of the Cone Vertigo, measured at its widest point, follows an approximate normal distribution with mean 46 mm with a standard deviation of 16 mm.

    (a). On a recent field trip a scientist found a Cone Vertigo measuring 74 mm wide. What is the probability that a randomly selected Cone Vertigo is wider than 74 mm?

    (b). Many of the Cone Vertigoes collected during a field trip to Pony Pasture Park in Richmond, Virginia were very small. It was determined that the width of a majority of the snails fell in the bottom 18% of the population. How wide must a randomly selected Cone Vertigo be for it to fall in the bottom 18% of the distribution?

VI. 14. Scientists are working on a new sleep aid product and they are testing it on laboratory rats. Based on their observations, the scientists know that the length of time that the laboratory rats sleep after taking 25 mg of the sleep aid product follows an approximate normal distribution with mean 193 minutes and standard deviation of 23 minutes.

(a). What is the probability that a randomly selected laboratory rat will sleep for 240 minutes or longer (4 hours or longer) given that the rat has taken 25mg of the sleep aid product?

(b). How long must a laboratory rat sleep after taking the 25 mg of the sleep aid product if the sleep duration will fall in the bottom 64.43% of the distribution?

(c). Between what two values must a laboratory rat sleep after taking the 25 mg of the sleep aid product if the sleep duration will fall in the <u>middle</u> 50% of the distribution?

VI. 15. Suppose that the number of characters per text message sent by all college students follow an approximate normal distribution with mean 28.5 characters and standard deviation 7.1 characters.

(a). Suppose a student sent a text message to a friend with 26 characters, and the friend responded with a text message with 31 characters. What is the probability that the number of characters in a text message will be between 26 and 31 characters?

(b). How many characters must a text message have to fall in the bottom 11.90% of the distribution?

(c). What is the probability that the number of characters in a text message will be 50 characters or more?

(d). Between what <u>two values</u> must the number of characters in a text message fall to enclose the middle 80% of the data?

VI. 16. Consider each of the following situations. Give the value of the t-distribution for the given degrees of freedom and upper-tail probability p.

(a). degrees of freedom = 18, p = .10

(b). degrees of freedom = 7, p = .0025

(c). degrees of freedom = 47, p = .01

VI. 17. Consider each of the following situations. Give the value of the upper-tail probability p that corresponds to each degrees of freedom and t-value.

(a). degrees of freedom = 20, t = 2.086

(b). degrees of freedom = 50, t = 1.047

(c). degrees of freedom = 12, t = 3.930

Normal Distributions - Extra Problems

1. The length of the western rattlesnake is normally distributed with a mean of 42 inches and a standard deviation of 12 inches. Additionally, the length of the Texas rattlesnake is normally distributed with a mean of 48 inches and a standard deviation of 2 inches. A tourist finds a rattlesnake that is 50 inches long, but does not know whether it is a western rattlesnake or a Texas rattlesnake.

    (a). Find the probability that a western rattlesnake will be 50 inches or longer.

    (b). Find the probability that a Texas rattlesnake will be 50 inches or longer.

    (c). Based on your calculations above, which of the two types of rattlesnakes do you think the tourist has found? Briefly explain your answer.

    (d). How long must a western rattlesnake be such that 72.57% of all western rattlesnakes are shorter than it?

    (e). How long must a Texas rattlesnake be such that 72.57% of all Texas rattlesnakes are shorter than it?

2.   Many knee injuries are extremely painful, particularly injuries to the medial collateral ligament (MCL). Between 15 and 20% of skiing injuries involve tears of the medial collateral ligament, and this injury is common in other sports as well. Fortunately, modern surgical techniques are making full recoveries from these injuries possible. In particular, it is known that the recovery times following surgery to repair a torn medial collateral ligament have a mean of 180 days and a standard deviation of 25 days, and that the distribution of these recovery times follows an approximate normal distribution.

(a). Joel suffered a torn medial collateral ligament in a traffic accident, underwent surgery, and his recovery time was 210 days. He was upset that his recovery time was so long. Based on the distribution described above, what is the probability that someone's recovery time will be at least 210 days? (Note: at least 210 days means 210 days or more)

(b). Jamie has just suffered a torn medial collateral ligament while playing basketball. The doctor recommends surgery, and tells Jamie that the expected recovery time following surgery will be between 175 and 200 days. Based on the distribution described above, what is the probability that someone's recovery time will be between 175 and 200 days?

(c). Mark is an avid skier who suffered a torn medial collateral ligament on his last ski trip. He just had surgery, and being a fitness guru is striving for a quick recovery and hence a short recovery time. Based on the distribution above, how long must Mark's recovery take if it falls in the bottom 5% of the distribution?

(d). James suffered a gruesome medial collateral ligament injury that was so serious that the doctor tells James that it is among the worst 8% of all MCL injuries that he has seen. Based on the distribution above, what recovery time should James expect if it is going to be in the top 8% of the distribution?

3. The U.S. National Center for Health Statistics compiles data on the length of stay of patients in short-term hospitals and publishes its findings in *Vital and Health Statistics*. A recent report indicates that the distribution of patient stays in Hospital V is approximately normal with mean 9.5 days and standard deviation 1.8 days.

    (a). What is the probability that a patient from hospital V will spend less than one week (less than 7 days) in the hospital?

    (b). How long must a Hospital V patient remain in the hospital if only 30% of the patients spend more time in the hospital (and hence falls in the top 30% of the distribution)?

    (c). Between what two values must a Hospital V patient remain in the hospital if her hospital stay falls in the middle 50% of the distribution?

    (d). What is the probability that a patient from hospital V will spend between 10 and 14 days in the hospital?

VII. Statistical Inference

In Moore: Read Chapter 14 (pages 359 – 364 and 368 – 376)

The objective of inferential statistics is to make statements about population parameters based on statistics computed from a sample. The field of statistical inference involves two things: <u>estimation</u> in the form of confidence intervals and <u>statistical tests</u> (also known as significance tests or tests of significance). In this chapter we introduce the basic concepts associated with these two types of inferences, and then in future chapters apply them to the different parameters under consideration.

The first step in any inference procedure is to state the <u>practical question</u> that needs to be answered. This involves specifying the **population** of interest, and then the specific **parameter** that inferences need to be made about. For example, suppose one is interested in determining the mean IQ of all students at this university. This implies that the population of interest would be all students at this university, and the parameter of interest is μ = the mean IQ of all students. In order to determine the exact value of μ = the mean IQ of all students one would need to know the IQ of every student, which is likely not possible. Hence there is a need to make inferences about this <u>unknown</u> population parameter.

The first section introduces the concepts of confidence intervals, which can be used to estimate the unknown population parameters, and then the second section introduces the concepts of statistical tests in which one hypothesizes the value of the unknown population parameter and then uses data to test whether this hypothesized value is accurate or not.

A. Confidence Intervals

Confidence intervals are statistical procedures that allow for the <u>estimation</u> of unknown population parameters. The procedures involve the <u>calculation</u> of the intervals, and then the <u>interpretation</u> of the intervals. The interpretation is actually the statistical inference because it uses the calculated interval to makes statements about the unknown quantity (the parameter of interest).

For example, as above suppose we are interested in μ = the mean IQ of all students at this university. Unless data for all students at the university is known, it will not be possible to compute the value of the mean IQ for all students. Hence it must be estimated.

To estimate an unknown parameter, one must begin by selecting a <u>sample</u> from the population of interest and collecting the required data for the individuals in the sample. This data is then used to compute a statistic, with this statistic becoming the starting point for the statistical inference.

For example, since the IQ's of all students at this university are not known, we must select a sample of students and then collect the IQ's of the students in this sample. This is not too difficult – one could easily select a sample of 100 students from this university and acquire the IQ of each of these 100 students. Obviously we would like for the sample to be selected <u>randomly</u> as opposed to haphazardly or voluntarily, and this is a point of emphasis in later chapters. Once the IQ of each of these 100 students is determined, one could easily compute the mean IQ of this sample of 100 students. This would be the sample mean $\overline{X}$.

The value that is computed from the sample data collected is referred to as the **point estimate** of the unknown population parameter. As in the example above, if estimating the mean of a population (μ), the point estimate of this population mean μ is the sample mean $\overline{X}$. If the sample is <u>representative</u> of the population, then one would expect that the point estimate will be a good estimate of the population parameter and hence will be very close to the actual (but unknown) value of the parameter. But it is very unlikely that the actual value of the population parameter will equal the point estimate value exactly.

For example, suppose a sample of 100 current students is selected, the IQ of each student recorded (105, 118, 95, 92, 114 and so forth), and then the sample mean IQ is calculated to be $\overline{X} = \dfrac{\text{sum of IQ's}}{100} = 106$. If this sample of 100 students is representative of the population of all students at this university, then one would expect that the unknown mean IQ of all students at this university (μ) should be close to 106, but it probably will not equal to 106 <u>exactly</u>.

Therefore, to this point estimate one would subtract and add a quantity called a **margin of error** to create an interval of values that it is hoped the unknown population parameter is contained between. This interval (or range) of values that is generated by subtracting and adding the margin of error is called a **confidence interval**.

The margin of error is defined to be a practical upper bound for the distance between the point estimate and the parameter that is being estimated.

For example, suppose one made decisions (to be described in later chapters) such that the margin of error was 10 points. With a point estimate of $\overline{X} = 106$ IQ points, if we subtract and add 10, we end up with an interval from $106 - 10 = 96$ to $106 + 10 = 116$. The interval (96, 116) is called the confidence interval. The margin of error of 10 implies that an upper bound on the difference between the point estimate $\overline{X} = 106$ and the unknown mean IQ of all current students is 10 points.

Hence in general terms, a confidence interval is defined to be the point estimate of the unknown population parameter, plus and minus the margin of error.

Confidence interval: point estimate $\pm$ margin of error

The margin of error is determined from the sampling distribution of the statistic being used as the point estimate. Many more are details to come in later chapters.

The term "confidence" interval originates from the concept that once the interval is calculated, one has a certain amount of confidence that the unknown population parameter will be contained in the interval. This is incorporated into the calculation of the margin of error, with more details to come in later chapters.

When directed to estimate an unknown population parameter using a confidence interval, one usually specifies the amount of confidence that is desired. The most common values are 90% confidence, 95% confidence, 98% confidence and 99% confidence, and this amount of confidence is often referred to as the **confidence level**. As mentioned above the margin of error is derived from the sampling distribution of the point estimate, and hence the definition of the confidence level shares the repeated sampling concept as defined in the last chapter for sampling distributions:

The confidence level C implies that if repeated simple random samples of the same size are taken from the same population and a confidence interval is computed for each sample, then 100 x C% of these <u>confidence intervals</u> would contain the true value of the parameter and 100 x (1 - C)% of these confidence intervals would <u>not</u> contain the true value of the parameter.

For example, if one computes a 90% confidence interval, 90% confidence means that if we select 100 simple random samples from the population and calculate a 90% confidence interval for each sample, approximately 90 of the confidence intervals will contain the unknown population parameter and approximately 10 of the confidence intervals will not contain the unknown population parameter.

This is a theoretical concept, because in practical applications only one sample will be selected and hence only one confidence interval will be calculated.

Once the confidence interval has been calculated (recall that the calculation is point estimate $\pm$ margin of error), it then becomes essential to understand the meaning and <u>interpretation</u> of this interval. This interpretation depends on the amount of confidence used to calculate the interval.

The confidence interval is interpreted by stating that we have $100 \times C\%$ confidence that the population parameter of interest falls between the <u>lower limit</u> L = point estimate – margin of error and the <u>upper limit</u> U = point estimate + margin of error. <u>This interpretation is the statistical inference</u>, and it is important that this is written correctly to appropriately describe what is being concluded.

For example, suppose we are interested in estimating μ = the mean IQ of all students at this university. From a sample of 100 students the mean IQ of the students in the sample is $\overline{X} = 106$, and for a 90% confidence interval the margin of error is 10. Hence the lower limit is L = 106 – 10 = 96 and the upper limit is U = 106 + 10 = 116, and the interpretation is we have 90% confidence that the mean IQ of all students at this university is between 96 and 116. We have no idea if the mean IQ of all students is in this range or not (because it is not known), but we have 90% confidence that it is in the interval. Unless we have data for the entire population, we will not be able to be 100% confident in our statement.

Example 56:

Of interest is to estimate the mean number of passengers per car on the trains connecting the concourses at Hartsfield-Jackson Atlanta International Airport. Counting the number of passengers per car for all trains is impossible, and hence the parameter must be estimated. In a random sample of 40 cars the mean number of passengers per car was $\overline{X}$ = 33.5, and the margin of error associated with a 95% confidence interval is 8.4. Identify the population and parameter of interest, then use the results to calculate and interpret a 95% confidence interval for the mean number of passengers per car for all trains connecting the concourses at Hartsfield-Jackson Atlanta International Airport.

The **width** of a confidence interval is twice the margin of error: width = 2 × margin of error. Since the goal is to estimate an unknown population parameter, the confidence interval estimate would be better with a smaller margin of error and hence with a smaller width. This would give a more accurate estimate of the parameter.

One would also like to estimate the parameter with as high of a level of confidence as possible: being 99% confident is better than being 95% confident, which in turn is better than being 90% confident. However, for a given sample of data, as the confidence level increases the margin of error and hence interval width also increases, and therefore there is a tradeoff between choosing high confidence and creating a narrow (or precise) interval. This tradeoff is addressed in future chapters.

B. Tests of Significance

The goal of statistical inference is to use data collected in a sample and statistics computed from this data to make statements about some unknown population parameter. In the previous section we discussed concepts related to calculating and interpreting confidence intervals as a means of estimating unknown population parameters. In this section we conjecture (or hypothesize) that the parameter equals some value (a **statistical hypothesis**) and we use the data collected to test whether this value is reasonable or not.

For example, the University President may believe that the mean IQ of all students at this university is 110. Based on this, the President would conjecture (hypothesize) that μ = the mean IQ of all students at this university = 110, and then use data collected from a sample to test whether this conjecture (that $\mu = 110$) is correct or not. Once again, a definitive answer cannot be determined unless data for the entire population (all students) is known, which usually is not the case.

By definition, a **statistical hypothesis** is a statement about a population parameter. Population parameters that we have discussed include the population mean μ, the population median η, the population variance σ^2, the population standard deviation σ, and the population correlation coefficient ρ. We will also learn in a future chapter about the population proportion π. Note that each of these parameters is specified using a Greek letter or symbol. Therefore, each of the following is an example of a statistical hypothesis:

$$\mu = 86 \qquad \eta < 66 \qquad \sigma^2 > 5 \qquad \sigma \neq 71 \qquad \pi < .60 \qquad \rho = .82$$

The sample mean $\overline{X}$, the sample median M, the sample variance s^2, the sample standard deviation s, the sample correlation coefficient r, and the sample proportion $\hat{p}$ (which we will learn about in a later chapter), are all statistics. Since a statistical hypothesis is a statement about a parameter and not a statistic, then the following are **not** examples of statistical hypotheses:

$$\overline{x} > 90 \qquad M < 42.3 \qquad s^2 = 14 \qquad s < 100 \qquad \hat{p} \neq .5 \qquad r > 0$$

This section introduces some general terms and characteristics of significance tests.

1. The **null hypothesis**, usually denoted by H_0 is a conjecture about a population parameter that is presumed to be true. It is usually a statement of no effect or no change.

    For example, if the University President believes that the mean IQ of all students at this university is 110, and since the null hypothesis is a statement of no change or no effect, then the null hypothesis is $H_0: \mu = 110$.

    Note that writing $H_0 = 110$ is not a statistical hypothesis because there is no parameter specified (including the μ to represent the population mean is very important).

2. The **alternative** (or **research**) **hypothesis**, usually denoted by H_a or H_1 is a conjecture about a population parameter that the researcher suspects or hopes is true.

    For example, suppose that with the growth in the number of applicants to the university the university is now more selective in which students it admits and hence the belief is the mean IQ is higher than in the past. Since the null hypothesis is $H_0: \mu = 110$, then for this belief the alternative hypothesis would be $H_a: \mu > 110$.

    The null hypothesis will <u>always</u> contain an equality statement, <u>and we carry out the significance test assuming that the null hypothesis is true.</u> We would like for our test to provide sufficient evidence against the null hypothesis so that we can conclude that the alternative hypothesis is true.

    Since the null hypothesis always contains an equality statement ($H_0: \mu = 110$), there are three possible expressions for the alternative hypothesis.

    (1) There can be a greater than sign, as in the example above ($H_a: \mu > 110$). With such an alternative hypothesis the test is called an <u>upper one-sided test</u>.

    (2) There can be a less than sign, such as $H_a: \mu < 110$. This would result if for some reason one thinks the mean IQ of all students is now less than what it has been in the past. With such an alternative hypothesis the test is called a <u>lower one-sided test</u>.

    (3) Many times there is no direction indicated for the alternative hypothesis, one just wants to test to see if the parameter is different from the value specified in the null hypothesis. For example, if one wants to test to see if the mean IQ of all students is different from 110, then the alternative hypothesis becomes $H_a: \mu \neq 110$. With such an alternative hypothesis the test is called a <u>two-sided test</u>.

3. The **test statistic** is some quantity calculated from the sample data that we have collected that we use to assess the strength of the evidence against the null hypothesis. Test statistic formulas will be derived and presented in each subsequent chapter as the different applications are introduced. The general idea, however, is as follows.

After the null and alternative hypotheses have been stated (for example in the case of the mean IQ score for all students H_0: $\mu = 110$ and H_a: $\mu > 110$), a sample is selected from the population that the inferences are being made about. In the example, a sample of n = 50 students can be selected, and the IQ score of each student can be recorded. This data can then be used to calculate a statistic, for example the 50 IQ scores can be added and then divided by 50 to produce the sample mean IQ score $\overline{X}$. This sample mean $\overline{X}$ could be used as the test statistic.

If the sample mean is close to the hypothesized value, for example if $\overline{X}$ equals a value close to 110, then it is likely that the null hypothesis $\mu = 110$ is correct. If, however, $\overline{X}$ equals a value much greater than 110, say 125 or 130, then likely the null hypothesis $\mu = 110$ is not correct and we would conclude that the alternative hypothesis $\mu > 110$ is much more likely to be correct.

The test statistic is similar to evidence in a court case: the more evidence that can be presented, the more likely that a person would be found guilty of the crime he or she is charged of committing. In our example, the more that the sample mean $\overline{X}$ is above the hypothesized value 110, the more evidence against the null hypothesis and the more likely the alternative hypothesis is correct.

4. As mentioned above, we carry out the test assuming the null hypothesis is true. Hence a significance test will result in one of the following two decisions:

(i) We decide to **reject the null hypothesis (reject H_0)** and hence conclude that there is sufficient evidence that the alternative hypothesis is true. A test that rejects H_0 is said to be **significant.**

In the above example with H_0: $\mu = 110$ and H_a: $\mu > 110$, if the sample of n = 50 students produces a sample mean IQ of $\overline{X} = 125$, then this is far above 110 and hence would likely lead us to reject the null hypothesis and conclude that the alternative hypothesis that mean IQ of all students is greater than 110 is likely correct (H_a: $\mu > 110$ is likely correct).

(ii) We decide to **fail to reject the null hypothesis (fail to reject H_0)** meaning that the data does not provide significant evidence against the null hypothesis, and hence we conclude that there is insufficient evidence that the alternative hypothesis is true. A test that fails to reject H_0 is said to be **insignificant**.

In the above example with H_0: $\mu = 110$ and H_a: $\mu > 110$, if the sample of n = 50 students produces a sample mean IQ of $\overline{X} = 112$, then this is very close to 110 and hence would likely lead us to fail to reject the null hypothesis and hence we <u>cannot</u> conclude that the mean IQ of all students is greater than 110 (H_a: $\mu > 110$ is likely not correct).

The question now becomes: what is the cut-off value for the test statistic for deciding to reject the null hypothesis versus fail to reject the null hypothesis?

5. When conducting a test the null hypothesis is either correct or it is not correct, the issue is that we do not know which. For example, when testing H_0: $\mu = 110$ versus H_a: $\mu > 110$, we do not know the mean IQ score of all students, and it may be 110 or it may not be 110. Also, the decision of the test will be either to reject the null hypothesis or fail to reject the null hypothesis. Hence there are four combinations that could occur, as follows.

It is possible that the null hypothesis is not true and we decide to reject the null hypothesis. This would be a correct decision. For example, if we reject H_0: $\mu = 110$ and the mean IQ of all students truly is greater than 110, then we have made the correct decision.

It is possible that the null hypothesis is true and we decide to fail to reject the null hypothesis. This also would be a correct decision. For example, if we fail to reject H_0: $\mu = 110$ and the mean IQ of all students truly is 110, then we have made the correct decision.

It is possible that the null hypothesis is true and we decide to reject the null hypothesis. This would be an error, and an error of this type is referred to as a **type I error**. For example, if we reject H_0: $\mu = 110$ and the mean IQ of all students truly is 110, then we have made an incorrect decision and this incorrect decision would constitute a type I error.

It is possible that the null hypothesis is not true and we decide to fail to reject the null hypothesis. This would also be an error, and an error of this type is referred to as a **type II error**. For example, if we fail to reject H_0: $\mu = 110$ and the mean IQ score of all students truly is greater than 110, then we have made an incorrect decision and this incorrect decision would constitute a type II error.

It would be desirable to minimize the probability of making any type of error, hence our goal is to minimize the probability of making a type I error and minimize the probability of making a type II error. Unfortunately, as one of these decreases (which is good), the other increases (which is bad). Since a type I error is usually considered more serious than a type II error, in a statistical test we usually attempt to control the probability of a type I error.

The maximum probability of a type I error (maximum probability of rejecting the null hypothesis when it is actually true) that a researcher is willing to risk is referred to as the **significance level** (or **α-level**) of the test and is denoted by the Greek letter α (read alpha). The significance level is usually set at some small probability level, such as α = .01, α = .05 or α = .10. The significance level that is going to be used should be stated at the beginning of the process, when the null and alternative hypotheses are being stated.

For example, consider the IQ scores example where we are testing H_0: $\mu = 110$ versus H_a: $\mu > 110$. In real applications we would not know the mean IQ score for all students (μ), but for the sake of illustration suppose it actually is 110 (so the null hypothesis H_0: $\mu = 110$ is correct). Data is collected, the sample mean $\overline{X}$ is calculated to be 118 and the decision is to reject the null hypothesis and conclude that the mean IQ score for all students is greater than 110. This obviously would be an incorrect decision, more specifically a type I error. The significance level is the maximum probability of making such an incorrect decision that the researcher is willing to take. Hence the smaller the significance level the more difficult it will be to reject the null hypothesis.

To make a decision to either reject or fail to reject the null hypothesis, the significance level is used with one of two approaches. One approach involves computing the p-value of the test and comparing the p-value directly to the significance level. The other approach involves using the significance level to create a rejection region, and then comparing the test statistic to this rejection region to make a decision. The two approaches are described below, and only one is necessary. Different users may have a preference for one over another, but with either at a particular significance level the same decision should be made.

6. The **p-value** of a test is the probability, assuming the null hypothesis is true, that the test statistic takes a value as extreme or more extreme than the value actually observed. Hence small p-values provide evidence against the null hypothesis.

When conducting a test of significance, the step of computing the p-value requires that two questions are answered. First, the distribution of the test statistic must be identified, and second the type of test that is being conducted must be identified. The calculation of the p-value is dependent on the answers to these two questions.

Regarding the distribution of the test statistic, we will discuss procedures based on a standard normal (Z) distribution and on a Student's t-distribution (see the last chapter for details).

Regarding the type of test, since the null hypothesis will always contain an equality statement, the type of test depends on the <u>alternative hypothesis</u>. As defined earlier in this section there are **upper one-sided tests** (for example, H_a: $\mu > 110$), **lower one-sided tests** (for example, H_a: $\mu < 110$), and **two-sided tests** (for example, H_a: $\mu \neq 110$). The p-value calculation will depend on which of the three alternative hypotheses is stated in a given problem.

(1) For an <u>upper</u> one-sided test   (H_a: $\mu > 110$)

p-value = $P(Z \geq Z_{OBS})$ or   p-value = $P(t_{df} \geq t_{OBS})$

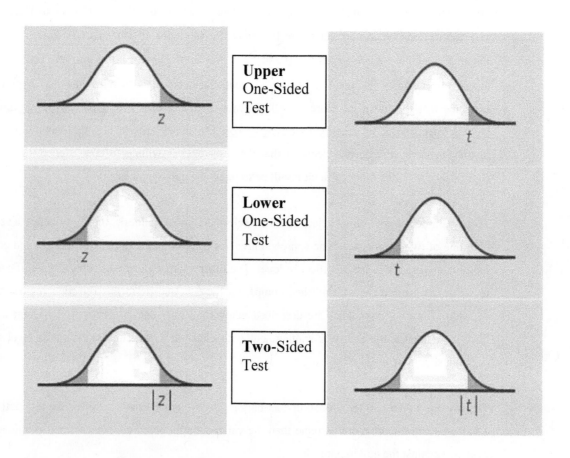

	Upper One-Sided Test	
	Lower One-Sided Test	
	Two-Sided Test	

(2) For a <u>lower</u> one-sided test   (H_a: $\mu < 110$)

p-value = $P(Z \leq Z_{OBS})$ or   p-value = $P(t_{df} \leq t_{OBS})$

(3) For a two one-sided test   (H_a: $\mu \neq 110$)

p-value = $P\!\left(Z \leq -\left|Z_{obs}\right|\right) + P\!\left(Z \geq \left|Z_{obs}\right|\right) = 2 \times P\!\left(Z \geq \left|Z_{obs}\right|\right)$

or

p-value = $P\!\left(t_{df} \leq -\left|t_{obs}\right|\right) + P\!\left(t_{df} \geq \left|t_{obs}\right|\right) = 2 \times P\!\left(t_{df} \geq \left|t_{obs}\right|\right)$

When using the standard normal (Z) table the p-value can usually be determined to four decimal places. However, if using the t-distributions the t-table only contains twelve probability values for each degrees of freedom, and hence the p-value is usually given in the form of an <u>interval</u>. Also recall that to use the Z-table the problem must be a <u>less than</u> problem, but to use the t-table the problem must be a <u>greater than</u> problem. The following two examples allow practice calculating p-values.

Example 57

For each of the following computed test statistics Z, calculate the p-value for the test indicated.

(a). Upper one-sided test; z = 2.65

(b). Lower one-sided test; z = -1.19

(c). Two-sided test; z = -2.12

Example 58

For each of the following computed test statistics, calculate the p-value for the test indicated.

(a). Upper one-sided test, df = 8, t_{obs} = 2.000

(b). Lower one-sided test, df = 40, t_{obs} = -1.53

(c). Two-sided test, df = 15, t_{obs} = -2.680

Note that when using either table (and particularly the t-table), if the value of the test statistic is not contained in the table, you use the most extreme value presented. Therefore, if the t_{obs} value is off the edge of the table to the left, then the probability is greater than .25; and if the t_{obs} value is off the edge of the table to the right, then the probability is less than .0005.

Once the p-value is calculated, we need to use it to make a decision about the significance of the test by comparing it directly to the significance level of the test.

(i). If p-value $\leq \alpha$, then we reject the null hypothesis H_0, say that the test is statistically significant at significance level α, and conclude that there is sufficient evidence that the alternative hypothesis is true.

(ii). If p-value $> \alpha$, then we fail to reject the null hypothesis H_0, say that the test is not statistically significant at significance level α, and conclude that there is insufficient evidence that the alternative hypothesis is true.

Note that "small" p-values lead us to reject the null hypothesis and "large" p-values lead us to fail to reject the null hypothesis.

Example 59

Consider the hypothesis testing situations and p-values calculated in example 57. For each test, state whether you would reject H_0 or fail to reject H_0 at significance level $\alpha = .05$.
(a). p-value = .0040

(b). p-value = .1170

(c). p-value = .0340

Example 60

Consider the hypothesis testing situations and p-values determined in example 58. For each test, state whether you would reject H_0 or fail to reject H_0 at significance level $\alpha = .05$.

(a). $.025 < \text{p-value} < .05$

(b). $.05 < \text{p-value} < .10$

(c). $.005 < \text{p-value} < .01$

7. The **rejection region** defines a range of values that the test statistic can take that would lead us to reject the null hypothesis in favor of the alternative hypothesis. As for the p-value approach, the determination of the rejection region is dependent on the type of test (upper one-sided, lower one-sided, or two-sided) and the distribution of the test statistic. The type of test is dependent on the alternative hypothesis, and the distribution of the test statistic will either be a standard normal (Z) distribution or a t-distribution.

    The rejection region is dependent on finding a critical value from a distribution table. In this book we will use the Table of t-Distribution Critical Values on page 340. Using the stated significance level α, proceed as follows for the type of test that you have.

    (1) For an <u>upper</u> one-sided test (H_a: $\mu > 110$)

        Find the significance level value across the top row, and then find the critical value from the appropriate row below. For test statistics based on the standard normal (Z) distribution these are the z^* values in the bottom row of the table, and for t-distributions the critical value is read from the row with the appropriate degrees of freedom, df. If the calculated degrees of freedom does not appear in the table, use for the critical value the corresponding value for the closest degrees of freedom value given in the table. Then the rejection region is:

Using Z: reject the null hypothesis if the observed test statistic value z_{obs} is <u>greater</u> than or equal to the critical value z^*. Reject H_0 if $z_{obs} \geq z^*$.

Using t: reject the null hypothesis if the observed test statistic value t_{obs} is <u>greater</u> than or equal to the critical value t^*. Reject H_0 if $t_{obs} \geq t^*$.

(2) For a <u>lower</u> one-sided test (H_a: $\mu < 110$)

Find the significance level value across the top row, and then find the critical value from the appropriate row below. For test statistics based on the standard normal (Z) distribution these are the z^* values in the bottom row of the table, and for t-distributions the critical value is read from the row with the appropriate degrees of freedom df. Then the rejection region is:

Using Z: reject the null hypothesis if the observed test statistic value z_{obs} is <u>less</u> than or equal to the **<u>negative</u>** of the critical value z^*. Reject H_0 if $z_{obs} \leq -z^*$.

Using t: reject the null hypothesis if the observed test statistic value t_{obs} is <u>less</u> than or equal to the **<u>negative</u>** of the critical value t^*. Reject H_0 if $t_{obs} \leq -t^*$.

(3) For a two-sided test (H_a: $\mu \neq 110$)

Divide the significance level by 2 and find the value $\alpha/2$ across the top row, and then find the critical value from the appropriate row below. For test statistics based on the standard normal (Z) distribution these are the z^* values in the bottom row of the table, and for t-distributions the critical value is read from the row with the appropriate degrees of freedom df. Then the rejection region is:

Using Z: reject the null hypothesis if the observed test statistic value z_{obs} is <u>less</u> than or equal to the <u>negative</u> of the critical value z^* or if the observed test statistic value z_{obs} is <u>greater</u> than or equal to the critical value z^*. Reject H_0 if $z_{obs} \leq -z^*$ or if $z_{obs} \geq z^*$.

Using t: reject the null hypothesis if the observed test statistic value t_{obs} is <u>less</u> than or equal to the <u>negative</u> of the critical value t^* or if the observed test statistic value t_{obs} is <u>greater</u> than or equal to the critical value t^*. Reject H_0 if $t_{obs} \leq -t^*$ or if $t_{obs} \geq t^*$.

Example 61

For each of the following situations based on the standard normal (Z) distribution, find the rejection region for a test at significance level $\alpha = .05$.

(a). Upper one-sided test

(b). Lower one-sided test

(c). Two-sided test

Example 62

Consider the rejection regions determined in example 61. For each consider the given observed test statistic value and state whether you would reject or fail to reject the null hypothesis. Note that the observed test statistic values are the same as those given in Example 57, so the decisions should match the decisions made in Example 59.

(a). Upper one-sided; $z_{obs} = 2.65$

(b). Lower one-sided; $z_{obs} = -1.19$

(c). Two-sided; $z_{obs} = -2.12$

Example 63

For each of the following tests based on the t-distribution, give the rejection region that would be used if the significance level for the test is $\alpha = .05$.

(a).   Upper one-sided test, df = 8

(b).   Lower one-sided test, df = 40

(c).   Two-sided test, df = 15

Example 64

Consider the rejection regions determined in example 63. For each consider the given observed test statistic value and state whether you would reject or fail to reject the null hypothesis. Note that the observed test statistic values are the same as those given in Example 58, so the decisions should match the decisions made in Example 60.

For each of the following computed test statistics, calculate the p-value for the test indicated.

(a).   Upper one-sided test, df = 8, $t_{obs} = 2.000$

(b).   Lower one-sided test, df = 40, $t_{obs} = -1.53$

(c).   Two-sided test, df = 15, $t_{obs} = -2.680$

The general significance testing procedure is as follows:

(1). State the null and alternative hypotheses, and the significance level α that is going to be used. This should be done <u>before</u> the data is collected.

(2). Carry out the experiment, collect data, verify that the assumptions are satisfied, and compute the value of the test statistic.

(3). Calculate the p-value of the test or determine the rejection region.

(4). Make a decision on the significance of the test (reject or fail to reject the null hypothesis).

(5). Make a **conclusion** statement <u>in the words of the original problem</u>. This conclusion is the statistical inference.

Note that steps (2) and (3) involve the mathematical calculations, and steps (1) and (4) require thought and that decisions be made. However, the most important step is the last step, because even if the calculations are done correctly, and all the decisions and notation expressed correctly, the result of the test is meaningless unless a conclusion can be expressed in words that can be understood by the typical person.

Additional Reading and Examples

1. The purpose of a confidence interval is to estimate an unknown population parameter with an indication of how accurate the estimate is and how confident we are that the result is correct. If the sample is representative of the population then the point estimate should be close to the unknown parameter, although it is likely not equal to it exactly.

2. To conduct inferences using formulas presented in future chapters the data must be a simple random sample from the population. If a more complex sampling design (such as a stratified or multistage random sample) is used then the formulas are not correct. Correct methods do exist for these sampling methods, but they are too complex for this book. However, there is no correct method for making inferences from data that is not randomly collected (such as a haphazard or volunteer response sample) that likely contains uncontrolled bias.

3. The margin of error and hence the width of the interval (**width = twice the margin of error**) are affected by the degree of confidence. For a given sample, the margin of error and interval width increase if the degree of confidence is increased and they both decrease if the degree of confidence is decreased.

4. A test of significance is intended to assess the evidence provided by data against a null hypothesis in favor of an alternative hypothesis. The null hypothesis will always contain an equal to sign (=), while the alternative hypothesis will contain a greater than sign (>, meaning an upper one-sided test), a less than sign (<, meaning a

lower one-sided test), or a not equal to sign ($\neq$, meaning a two-sided test). All statistical hypotheses involve a statement about a **population parameter**.

5 The decision to reject or fail to reject the null hypothesis is based on either the p-value of the test or the rejection region for the test. The **p-value** is the probability, assuming the null hypothesis is true, of observing a test statistic value as extreme or more extreme than the value actually calculated. Small p-values indicate strong (or significant) evidence against the null hypothesis in favor of the alternative hypothesis. The **rejection region** provides a range of values that the test statistic can fall within that would lead one to reject the null hypothesis. In either situation the decision is dependent on the **significance level** of the test, which is the maximum probability of rejecting the null hypothesis when the null hypothesis is actually true that the researcher is willing to risk.

6. For a given problem someone performing a test would either calculate the p-value or determine the rejection region. It is not necessary to do both. Consult with your instructor as to which approach he or she prefers. In the remainder of this book examples and practice problem solutions are given using both approaches, and you can use the one that is more appropriate for your situation.

7. A **two-sided** significance test is related to a confidence interval in the following way. If the hypothesized value under the null hypothesis (μ_0) falls in a $(1 - \alpha)100\%$ confidence interval then the test would be insignificant at significance level α and we would fail to reject the null hypothesis. However, if the hypothesized value under the null hypothesis does not fall in the $(1 - \alpha)100\%$ confidence interval then the test is significant at significance level α and we would reject the null hypothesis in favor of the two-sided alternative that the mean is different from μ_0.

For example, to estimate μ = the mean IQ of all students, assume a 90% confidence interval is computed for μ and works out to be (96, 116). Then $(1 - \alpha)100\% = 90\%$ implying that $\alpha = .10$. Hence if a test of H_0: $\mu = 112$ versus H_A: $\mu \neq 112$ is conducted at the $\alpha = .10$ significance level, since 112 is contained in the 90% confidence interval then 112 is a reasonable value for the mean IQ of all students and we would fail to reject the null hypothesis. However, if a test of H_0: $\mu = 120$ versus H_A: $\mu \neq 120$ is conducted at the $\alpha = .10$ significance level, since 120 is not contained in the 90% confidence interval then it is not a reasonable value for the mean IQ of all students and we would reject the null hypothesis. This is only true for two-sided tests (alternative hypothesis contains a $\neq$ sign).

Practice Problems:

VII.1.   (a). Of interest is to determine the mean income of all New York City taxi cab drivers. Identify the population and parameter of interest.

      (b). Collecting data on every member of the population is likely not possible, and hence the exact value of the parameter cannot be determined. In an effort to estimate the parameter, a newspaper selected a simple random sample of 65 New York City taxi cab drivers and reports that the mean income of the drivers in this sample is $\bar{x} = \$32,350$. The newspaper announced a margin of error of $2,250 for 95% confidence in its conclusions. Use this information to calculate and interpret a 95% confidence interval for the mean income of all New York City taxi cab drivers.

      (c). Why can't we say that the mean income of all New York City taxi cab drivers is exactly $32,350?

      (d). Explain clearly what is meant by 95% confidence.

VII. 2.   The United States Congress consists of 100 Senators and 435 members of the House of Representatives. A historian who is writing a book about the 107th Congress is interested in the intelligence of the members of Congress. One approach to measure the intelligence is to give a standard intelligence test to the members of Congress. The test that is to be used is scaled such that all scores are between 0 and 200, and such that the standard deviation of all scores is 20 points.

      (a). A simple random sample of 170 Congresspersons was selected and each of these Congresspersons took the standardized intelligence test and a score was determined for each. The mean score for this sample of 170 Congresspersons was 117.39. The margin of error of 3.95 was announced to coincide with 99% confidence. Use this information to calculate and interpret a 99% confidence interval for the mean score on this standard intelligence test for all members of Congress.

      (b). What would happen to the margin of error and width of the confidence interval if the degree of confidence were decreased from 99% to 90%?

VII. 3.   The YMCA Annual Giving campaign collects money to be used for children's programs, summer camps, and to purchase equipment for adult programs. Of interest is to estimate the mean contribution of all contributors and to do so the YMCA selected a simple random sample of 81 contributor forms, with the mean contribution of this sample of 81 forms being $62.50. For 99% confidence, a margin of error of 4.99 was announced, and hence the 99% confidence interval for the mean contribution of all YMCA Annual Giving campaign contributors is (57.51, 67.49). Identify whether each of the following is a correct interpretation of the confidence interval and the definition of confidence.

      (i). If repeated simple random samples of 81 contributors are selected and a 99% confidence interval computed for each, then the mean contribution of all YMCA Annual Giving campaign contributors will be contained in 99% of the confidence intervals.

(ii). If repeated simple random samples of 81 contributors are selected and a 99% confidence interval computed for each, then 99% of the sample means would be contained between $57.51 and $67.49.

(iii). The YMCA has 99% confidence that the mean contribution of all YMCA Annual Giving campaign contributors is between $57.51 and $67.49.

(iv). The probability that the mean contribution of all YMCA Annual Giving campaign contributors is between $57.51 and $67.49 is .99.

(v). 99% of all YMCA Annual Giving campaign contributions are between $57.51 and $67.49.

(vi). The mean contribution of all YMCA Annual Giving campaign contributors is equal to exactly $62.50.

VII. 4. Each of the following situations calls for a significance test for a population mean μ. State the parameter of interest and then null hypothesis H_0 and the alternative hypothesis H_a in each case.

(a). The diameter of a spindle in a small motor is supposed to be 5 millimeters. If the spindle is either too small or too large, the motor will not work properly. The manufacturer measures the diameter in a sample of motors to determine whether the mean diameter has moved away from the target.

(b). Designers report that the mean cost of the dresses worn by women who attended the 2009 American Music Awards show is $264.32. Since most presenters, entertainers, and/or nominees make large sums of money, ABC television believes the mean cost of the dresses worn by female presenters, entertainers, and/or nominees is greater than the mean for all attendees.

(c). The mean cost of meals in restaurants in St. Croix, U.S. Virgin Islands is $17.49. Travelers to the U.S. Virgin Islands want to test to determine if the mean cost of meals in restaurants in St. Thomas, another island in the U.S. Virgin Islands, is less than $17.49.

VII. 5. Suppose in the year 2000 the mean amount of money paid in taxes to the federal government by a single person in their 20's was $8,425. With revisions to the tax laws, it is suspected that currently the mean amount of money paid in taxes to the federal government by a single person in their 20's is less than $8,425.

(a). Based on the above, state the hypotheses that need to be tested.

(b). Suppose the test is to be conducted at the $\alpha = .10$ significance level. For each of the following calculated p-values, what decision should be made about the null hypothesis?

(i) p-value = .0355   (ii) p-value = .2519   (iii) p-value = .10   (iv) p-value = .0003

(c). For the p-values in part (b), how would the decisions regarding the null hypothesis have changed if the significance level had been set at $\alpha = .05$? What about $\alpha = .01$?

VIII. Inferences on Population Proportions

In Moore: Read Chapter 19

The goal of statistical inference is to use data collected in a sample and statistics computed from this data to make statements about some unknown parameter of the population. In this chapter the parameter of interest is the **population proportion**, denoted by the Greek letter π. If data for the entire population is known, then the value of the population proportion π can be computed and inferences are not required. However, in most situations data for the entire population is not known, and hence inferences in the form of confidence intervals and tests of significance must be made.

When making statistical inferences, the first step is to identify the population of interest and the specific parameter about which the inferences should be made. Consider the following examples.

1. Of interest is to estimate the proportion of all students at this university who have children. In this situation the population of interest is all students at this university, and the parameter of interest is π = the <u>proportion</u> of all students at this university with children.

2. MTV was launched on August 1, 1981 and initially played music videos guided by on-air hosts. Currently MTV plays a limited selection of music videos, but primarily broadcasts a variety of popular culture and reality television shows targeted at adolescents and young adults. However, since the show started in 1981 there is still a loyal following of viewers from the 1980's, and of interest is to estimate the proportion of current viewers who are age 30 or older. In this situation the population consists of current viewers of MTV, and the parameter of interest is π = the <u>proportion</u> of all current MTV viewers who are age 30 or older.

3. It is conjectured that at any given Major League Baseball game approximately 5% of fans in attendance are attending their first Major League Baseball game. Of interest is to test this claim versus the alternative that the proportion of fans in attendance at baseball games who are attending their first Major League Game is different from 0.05. In this situation the population consists of all fans attending Major League Baseball games, and the parameter of interest is π = the <u>proportion</u> of all fans attending Major League Baseball games who are attending their first Major League Baseball game.

Once the population and parameter of interest are determined, then a sample of the population is selected and data collected for the individuals in the sample. From this data the sample proportion, $\hat{p}$, can be calculated and this statistic used to make inferences about the population proportion π. In this case the sample proportion $\hat{p}$ is called the <u>point estimate</u> of the population proportion π.

In the remainder of this chapter we begin by discussing the sampling distribution of the sample proportion $\hat{p}$, and then talk about using the sample proportion to make inferences, both confidence intervals and tests of significance, about the population proportion.

Note: in Moore, he refers to the population proportion as p instead of π.

A. Sampling Distribution of the Sample Proportion $\hat{p}$

In Moore: Read Chapter 19 (pages 501 - 504)

Consider a random variable X that can take only two possible values, a "success" or a "failure". For example, suppose a new television set is purchased. The television set either works properly (a "success") or it does not work properly (a "failure"). As another example, a student takes a test. The student will either pass the test (a "success") or will fail the test (a "failure").

Numerically we usually code the successes as 1's and the failures as 0's, and assume that the proportion of successes (of 1's) in the population is π. Hence the proportion of failures in the population is $1 - \pi$.

With our first example, a television set that works properly is a "success" that is coded as a 1 and π is the proportion of all television sets that work properly, while a television set that does not work properly is a "failure" that is coded as a 0 and $1 - \pi$ is the proportion of all television sets that do not work properly.

Similarly for the second example, a student who passes the test is a "success" coded as a 1 and π is the proportion of all students who pass the test, while a student who fails the test is a "failure" coded as a 0 and $1 - \pi$ is the proportion of all students who do not pass the test.

This creates what is called a **0-1 random variable**, and in this section we assume that π, the proportion of successes in the population, is known.

Recall that a **sampling distribution** of a statistic is the distribution of values taken by the statistic in a large number of simple random samples of the same size n from the same population. Describing a sampling distribution involves theoretically describing the shape, center, spread and any unusual features in the distribution. To do so we must assume the population parameters are known, so for the current application we are assuming that the population proportion π is known.

The assumptions required for proportions are very similar to those for means, namely (1) the data being used to make inferences must be a <u>simple random sample</u> selected from the population and (2) the sample size must be "large enough" for the <u>central limit theorem</u> to apply.

For means in addition to "large sample" we allowed the population distribution to be normal, but this will never be the case when analyzing proportions because there are only two possible values (success and failure, or equivalently 1 and 0) so the distribution will be two spikes (bimodal) and not normal.

The other difference for proportions is that the sample is considered "large enough" for the central limit theorem to apply if <u>both</u> the expected number of successes in the sample, $n\pi$, and the expected number of failures in the sample, $n(1-\pi)$, are greater than or equal to 10. If either $n\pi$ or $n(1-\pi)$ is less than 10 (or both less than 10) then the sample size is not large enough for the central limit theorem to apply. Note that if π is close to 0 or to 1, then the required sample size n will be much larger than if π is close to .50.

Then if the population proportion π is known, and **if both assumptions are satisfied**, then the sampling distribution of the sample proportion $\hat{p}$ can be theoretically described as follows.

(1) Center: the mean of the sampling distribution of $\hat{p}$ is $\mu_{\hat{p}} = \pi$.

(2) Spread: the standard deviation of sampling distribution of $\hat{p}$ is $\sigma_{\hat{p}} = \sqrt{\dfrac{\pi(1-\pi)}{n}}$.

(3) Shape: the shape of the sampling distribution will be normal.

(4) Unusual features: since the shape will be normal, then there are no unusual features in the sampling distribution.

Hence the <u>sampling distribution</u> of $\hat{p}$ is $\hat{p} \sim N\left(\pi, \sqrt{\dfrac{\pi(1-\pi)}{n}}\right)$.

Example 65

Television executives report that only 6% of all people who have called to vote for a contestant on "American Idol" have voted at least once each season. To test this claim, a special number was created and the first 400 people who voluntarily called the number were asked if they had called in at least once during each season. Of interest is to determine the proportion of this sample of 400 people who have called in at least once each season. If appropriate, describe the sampling distribution of the sample proportion $\hat{p}$.

Example 66

Using data from past semesters it is known that 80% of students who take introductory statistics pass the course; the other 20% either fail or drop/withdraw from the class. The current statistics instructor selects a simple random sample of 64 students enrolled in introductory statistics during the current semester and computes $\hat{p}$ = the proportion of the 64 students who are passing the course. If appropriate, describe the sampling distribution of the sample proportion $\hat{p}$.

Example 67

It is known that 85% of all attempted bank robberies in this country are successful. By successful we mean the robber left the bank with stolen money (whether or not they are later caught does not matter). A simple random sample of 120 attempted bank robberies is studied, and the proportion of these bank robberies that are successful determined. If appropriate, describe the sampling distribution of the sample proportion $\hat{p}$.

The primary use of these sampling distributions is to make inferences about the unknown population proportion π, and the next two sections of this chapter will discuss confidence intervals and tests of significance, respectively. However, another use is to use the sampling distribution theory together with the Table of Standard Normal Probabilities on pages 338 and 339 to make probability statements about $\hat{p}$.

The Z-score transformation takes the value of the variable, subtracts the mean, and then divides by the standard deviation: $Z = \dfrac{\text{value - mean}}{\text{s tan dard deviation}}$. This Z-score transformation procedure can be used to make probability statements about the sample proportion $\hat{p}$ by putting the value of $\hat{p}$ into the equation along with the mean $\mu_{\hat{p}} = \pi$ and the standard deviation $\sigma_{\hat{p}} = \sqrt{\dfrac{\pi(1-\pi)}{n}}$. So to make probability statements about the sample proportion $\hat{p}$ the appropriate Z-score transformation is $Z = \dfrac{\hat{p} - \pi}{\sqrt{\dfrac{\pi(1-\pi)}{n}}}$.

Example 68

Television executives report that only 6% of all people who have called to vote for a contestant on "American Idol" have voted at least once each season. To test this claim, a special number was created and the first 400 people who voluntarily called the number were asked if they had called in at least once during each season. Of interest is to determine the proportion of this sample of 400 people who have called in at least once each season. If appropriate, use the sampling distribution determined in example 65 to determine the probability that the proportion of the 400 people in the sample who have called in at least once during each season is less than .07.

Example 69

Using data from past semesters it is known that 80% of students who take introductory statistics pass the course; the other 20% either fail or drop/withdraw from the class. The current statistics instructor selects a simple random sample of 64 students enrolled in introductory statistics during the current semester and computes $\hat{p}$ = the proportion of the 64 students who are passing the course. If appropriate, use the sampling distribution determined in example 66 to determine the probability that the proportion of the sample of 64 students who will pass the course this semester is greater than .75.

194

Example 70

It is known that 85% of all attempted bank robberies in this country are successful. By successful we mean the robber left the bank with stolen money (whether or not they are later caught does not matter). A simple random sample of 120 attempted bank robberies is studied, and the proportion of these bank robberies that are successful determined. If appropriate, use the sampling distribution determined in example 67 to determine the probability that the proportion of the 120 bank robberies in the sample that are successful is between .80 and .90.

B. Confidence Interval for π

In Moore: Read Chapter 19 (pages 504 – 512)

Consider the first example mentioned at the beginning of this chapter, namely that of interest is to estimate the proportion of all students at this university who have children. In this situation the population of interest is all students at this university, and the parameter of interest is π = the proportion of all students at this university with children. Unless data for every student at this university is known, then the proportion of all students who have children is unknown and must be estimated. This section talks about how confidence intervals can be used to estimate such unknown population proportions.

If one selects a simple random sample from the population, and uses the data in the sample to compute the sample proportion $\hat{p}$, then $\hat{p}$ is the **point estimate** of the population proportion π. If the sample is a representative sample of the population then the sample proportion $\hat{p}$ should be close to the population proportion π, but it most likely will not equal to the unknown value exactly. Hence to the point estimate $\hat{p}$ we will subtract and add a **margin of error** to create an interval of values that we hope the unknown population proportion π is between. This interval is called a **confidence interval** and below we discuss how to calculate and interpret such confidence intervals.

As in the last chapter, the term confidence refers to the amount of confidence we have that our interval contains the population proportion π. Recall that π is an unknown value – if it is known it does not need to be estimated and there is no reason to compute a confidence interval. Since π is unknown, there is no way of knowing whether it will be in the confidence interval or not. Hence we state a confidence level C that indicates the amount of confidence we have that our calculated 100*C% confidence interval will contain the unknown population proportion π. This confidence level is used in calculating the intervals, and again the most common values are .90, .95, .98 and .99 corresponding to 90%, 95%, 98% and 99% confidence intervals, respectively.

The confidence interval formula below requires the same two basic assumptions that were required for the sampling distribution in the previous section, namely (1) that a simple random sample is selected from the population and (2) the sample size is "large enough" for the central limit theorem to apply. The sample is considered "large enough" for the central limit theorem to apply if both the expected number of successes in the sample, $n\pi$, and the expected number of failures in the sample, $n(1-\pi)$, are greater than or equal to 10.

If these two assumptions are satisfied then the sampling distribution of $\hat{p}$ is $\hat{p} \sim N\left(\pi, \sqrt{\dfrac{\pi(1-\pi)}{n}}\right)$, and

doing a Z-score transformation we get $Z = \dfrac{\hat{p} - \pi}{\sqrt{\dfrac{\pi(1-\pi)}{n}}}$. Solving this for the unknown population

proportion π yields the following 100*C% confidence interval formula: $\hat{p} \pm Z^* \sqrt{\dfrac{\pi(1-\pi)}{n}}$. The value of Z^*

can be found in the t-Table on page 340 by looking up the confidence level across the bottom row and then finding the Z^* value directly above.

The only remaining issue is that the unknown population proportion π appears in the formula above. To correct this issue, the sample proportion $\hat{p}$ (the point estimate) is substituted into the formula for π. In doing so the assumptions become (1) that a simple random sample is selected from the population and (2) the sample size is "large enough" for the central limit theorem to apply. For a **confidence interval** the sample is considered "large enough" for the central limit theorem to apply if both the observed number of successes in the sample, $n\hat{p}$, and the observed number of failures in the sample, $n(1 - \hat{p})$, are greater than or equal to 10. Hence the formula for a 100*C% confidence interval for the population proportion π is:

$$\hat{p} \pm Z^* \sqrt{\frac{\hat{p}(1-\hat{p})}{n}}$$

Hence $\hat{p} - Z^* \sqrt{\frac{\hat{p}(1-\hat{p})}{n}}$ is the lower limit of the confidence interval, $\hat{p} + Z^* \sqrt{\frac{\hat{p}(1-\hat{p})}{n}}$ is the upper limit of

the confidence interval, and $Z^* \sqrt{\frac{\pi(1-\pi)}{n}}$ is the <u>margin of error</u> of the confidence interval.

The interpretation of the interval is similar to that for population means, and this interpretation is the statistical inference. For example, if when estimating the proportion of all students at this university who have children the 90% confidence interval is .08 to .14, then we write "we have 90% confidence that the proportion of all students at this university who have children is between .08 and .14."

Note that the above interpretation can be equivalently written in terms of the <u>percentage</u> instead of proportion, as follows: "we have 90% confidence that the percentage of all students at this university who have children is between 8% and 14%."

Example 71

Of interest is to estimate the proportion of all current college presidents who favor a plan whereby scholarship athletes would receive a salary equal to the minimum wage for each hour of official sports-related participation. Begin by identifying the population of interest and the parameter of interest. A simple random sample of 100 college presidents was selected, and 6 indicated that they favor the plan. If appropriate, use this data to calculate and interpret a 95% confidence interval for the proportion of all college presidents who favor the plan.

Example 72

Of interest is to estimate the proportion of all current athletic directors who favor a plan whereby scholarship athletes would receive a salary equal to the minimum wage for each hour of official sports-related participation. Begin by identifying the population of interest and the parameter of interest. A simple random sample of 100 athletic directors was selected, and 25 indicated that they favor the plan. If appropriate, use this data to calculate and interpret a 98% confidence interval for the proportion of all athletic directors who favor the plan.

Example 73

Of interest is to estimate the proportion of all current college students who have received at least one speeding ticket. Begin by identifying the population of interest and the parameter of interest. A simple random sample of 225 current college students is selected and 140 of these students have received at least one speeding ticket. If appropriate, calculate and interpret a 90% confidence interval for the proportion of all current college students who have received at least one speeding ticket.

All the properties regarding the confidence intervals for means also apply to these confidence intervals for proportions. Specifically, increasing the degree of confidence will increase the margin of error and hence the width of the interval, while decreasing the degree of confidence will decrease both the margin of error and interval width. Similarly, increasing the sample size will decrease the margin of error and interval width while decreasing the sample size to save resources will result in an increase in the margin of error and interval width.

Now suppose that before the experiment is carried out or before the sample is selected, we specify the degree of confidence that we desire and the maximum margin of error (or maximum interval width) that we will allow. Our goal is to find the sample size n necessary to guarantee this degree of confidence and simultaneously this margin of error m. The margin of error for a confidence interval for π is

$$m = Z^* \sqrt{\frac{\pi(1-\pi)}{n}}$$, and solving for n yields $n = \left(\frac{Z^*}{m}\right)^2 \pi(1-\pi)$.

However, the population proportion π is unknown and without data the sample proportion $\hat{p}$ cannot be calculated and used as we did in the confidence interval calculation. So we must find a value for π from a different source.

(1) If a previous estimate π^* for π exists, approximate π with this previous estimate π^*, or
(2) Do a small pilot study to determine an estimate of π, or
(3) If no value is available, use $\pi = .50$. Using $\pi = .50$ will give a sample size n that is at least large enough, and works well if the true value of it is anywhere between .3 and .7.

π	$\pi(1-\pi)$
.2	.2(1-.2) = .16
.3	.3(1-.3) = .21
.4	.4(1-.4) = .24
.5	**.5(1-.5) = .25**
.6	.6(1-.6) = .24
.7	.7(1-.7) = .21
.8	.8(1-.8) = .16

The pilot study usually involves some nonrandom collection of data that is easily available and from which an estimate of π can be calculated. In practical situations this is an option, but in classroom or other academic settings it is usually not an option.

Then the sample size required for a 100*C% confidence interval for π with maximum margin of error m is

$$n = \left(\frac{Z^*}{m}\right)^2 \pi(1-\pi).$$ This numerical result is usually a fraction of a whole number and the result should always be rounded up to the next largest integer.

Example 74

Of interest is to estimate the proportion of all current athletic directors who favor a plan whereby scholarship athletes would receive a salary equal to the minimum wage for each hour of official sports-related participation. In example 72 a total of 100 athletic directors was selected and the margin of error of the confidence interval was .1007. For this situation, determine the sample size n required to give a 98% confidence interval for the proportion of all current athletic directors who favor the plan with margin of error no larger than .06. Do this first assuming that the true proportion is .25 (the $\hat{p}$ valued used in example 72) and then second using $\pi = .50$.

C. Significance Test for π

In Moore: Read Chapter 19 (pages 512 – 516)

Now our attention is turned to significance tests for population proportions. Our goal is to test the null hypothesis that the population proportion π equals some specified value π_0 (H_0: $\pi = \pi_0$) versus the alternative hypothesis that π is greater than π_0 (H_A: $\pi > \pi_0$), π is less than π_0 (H_A: $\pi < \pi_0$), or π is not equal to π_0 (H_A: $\pi \neq \pi_0$). We need to define a test statistic appropriate for testing these hypotheses, and once the test statistic is calculated a p-value or rejection region is calculated and an appropriate decision and conclusion are made regarding the hypotheses, similar to what was done for the mean in the last chapter.

For example, consider the third example listed at the beginning of this chapter.

It is conjectured that at any given Major League Baseball game approximately 5% of fans in attendance are attending their first Major League Baseball game. Of interest is to test this claim versus the alternative that the proportion of fans in attendance at baseball games who are attending their first Major League Game is different from 0.05. In this situation the population consists of all fans attending Major League Baseball games, and the parameter of interest is π = the <u>proportion</u> of all fans attending Major League Baseball games who are attending their first Major League Baseball game.

Hence the null hypothesis would be H_0: $\pi = .05$ and the alternative hypothesis would be H_A: $\pi \neq .05$.

Recall that the <u>point estimate</u> of the population proportion π is the sample proportion $\hat{p}$. The test statistic formula is derived from the sampling distribution of $\hat{p}$, which requires the assumptions that (1) the data is a simple random sample selected from the population and (2) that the sample size is large enough for the central limit theorem to apply, meaning both $n\pi \geq 10$ and $n(1 - \pi) \geq 10$. With these two assumptions the sampling distribution of $\hat{p}$ is $\hat{p} \sim N\left(\pi, \sqrt{\dfrac{\pi(1-\pi)}{n}}\right)$, and by a Z-score transformation we have the statistic

$$Z = \dfrac{\hat{p} - \pi}{\sqrt{\dfrac{\pi(1-\pi)}{n}}}$$, which is a candidate for the test statistic.

However, this statistic cannot be calculated because the population proportion π is unknown. Since we perform the test assuming that the null hypothesis H_0: $\pi = \pi_0$ is true, our best estimate of π is π_0 and the test statistic that can be used to conduct tests on population proportions is:

$$Z = \frac{\hat{p} - \pi_0}{\sqrt{\frac{\pi_0(1 - \pi_0)}{n}}}$$

Note that by substituting the hypothesized value π_0 for the unknown population proportion π, the requirement for a large sample becomes both the hypothesized number of successes in the sample $n\pi_0$ and the hypothesized number of failures in the sample $n(1 - \pi_0)$ <u>both</u> must be greater than or equal to 10.

Also note that this requirement is slightly different than the requirement for confidence intervals, which substituted the sample proportion $\hat{p}$ for the unknown population proportion π and hence the requirement for a large sample was $n\hat{p}$ and $n(1 - \hat{p})$ <u>both</u> must be greater than or equal to 10.

Example 75

It is conjectured that at any given Major League Baseball game approximately 5% of fans in attendance are attending their first Major League Baseball game. Of interest is to test this claim versus the alternative that the proportion of fans in attendance at baseball games who are attending their first Major League Game is different from 0.05. In this situation the population consists of all fans attending Major League Baseball games, and the parameter of interest is π = the <u>proportion</u> of all fans attending Major League Baseball games who are attending their first Major League Baseball game. The null hypothesis is H_0: π = .05 and the alternative hypothesis is H_A: $\pi \neq .05$. A simple random sample of 160 fans was selected and asked if this was their first Major League Baseball game or not. 12 of the fans indicated that it was their first Major League Baseball game. If appropriate, use this data to test the hypotheses at significance level α = .10.

Example 76

In 2000 the proportion of students taking business courses at a large college was .28. A group of faculty advisors claim that this proportion has changed since 2000. Begin by stating the population of interest, the parameter of interest, and the hypotheses that should be tested. A simple random sample of 300 currently enrolled students was selected and it was found that 110 are taking business courses. If appropriate, use this data to test the faculty advisor's claim at significance level $\alpha = .10$.

Example 77

A recent survey published by the Higher Educational Research Institute stated that 22 percent of entering college students classified themselves as politically liberal. Administrators at a large urban university feel that the proportion of entering students at their university who classify themselves as politically liberal is greater than this national figure. Begin by stating the population of interest, the parameter of interest, and the hypotheses that should be tested. A simple random sample of 264 students who started at the large urban university in 2009 were selected, of which 65 classified themselves as being politically liberal. If appropriate, at significance level $\alpha = .05$, test to determine if the claim made by the administrators is accurate.

Additional Reading and Examples

1. Sampling distributions are theoretical concepts that require that the population parameters are known. In the case of proportions this implies the population proportion π must be known. In real inference problems these parameters are unknown and our goal is to either estimate the parameters or test hypotheses about the parameters.

2. The assumptions necessary for the sampling distribution theory to be appropriate are (1) the data must be a simple random sample selected from the population and (2) the sample size must be "large enough" for the central limit theorem to apply. For problems involving <u>proportions</u> the sample size is considered large enough if the expected number of successes $n\pi \geq 10$ <u>and</u> the expected number of failures $n(1-\pi) \geq 10$. When making statistical inferences on population proportions π is unknown, and for confidence intervals it is replaced by the sample proportion $\hat{p}$ in the expressions above and for tests of significance it is replaced by the hypothesized value π_0 in the expressions above. The normal approximation used to describe the shape of the sampling distribution gets better and better as the sample size increases. In cases in which the sample size is not large enough for the central limit theorem to apply the shape of the distribution is not necessarily normal but <u>it can still be described</u>. However, this description depends on knowledge of the real population distribution and in most cases is beyond the difficulty level of this book.

3. Manufacturers of food products report that approximately 2% of all the coupons they circulate are redeemed for discounts on the food purchased. Different manufacturers rely more heavily on coupon advertising than others, and hence this figure is quite alarming to them. They decide to market test their coupons by selecting a simple random sample of 400 coupons that are marked with a special code. Of interest is to determine the proportion of this sample of 400 coupons that are returned. State as completely as possible the sampling distribution of this sample proportion.

    We must specify the mean, the standard deviation, and the shape. Since there is a simple random sample the mean and standard deviation formulas can be used, as follows.

    Mean: $$\mu_{\hat{p}} = \pi = .02$$

    Standard deviation: $$\sigma_{\hat{p}} = \sqrt{\frac{\pi(1-\pi)}{n}} = \sqrt{\frac{.02(1-.02)}{400}} = .007$$

    Shape: Since $n\pi = 400(.02) = 8 < 10$, the central limit theorem does <u>not</u> apply and we cannot state that the distribution is normal. In this case a sample of size 400 is <u>not</u> "large enough."

4. A local cable company reports that approximately 12% of their subscribers have made complaints against the cable company in the past two years. A local neighborhood group feels that their area is having a larger number of problems than the cable company is willing to admit. They select a simple random sample of 100 cable subscribers in their neighborhood, of which 17 have reported problems. If such a sampling procedure were repeated, what is the probability of getting a sample proportion of .17 or greater?

    The local residents fear that there are more problems in their area than the cable company is reporting because the sample proportion is $\hat{p} = \dfrac{17}{100} = .17$. To answer the question, the sampling distribution of $\hat{p}$ must first be determined. There is a simple random sample, so the mean and standard deviation are:

    Mean: $\mu_{\hat{p}} = \pi = .12$

    Standard deviation: $\sigma_{\hat{p}} = \sqrt{\dfrac{\pi(1-\pi)}{n}} = \sqrt{\dfrac{.12(1-.12)}{100}} = .0325$

    Shape: Since $n\pi = 100(.12) = 12$ and $n(1 - \pi) = 100(1 - .12) = 88$ are both greater than 10, then the central limit theorem applies and the sampling distribution is normal: $\hat{p} \sim N\,(.12, .0325)$.

    Then $P(\hat{p} \geq .17) = P\left(Z \geq \dfrac{.17 - .12}{.0325} \right) = P(Z \geq 1.54) = 1 - P(Z < 1.54) = 1 - .9382 = .0618$

5. The inferences for population proportions are similar to those for population means. Both the confidence interval formula and the test statistic are derived from the sampling distribution of the point estimate $\hat{p}$ (the sample proportion) and require a large simple random sample from the population. The properties of the confidence intervals and the conclusions of the significance tests are the same as those for means except they reference a proportion instead of a mean.

6. In 2009 a large group of Americans were interested in determining the proportion of all American citizens who felt that President Obama's most recent budget represented "a positive change in the direction of the country." Since all American citizens could not be contacted for their opinion, this proportion was estimated using a 95% confidence interval. To keep the estimate as accurate as possible they decided to restrict the margin of error of the interval to 0.035.

    The first decision was to determine how large of a sample of American citizens they should select. With π unknown and no previous estimate available, they used $\pi^* = .50$. For a 95% confidence interval, $Z^* = 1.960$, and we want to restrict the margin of error to m = .035.

$$n = \left(\frac{Z^*}{m}\right)^2 \pi(1-\pi) = \left(\frac{1.960}{.035}\right)^2 (.50)(1-.50) = 784$$

(Note: in this case the calculation worked out to be a whole number. Usually the result would be a fraction and the number calculated would be rounded <u>up</u> to the next largest integer.)

Hence researchers need to randomly select at least 784 American citizens to assure that the 95% confidence interval has a margin of error no larger than 0.035. Given this calculation, researchers selected a simple random sample of 800 American citizens, of which 368 agreed that the 2009 budget was a positive change in the direction of the country. The other 432 either disagreed or had no opinion. This data was used to calculate a 95% confidence interval for the proportion of all Americans who agreed that the 2009 budget was a positive change for the country.

From the sample of $n = 800$ Americans, the sample proportion is $\hat{p} = \frac{368}{800} = .46$. Both the number of successes in the sample $n\hat{p} = 368$ and the number of failures in the sample $n(1-\hat{p}) = 432$ are greater than 10, so the confidence interval formula presented in this chapter is appropriate.

Then the 95% confidence interval, using $Z^* = 1.960$, is

$$\hat{p} \pm Z^* \sqrt{\frac{\hat{p}(1-\hat{p})}{n}} = .46 \pm 1.960 \sqrt{\frac{.46(1-.46)}{800}} = .46 \pm .0345 = (.4255, .4945)$$

One has 95% confidence that the proportion of all Americans who agreed that the 2009 budget was a positive change for this country is between .4255 and .4945.

Note that the observed margin of error is .0345, which is less than .035. Also, from a practical standpoint, since .50 is not in the interval people at the time could be fairly confident that a majority (50% or more) of all American people did not agree that the 2009 budget was a positive change for the country.

7. A southern book company believes that 90% of all statistics books are returned at the end of the semester. They have an interest in conducting an experiment to determine if this is true or not. With π = the proportion of all statistics books that are returned at the end of the semester, they want to test the null hypothesis that π is equal to .90 (H_0: $\pi = .90$) versus the alternative hypothesis that it is different from .90 (H_A: $\pi \neq .90$).

The book company selected a simple random sample of 90 students who had purchased statistics books, and asked each whether they had returned their book. In the sample 82 had returned their books and 8 had not, so the sample proportion is $\hat{p} = 82/90 = .9111$. There is a simple random sample, however, since the expected number of failures $n(1 - \pi_0) = 90(1 - .90) = 9$ is less than 10, the central limit theorem does not apply and using inference procedures based on the standard normal (Z) statistic are not appropriate. Therefore, this data should not be used to test the hypotheses of interest. While one may think that a sample of size 90 is "large", in this example it is not "large enough" for the central limit theorem to apply.

8. A study was conducted on the incidence of learning disabilities in adolescents staying at emergency shelters. Complete evaluations were obtained on a simple random sample of 61 such adolescents, of which 42 were diagnosed as having a learning disability. Does this data provide sufficient evidence at the 1% significance level that a majority of all adolescents living at emergency shelters have learning disabilities?

    The parameter of interest is π = the proportion of all adolescents living at emergency shelters with learning disabilities, and since a majority is more than half, the hypotheses are: $H_0: \pi = .50$ versus $H_A: \pi > .50$.

    From the data, $n = 61$ and the sample proportion is $\hat{p} = 42/61 = .6885$. Since both the expected number of successes $n\pi_0 = 61(.50) = 30.5$ and the expected number of failures $n(1 - \pi_0) = 61(1 - .50) = 30.5$ are greater than 10, the central limit theorem applies and the test statistic formula of this chapter is valid.

    Hence the observed test statistic is $Z = \dfrac{\hat{p} - \pi_0}{\sqrt{\dfrac{\pi_0(1 - \pi_0)}{n}}} = \dfrac{.6885 - .50}{\sqrt{\dfrac{.50(1 - .50)}{61}}} = \dfrac{.1885}{.0640} = 2.94$.

    P-value: this is an upper one-sided test, so p-value = $P(Z \geq 2.94) = 1 - P(Z < 2.94) = 1 - .9984 = .0016$.
    Rejection region: with $\alpha = .01$ and an upper one-sided test, we reject the null hypothesis if $z_{obs} \geq 2.326$.

    Using the p-value, since the p-value is less than .01 we reject the null hypothesis. Using the rejection region, since the observed test statistic $Z = 2.94$ is greater than 2.326, we reject the null hypothesis. Hence we conclude that there is sufficient evidence that the proportion of all adolescents staying at emergency shelters with learning disabilities does exceed .50.

TI-83/84 Calculator

To calculate a confidence interval for the population proportion π or to conduct a significance test for the population proportion π on the TI-83/84 calculator, all you need is the number of successes in the sample and the sample size.

1. Confidence interval: press **STAT** and use the right-arrow button to scroll over to **TESTS**. Then use the down-arrow button to scroll down to **A: 1-PropZInt** and press **ENTER**. At this prompt you need to enter the number of successes in the sample next to **x:**, the sample size next to **n:**, and give the desired confidence level

in terms of a proportion next to **C-Level:**. After entering these three values, scroll down to **Calculate** and hit **ENTER** and the results are displayed. In addition to the confidence interval you also receive the calculated value of the sample proportion $\hat{p}$ and the sample size n.

2.   Test of significance: the steps are very similar to those for a confidence interval. First, press **STAT** and use the right-arrow button to scroll over to **TESTS**. Then use the down-arrow button to scroll down to **5:1-PropZTest** and press **ENTER**. Now you have to enter four values: next to p_0 enter the hypothesized proportion in the null hypothesis; next to **x:** enter the number of successes; next to **n:** enter the sample size; and then choose the type of test: two-sided ($\neq p_0$), lower one-sided ($<p_0$), or upper one-sided ($>p_0$) Once these values are entered scroll down to **Calculate** and hit **ENTER**. The values of the Z test statistic, the p-value, the sample proportion $\hat{p}$ and the sample size n are all displayed.

Practice Problems:

VIII. 1. A college president says "99% of the alumni support my firing of the football coach." You contact a simple random sample of 200 of the college's 15,000 living alumni and find that 76 of them support firing the coach. Describe in words the population of interest and what the parameter π is for this problem. Then give a numerical value for the statistic $\hat{p}$ that estimates π.

VIII. 2. According to government data, 22% of American children under the age of 6 live in households with incomes less than the official poverty level. A study of learning in early childhood chooses a simple random sample of 300 children.

(a). What is the probability that more than 20% of the sample are from poverty households?
(b). What is the probability that more than 30% of the sample are from poverty households?

VIII. 3. Following a budget impasse, it was reported that only 2.5% of all state of Virginia employees agreed that they should sacrifice a raise last year so that the governor could balance the state budget. To test this report, a simple random sample of 500 employees of the state of Virginia was selected and the proportion of the 500 employees that agreed that they should sacrifice a raise last year so that the governor could balance the state budget determined.

(a). If $\hat{p}$ is the proportion of the sample that agreed that they should sacrifice a raise last year so that the governor could balance the state budget, describe completely the sampling distribution of this sample proportion.
(b). Find the probability that the sample proportion $\hat{p}$ will take a value less than .02.

VIII. 4. The 2001 Rock and Roll Hall of Paine induction class consisted of the following performers: Aerosmith, Solomon Burke, The Flamingos, Michael Jackson, Queen, Paul Simon, Steely Dan, and Ritchie Valens. Suppose a simple random sample of 300 people is selected, and $\hat{p}$ = the proportion of the sample who think Michael Jackson is the most deserving inductee, is determined.

    (a). If each inductee is equally preferred, then the proportion of all people who think each contestant is the most deserving inductee is π = .125. Based on this, what is the sampling distribution of $\hat{p}$, the proportion of the sample who think Michael Jackson is the most deserving inductee?

    (b). What is the probability that the proportion of a sample of 300 people who think Michael Jackson is the most deserving inductee is greater than .10?

VIII. 5. Six percent of the students taking summer courses at a large urban university last summer were not regular students of that university, but instead are enrolled at another university and transferred the credit from their summer class to their regular university. These students are referred to as transcient students. A simple random sample of 200 students who took courses at the large urban university last summer is selected, and the proportion of the students in the sample who transferred the credit to their regular university determined.

    (a). If a simple random sample of 200 students who took summer courses at this urban university last summer is selected and the sample proportion $\hat{p}$ computed for the sample, describe completely the sampling distribution of the sample proportion.

    (b). What is the probability that the proportion of the 200 students in the sample who will transfer the credit back to their regular university exceeds .10?

VIII. 6. An internet service provider recently announced that 25% of the emails that pass through their server are classified as "chain emails." A subscriber decides to test this report by selecting a simple random sample of 500 emails sent through the mail server and determining the proportion of the emails that are "chain emails."

    (a). Describe completely the sampling distribution of this sample proportion of the 500 emails that are "chain emails."

    (b). What is the probability that the proportion of the 500 emails that are "chain emails" is less than .20?

VIII. 7. In the population of American adults, 67% watched some of the figure skating and/or ice dancing competitions at the 2010 Winter Olympics. A simple random sample of 500 American adults is selected and the proportion of the sample who watched some of the figure skating and/or ice dancing competitions at the 2010 Winter Olympics is determined.

    (a). What is the sampling distribution of this sample proportion?

    (b). What is the probability that the proportion of the 500 American adults who watched some of the figure skating and/or ice dancing competitions at the 2010 Winter Olympics is between .65 and .70?

VIII. 8. A study was initiated to determine what proportion of all Americans agree with the statement that the 2000 Presidential race would not have ended up so close and in such controversy if Ralph Nader had not been running. A simple random sample of 950 Americans was selected and each was asked if they agreed with the above statement. In the sample, 627 answered "yes, I agree", If appropriate, use this data to calculate and interpret a 99% confidence interval for the proportion of all Americans who agree with the statement.

VIII. 9 In which of the following situations can you safely use the methods of this section for a significance test? Explain your answers.

   (a).   You toss a coin 10 times in order to test the hypothesis H_0: $\pi = .5$ that the coin is balanced.

   (b).   A college president says "99% of the alumni support my firing of the Provost." You contact a simple random sample of 200 of the college's 15,000 living alumni to test the hypothesis H_0: $\pi = .99$.

   (c).   To determine if a majority of the 250 students in a statistics course agree that knowing statistics will help them in their future careers, you interview a simple random sample of 20 students to test $H_0 : \pi = .5$.

   (d).   You set up a toll-free 1-800 number to determine if less than a quarter of all parents support allowing students diagnosed as being HIV-positive to participate in physical education classes with other students. 364 people respond and you use the data to test the hypothesis: H_0: $\pi = .25$.

VIII. 10. With enrollments up, particularly among freshmen, officials at University X are concerned about the retention rates of the students. Of particular concern are students classified as "high risk" students. Between 1993 and 1995 only 53% of the students classified as "high risk" remained at University X after two years. To increase the retention rate for these students, in 1996 University X started offering a one-credit orientation course designed to better prepare the students for college and therefore increase their chances for success at University X. In a simple random sample of 88 "high risk" students who entered University X in the fall of 2008 and completed the orientation course, 66 were still at University X after the 2009-10 academic year. Is this good evidence that the orientation course has been successful in increasing the proportion of "high risk" students who are retained at University X? If appropriate, test at significance level $\alpha = .05$.

VIII 11. In 1994 the American Academy of Pediatrics began advising parents to have infants sleep on their backs. This was an effort to reduce occurrences of Sudden Infant Death Syndrome (or SIDS). In 1989 it was found that 40 percent of all deaths among infants less than 1 year of age could be attributed to SIDS. The American Academy of Pediatrics believes that the proportion of all deaths among infants less than 1 year of age in the year 2009 is less than .40, and they want to test this claim at the $\alpha = .05$ significance level. To do so they selected a simple random sample of 400 deaths among infants less than 1 year of age and found that 130 of the deaths could be attributed to SIDS.

VIII. 12. The federal government has set up a website where heads of single parent homes can find information, forms, and references to assist them with raising their children. The website is available to single parents throughout the country, but due to different levels of publicity they are interested in whether the number of hits from each region of the country is in line with the number of people living in each region of the country. The regions of the country will correspond to the time zones, coded as follows: A – Alaskan, C – Central, E – Eastern, H – Hawaiian, M – Mountain and P – Pacific.

(a). Since the federal government is housed in the **Eastern** time zone, of interest is to estimate the proportion of all hits to the website that are by single parents in the **Eastern** time zone (code **E**). The goal is to do this by calculating a 98% confidence interval with margin of error no larger than .10. What is the minimum sample size required that guarantees that this can be done? Note that the data presented in part (b) cannot be used to solve this question.

(b). Federal government officials contacted a simple random sample of 150 single parents who had visited the website and asked each in which region of the country she or he lived. Using the time zone codes listed above, the results were as follows.

P E M C E P C E E C M E C E E C P C E C E E C C P E C E P E C M P C E P C
E C E A C E E C E P C E E E C C E P P C E E P C E E C M E C P E C P E C E P
C E P E C E P E C E C H E C P E E P E C P E P E C P P E C E P E C P H E P E
P C E E P E C M E P C E E E P M E P E C E P C E C E E P C E P C E M E E C

If appropriate, use this information to calculate and interpret a 98% confidence interval for the proportion of all hits to the website that are by single parents in the **Pacific** time zone (code **P**).

(c). Those responsible for creating the program and establishing the website are originally from Chicago in the **Central** time zone (code **C**). They believe that a third of all hits will be from single parents living in the **Central** time zone. If appropriate, use the data in part (b) to test at level $\alpha = .05$ to determine if the proportion all hits to the website that are by single parents in the **Central** time zone is equal to .33 or if it is different from .33.

VIII. 13. The YMCA wants to determine the proportion of all its members and employees who contribute to the YMCA Annual Giving campaign. The campaign director obtained the staff directory and membership role, combined these lists, and selected a simple random sample of 150 people from the combined list. In this sample of 150 people, 18 indicate that they are contributing to the YMCA Annual Giving campaign. Using this information, if appropriate, calculate and interpret a 90% confidence interval to estimate the proportion of all members and employees who contribute to the YMCA Annual Giving campaign.

VIII. 14. In 1995 researchers at Stanford University reported that 70% of all truck drivers suffered from obstructive sleep apnea. Obstructive sleep apnea is a sleep disorder that causes a person to stop breathing momentarily and then awaken briefly. These sleep interruptions, which may occur hundreds of times in a night, can drastically reduce the quality of rest and cause fatigue during waking hours. Researchers feel that more than

70% of all truck drivers suffer from obstructive sleep apnea. To test this claim, the researchers collected a simple random sample of 159 commercial truck drivers and found that 122 of them suffered from obstructive sleep apnea. Does the data suggest that more than 70% of all truck drivers suffer from obstructive sleep apnea? If appropriate, test at significance level $\alpha = .01$.

VIII. 15. There were 4228 people in attendance at the 2001 American Music Awards show. ABC television wants to determine the proportion of these people who live in California.

(a). They decide to estimate this proportion using a 95% confidence interval and they want the margin of error associated with this interval to be no larger than .05. How large of a sample of attendees should they sample to guarantee this level of confidence and this margin of error?

(b). A simple random sample of 400 people in attendance at the 2001 American Music Awards show was selected, and 188 of these people live in California. If appropriate, use this information to calculate and interpret a 95% confidence interval for the proportion of all attendees who live in California.

(c). Airlines promised a special rate for people traveling to future American Music Awards shows if more than half of the attendees at the 200! American Music Awards show were from <u>outside</u> California. If appropriate, use the information in part (b) to test at level $\alpha = .05$ to determine if more than half of all attendees were from outside California.

VIII. 16. A recent survey by National Public Radio, the Kaiser Family Foundation, and Harvard's Kennedy School of Government found that vast majorities of people in the top income categories have very few problems getting health care or paying for it. Researchers are now interested in determining the percentage of Americans that have stayed in a job longer than they otherwise would in order to keep their health insurance. Determine the minimum sample size required to give a 95% confidence interval for the proportion of all Americans that have stayed in a job longer than they otherwise would in order to keep their health insurance with a margin of error no larger than .05.

VIII. 17. The American Academy of Pediatrics issued new recommendations recently telling pediatricians to screen all children for snoring because it could be a sign of a serious illness. Children who snore loudly may suffer from obstructive sleep apnea syndrome (OSAS). Left untreated, the disorder can lead to growth, heart and pulmonary problems. Local physicians are interested in estimating the proportion of all children in the Richmond, Virginia area who snore.

(a). Determine the minimum sample size required to give a 95% confidence interval for the proportion of all children in the Richmond, Virginia area who snore with a margin of error no larger than .10.

(b). A simple random sample of 100 children in the Richmond, Virginia area was selected. In the sample 37 children snored. If appropriate, use this information to calculate and interpret a 95% confidence interval for the proportion of all children in the Richmond, Virginia area who snore.

VIII. 18. In a 1998 survey of medical students by Brushkin-Goldring Research, it was found that 3 out of 4, or 75%, of medical students who took a commercial MCAT prep course were enrolled in courses offered by Kaplan. Medical College of Virginia officials are interested in determining the proportion of all medical students enrolled in Virginia universities that have taken the Kaplan MCAT preparatory courses.

(a). Determine the minimum sample size required to give a 99% confidence interval for the proportion of all Virginia medical students that have taken the Kaplan MCAT preparatory courses with a margin of error no larger than .10.

(b). In an attempt to estimate the proportion of all medical students enrolled in Virginia universities that have taken the Kaplan MCAT preparatory courses, Medical College of Virginia officials decided that they could easily obtain a simple random sample of 200 medical students enrolled in Virginia universities. In doing so, they found that 148 of the 200 medical students in the sample have taken a Kaplan preparatory course before taking the MCAT exam. If appropriate, use this information to calculate and interpret a 99% confidence interval for the proportion of all medical students enrolled in Virginia universities that have taken the Kaplan MCAT preparatory courses.

Card Exercise

A standard deck of 52 playing cards consists of four suits: clubs, diamonds, hearts, and spades, with 13 cards of each suit. The clubs and spades are black, the diamonds and hearts are red.

1. What proportion of the playing cards in a standard 52-card deck are red?

2. Suppose we want to conduct a test to determine if π = the proportion of red cards in a deck is as we expect. Using the answer in question 1, what hypotheses may we want to test?

    Null hypothesis: Alternative hypothesis:

3. Drawing cards <u>with replacement</u> from the deck means that after a card is selected and observed, it is returned to the deck. This keeps the proportion of red cards the same for each draw, and satisfies the simple random sample assumption for the inference procedures.

    If we randomly select 25 cards from the deck with replacement, how many red cards do you expect to get?

4. If we randomly select 25 cards from the deck with replacement, and compute the proportion of the 25 cards that are red, this would be the sample proportion $\hat{p}$. If the null hypothesis made in question 2 is true, what is the sampling distribution of $\hat{p}$?

5. We will actually conduct this experiment by selecting, with replacement, 25 cards from the deck.
    Number of red cards in sample: Number of black cards in sample:

6. Does this data provide <u>some</u> evidence that the alternative hypothesis is true? Explain.

7. If appropriate, carry out a test at significance level $\alpha = .10$ to test the hypotheses stated in question 2. What do you conclude about this deck?

IX. Inferences on Populations Means

The goal of statistical inference is to use data collected in a sample and statistics computed from this data to make statements about some unknown parameter of the population. In this chapter the parameter of interest is the **population mean**, denoted by the Greek letter μ. If data for the entire population is known, then the value of the population mean μ can be computed and inferences are not required. However, in most situations data for the entire population is not known, and hence inferences in the form of confidence intervals and tests of significance must be formed.

When making statistical inferences, the first step is to identify the population of interest and the specific parameter about which the inferences should be made. Consider the following examples.

1. Of interest is to estimate the mean age of all students at this university. In this situation the population is all students at this university, and the parameter of interest is μ = the <u>mean</u> age of all students at this university.

2. It is conjectured that the mean cost of all women's swimwear purchased in 2009 was $60, and of interest is to test this conjecture versus the alternative that the mean cost of all women's swimwear purchased in 2009 was actually greater than $60. In this situation the population consists of all sales of women's swimwear in 2009, and the parameter of interest is μ = the <u>mean</u> cost of all women's swimwear purchased in 2009.

3. General Motors advertises that the 2010 Chevy Equinox averages 32 miles per gallon when driven on the highway. Of interest is to test this claim versus the alternative that the mean miles per gallon when driven on the highway for all 2010 Chevy Equinox vehicles is different from 32 miles per gallon. In this situation the population consists of all 2010 Chevy Equinox vehicles driven on the highway, and the parameter of interest is μ = the mean miles per gallon of all 2010 Chevy Equinox vehicles when driven on the highway.

Once the population and parameter of interest are determined, then a sample of the population is selected and data is collected for the individuals in the sample. From this data the sample mean, $\overline{X}$, can be calculated and this statistic is used to make inferences about the population mean μ. In this case the sample mean $\overline{X}$ is called the <u>point estimate</u> of the population mean μ.

In the remainder of this chapter we begin by discussing the sampling distribution of the sample mean $\overline{X}$, and then talk about using the sample mean to make inferences, both confidence intervals and tests of significance, about the population mean.

A. Sampling Distribution of the Sample Mean $\overline{X}$

In Moore: Read Chapter 11 (pages 299 – 308)

In chapter VI a sampling distribution was defined to be the distribution of values taken by the statistic in a large number of simple random samples of the same size n from the same population. This involves theoretically describing the shape, center, spread and any unusual features in the distribution.

To describe the sampling distribution of the sample mean $\overline{X}$, values for the population mean μ and the population standard deviation σ must be known. In inference problems the values for μ and σ are usually unknown, but in this section we assume that they are <u>known</u>. For example, in the first example above X is a student's age and suppose it is known that the mean age of all students in the population is $\mu = 28.9$ and that the standard deviation of the ages of all students in the population is $\sigma = 4.8$.

The sampling distribution theory that follows, along with all the inference procedures discussed later in the chapter, requires that two assumptions be satisfied. Prior to working any problem, these assumptions should be checked and the problem worked only if the assumptions are satisfied. If the assumptions are not satisfied there are appropriate procedures than can be used, but they are beyond the scope of this book.

Assumption 1: the data being used to make the inferences must be a <u>simple random sample</u> from the population.

Assumption 2: the <u>population distribution</u> must be known to be <u>normal</u>, or the <u>sample size</u> must be "large enough" for the **central limit theorem** to apply (or both). The central limit theorem is defined below, and for problems involving <u>means</u> the sample is considered "large enough" if the sample size n is greater than or equal to 15, unless the distribution is **heavily skewed** due to outliers and in the case where the population distribution is **heavily skewed** due to outliers the sample size must be greater than or equal to 40.

Note: different books may have different rules for what is considered a "large enough" sample. The two-tiered rule of 15/40 is fairly standard and will be used consistently in the rest of the book.

Then if the population mean μ and population standard deviation σ are known, and **if both assumptions are satisfied**, then the sampling distribution of the sample mean $\overline{X}$ can be theoretically described as follows.

(1) Center: the mean of the sampling distribution of $\overline{X}$ is $\mu_{\overline{x}} = \mu$.

(2) Spread: the standard deviation of sampling distribution of $\overline{X}$ is $\sigma_{\overline{x}} = \dfrac{\sigma}{\sqrt{n}}$.

(3) Shape: the shape of the sampling distribution will be normal.

(4) Unusual features: since the shape will be normal, then there are no unusual features in the sampling distribution.

We can summarize the sampling distribution by writing it as: $\overline{X} \sim N\left(\mu, \dfrac{\sigma}{\sqrt{n}}\right)$. This is read "the sampling distribution of the sample mean $\overline{X}$ is distributed normal with mean μ and standard deviation $\dfrac{\sigma}{\sqrt{n}}$.

The central limit theorem is a mathematical property that states that regardless of the shape of the original population (symmetric, bimodal, slightly skewed, heavily skewed due to outliers, etc), if the sample size is large enough the shape of the sampling distribution will be approximately normal. Hence if the population is normal, the sample size only needs to be 1 (or greater). However, if the population is not normal, or if the population distribution shape is unknown, then the central limit theorem must be used and the sample size rules of assumption 2 become important.

Example 78

Among Americans who took vacations last summer, the length of the vacations follows a normal distribution with mean 7 days and standard deviation 3.5 days. A simple random sample of 25 vacationers is selected and $\overline{X}$ = the mean length of the vacations in this sample of 25 vacations determined. If appropriate, describe the sampling distribution of the sample mean $\overline{X}$.

Example 79

At a particular university, scores on an organic chemistry test are skewed to the left with a mean of 70 and a standard deviation of 15. A simple random sample of 50 students taking organic chemistry is selected and $\overline{X}$ = the mean score on the organic chemistry test by this sample of 50 students determined. <u>If appropriate</u>, describe the sampling distribution of the sample mean $\overline{X}$.

Example 80

The incomes of employees at a large government agency are skewed heavily to the right with a mean of $115,870 and a standard deviation of $32,925. A simple random sample of 22 employees is selected and $\overline{X}$ = the mean income of this sample of 22 employees determined. <u>If appropriate</u>, describe the sampling distribution of the sample mean $\overline{X}$.

The primary purpose of sampling distributions is that they are used to make inferences about the population parameter of interest. For the remainder of this chapter the sampling distribution of $\overline{X}$ theory just described will be used to make inferences about the population mean μ.

However, since the sampling distribution theory describes the shape of the sampling distribution to be normal, another use of the sampling distributions is to use the sampling distribution together with the Table of Standard Normal Probabilities on pages 338 and 339 to make probability statements about $\overline{X}$.

The Z-score transformation takes the value of the variable, subtracts the mean, and then divides by the standard deviation: $Z = \dfrac{\text{value - mean}}{\text{s tan dard deviation}}$. This sample Z-score transformation procedure can be used to make probability statements about the sample mean $\overline{X}$ by putting the value of $\overline{X}$ into the equation along with the mean $\mu_{\overline{x}} = \mu$ and the standard deviation $\sigma_{\overline{x}} = \dfrac{\sigma}{\sqrt{n}}$.

So to make probability statements about the sample mean $\overline{X}$ the appropriate Z-score transformation is

$$Z = \frac{\overline{X} - \mu}{\sigma / \sqrt{n}}.$$

Example 81

Among Americans who took vacations last summer, the length of the vacations follows a normal distribution with mean 7 days and standard deviation 3.5 days. A simple random sample of 25 vacationers is selected and $\overline{X}$ = the mean length of the vacations in this sample of 25 vacations determined. If appropriate, use the sampling distribution determined in example 78 to determine the probability that the **mean** length of the vacations in this simple random sample of 25 vacationers will be between 5 and 10 days.

Example 82

At a particular university, scores on an organic chemistry test are skewed to the left with a mean of 70 and a standard deviation of 15. A simple random sample of 50 students taking organic chemistry is selected and $\overline{X}$ = the mean score on the organic chemistry test by this sample of 50 students determined. If appropriate, use the sampling distribution determined in example 79 to determine the probability that the **mean** organic chemistry test score in this simple random sample of 50 students will be less than 65.

Example 83

The incomes of employees at a large government agency are skewed heavily to the right with a mean of $115,870 and a standard deviation of $32,925. A simple random sample of 22 employees is selected and $\overline{X}$ = the mean income of this sample of 22 employees determined. If appropriate, use the sampling distribution determined in example 80 to determine the probability that the **mean** income of employees in this simple random sample of 22 employees will be greater than $100,000.

B. Confidence Intervals

Consider the first example mentioned at the beginning of this chapter, namely that of interest is to make statements about the mean age of all students at this university. In this situation the population is all students at this university, and the parameter of interest is μ = the <u>mean</u> age of all students at this university. Unless data for every student at this university is known, then this mean age of all students is unknown and must be estimated. This section talks about how confidence intervals can be used to estimate such unknown population means.

It is established that if one selects a simple random sample from the population, and uses the data in the sample to compute the sample mean $\overline{X}$, then $\overline{X}$ is the **point estimate** of the population mean μ. If the sample is a representative sample of the population then the sample mean $\overline{X}$ should be close to the population mean μ, but it most likely will not equal to the unknown value exactly. Hence as learned in the last chapter, to the point estimate $\overline{X}$ we will subtract and add a **margin of error** to create an interval of values that we hope the unknown population mean μ is between. This interval is called a **confidence interval** and the two subsections below give two situations for calculating and interpreting such confidence intervals.

The term confidence refers to the amount of confidence we have that our interval contains the population mean μ. Recall that μ is an unknown value – if it is known it does not need to be estimated and there is no reason to compute a confidence interval. Since μ is unknown, there is no way of knowing whether it will be in the confidence interval or not. Hence we state a <u>confidence level C</u> that indicates the amount of confidence we have that our calculated 100*C% confidence interval will contain the unknown population mean μ. This confidence level is used in calculating the intervals, and the most common values are .90, .95, .98 and .99 corresponding to 90%, 95%, 98% and 99% confidence intervals, respectively.

Both of the scenarios below require the same two assumptions that were required for the sampling distribution in the previous section, namely (1) that a simple random sample is selected from the population and (2) that either the population distribution is known to be normal or the sample size is "large enough" for the central limit theorem to apply. For problems involving <u>means</u> the sample is considered "large enough" if the sample size n is greater than or equal to 15, unless the distribution is **heavily skewed** due to outliers, and in the case where the population distribution is **heavily skewed** due to outliers the sample size must be greater than or equal to 40.

1. Confidence Intervals for μ When the Population Standard Deviation σ is Known

In Moore: Read Chapter 14 (pages 359 – 367)

In addition to assuming (1) that a simple random sample is selected from the population and (2) that either the population distribution is known to be normal or the sample size is "large enough" for the central limit theorem to apply, suppose it is also assumed that <u>the population standard deviation σ is known</u>. Situations where the population mean μ is unknown and the population standard deviation σ is known are rare, but it is possible.

We know that the point estimate of the population mean μ is the sample mean $\overline{X}$, and if the assumptions are satisfied the sampling distribution of $\overline{X}$ is $\overline{X} \sim N\left(\mu, \dfrac{\sigma}{\sqrt{n}}\right)$. From this a Z-score transformation can be done to produce $Z = \dfrac{\overline{X} - \mu}{\sigma / \sqrt{n}}$. Solving this for the unknown population mean μ yields the following 100*C% confidence interval formula: $\overline{X} \pm Z^{*}\left(\dfrac{\sigma}{\sqrt{n}}\right)$.

In this expression the symbol $\pm$ means subtract and add, so this is equivalent to $\overline{X} - Z^{*}\left(\dfrac{\sigma}{\sqrt{n}}\right)$ as the lower limit and $\overline{X} + Z^{*}\left(\dfrac{\sigma}{\sqrt{n}}\right)$ as the upper limit. Additionally, the quantity $Z^{*}\left(\dfrac{\sigma}{\sqrt{n}}\right)$ to the right of the $\pm$ symbol is the <u>margin of error</u> of the confidence interval.

The value of Z^{*} to use in the interval depends on the confidence level stated. The most common confidence intervals are 90%, 95%, 98% and 99%, corresponding to Z^{*} values of 1.645, 1.960, 2.326 and 2.576, respectively. These values, and values for other confidence levels, can be found in the t-Table on page 340 by looking up the confidence level across the bottom row and then finding the Z^{*} value directly above.

Hence the formula for a 100*C% confidence interval for the population mean μ when the population standard deviation σ is known is:

$$\overline{X} \pm Z^* \left(\frac{\sigma}{\sqrt{n}} \right)$$

Once the confidence interval is calculated a statement interpreting the interval should be written. The interpretation states that we have 100*C% confidence that the population mean μ falls between the lower limit $\overline{X} - Z^* \left(\frac{\sigma}{\sqrt{n}} \right)$ and the upper limit $\overline{X} + Z^* \left(\frac{\sigma}{\sqrt{n}} \right)$. <u>This interpretation is the statistical inference</u>, and it is important that this is written correctly to appropriately describe what is being concluded.

For example, if when estimating the mean age of all students at this university the 95% confidence interval is 20.5 to 28.5, then we write "we have 95% confidence that the mean age of all students at this university is between 20.5 and 28.5 years."

We use the term "confidence" because we still do not know if the population mean is in the interval or not – that will only be known if data for the entire population is known. Note that the interpretation does not involve the probability of something occurring, it does not talk about individual values (in the example, ages of individual students), and it does not mention the sample mean $\overline{X}$ (instead the population mean μ).

Example 84

Of interest is to estimate the mean salary of all employees at this university. Begin by identifying the population of interest and the parameter of interest. Suppose that it is known that the standard deviation of the salaries of <u>all</u> university employees is $6,000. A simple random sample of 49 employees at this university is selected, and the mean salary of the employees in the sample is $42,000. If appropriate, calculate and interpret a 95% confidence interval for the mean salary of all university employees.

Example 85

Of interest is to estimate the mean weight of all male runners. Begin by identifying the population of interest and the parameter of interest. Suppose that it is known that the standard deviation of the weights of <u>all</u> male runners is 5 kg. A simple random sample of 48 male runners is selected, and the mean weight of the men in the sample is 60 kg. If appropriate, calculate and interpret a 99% confidence interval for the mean weight of all male runners.

As mentioned in the previous chapter, the goal is to have as high of confidence as possible, while at the same time creating as precise (or narrow) of an interval as possible. Since the width of the confidence interval is twice the margin of error, one can reduce the width of the interval by making the margin of error smaller. There are two ways that this can occur.

First, the margin of error (and hence width of the interval) can be reduced by decreasing the value of Z^*, which occurs when the confidence level is decreased. This implies a trade-off, since we want high confidence but having higher confidence causes the margin of error and interval width to increase.

Second, the sample size n can be increased. Increasing the sample size means we are dividing by a larger number, and hence the margin of error and interval width decrease. This is the most practical method for reducing the margin of error, but increasing the sample size can be more expensive, more time consuming, and so forth.

Since the margin of error is $m = Z^* \left(\dfrac{\sigma}{\sqrt{n}} \right)$, if before the sample is obtained we specific the amount of confidence and the margin of error (or interval width) that are desired, then an appropriate sample size n can be determined that will guarantee both. Solving the margin of error expression for the sample size n, we obtain the following formula:

$$n = \left(\frac{Z^* \sigma}{m} \right)^2$$

The population standard deviation σ is assumed to be known, the Z^* value is determined when the confidence level is specified, and again m represented the stated margin of error (if the width is stated, divide the stated width by 2 to get the appropriate margin of error). When the calculation is complete, <u>round the result up to the next largest integer</u>. Rounding up (instead of down) assures that the sample size will be at least large enough, and the rounding is necessary because it is not possible to sample a fraction of a subject.

Once the appropriate sample size is determined the simple random sample can be obtained, and if the population is normal or if the calculated sample size is large enough for the central limit theorem to apply, a confidence interval can be formed that will have margin of error no larger than that specified.

Example 86

Returning to example 84, the margin of error for the confidence interval based on 49 employees was $1,680. Now suppose we want to design a new experiment to determine the mean salary of all employees at this university. Continuing to assume that the standard deviation of the salaries of all employees is $\sigma = 6000$, determine the sample size required to give a 95% confidence interval for μ = the mean salary of all employees with margin of error no larger than m = $500.

2. Confidence Intervals for μ When the Population Standard Deviation σ is Unknown

In Moore: Read pages 447 – 449

Our goal is to estimate the unknown population mean μ, just as we did in the last section. However, in the last section the procedures that used the standard normal (Z) distribution required that the population standard deviation σ was known. In most cases, if the population mean μ is unknown, then so too will the population standard deviation σ. In this section we repeat the confidence interval procedures of the last section, except now assuming the population standard deviation σ is unknown. The only significant difference is that when the population standard deviation σ is unknown we must compute the sample standard deviation s, and the inference is based on the t-distribution instead of the standard normal (Z) distribution.

The two assumptions of this chapter, (1) that the data being used to make the inferences must be a simple random sample from the population and (2) that the population distribution must be known to be normal, or the sample size must be "large enough" for the central limit theorem to apply (or both), still must be satisfied.

The point estimate of the population mean μ remains the sample mean $\overline{X}$, but the margin of error $Z^*\left(\dfrac{\sigma}{\sqrt{n}}\right)$ that was subtracted from and added to the point estimate when the population standard deviation σ was known is no longer valid. Instead the margin of error uses the calculated sample standard deviation s and instead of using the standard normal (Z) distribution it uses a t-distribution. The margin of error now becomes $t^*\left(\dfrac{s}{\sqrt{n}}\right)$, and the t^* value is based on a t-distribution with n – 1 degrees of freedom.

Hence the formula for a 100*C% confidence interval for the population mean μ when the population standard deviation σ is unknown is:

$$\overline{X} \pm t_{df}^*\left(\frac{s}{\sqrt{n}}\right)$$

where the t_{df}^* value is found from the t-Table on page 340 by looking up the confidence level across the bottom row, and then reading the t^* for the appropriate df = n – 1 degrees of freedom row.

This procedure requires that the sample standard deviation s be calculated so that it can be used. See pages 77 – 80 in chapter IV for details and examples of calculating the sample standard deviation s.

Example 87

A health club owner is interested in the mean amount of time that members spend per week at the club. Begin by identifying the population of interest and the parameter of interest. The owner knows that the distribution of club membership times is approximately normal, but knows little else about the distribution. To estimate the mean amount of time that members spend per week at the club, the owner obtains a simple random sample of 10 members and asks each the number of hours he/she spends at the club per week. The responses were 10, 8, 3, 2, 12, 3, 6, 14, 7, and 5 hours. If appropriate, use this data to calculate and interpret a 95% confidence interval for the mean amount of time that all members spend per week at the club.

Example 88

Officials at a large corporation located in New York City are interested in the mean travel time under standard traveling conditions from their home to the workplace for each of their employees. Standard travel conditions means no bad weather (such as snow), no construction projects that delay travel, and no accidents that delay traffic. Since some people live much further from the city than others, the corporation knows that the distribution of travel times is skewed to the right. Begin by identifying the population of interest and the parameter of interest. To estimate the mean travel time from their home to the workplace for each of the corporation's employees, a simple random sample of 11 employees was selected. The mean travel time for this sample of 11 employees was 27.2 minutes, with a standard deviation of 14.6 minutes. If appropriate, use this information to calculate and interpret a 99% confidence interval for the mean travel time from the home to the workplace for each of the corporation's employees.

Example 89

In the spring of 2010 the officers of a 2000 high school graduation class were preparing for their tenth year reunion. There are 835 members in the 2000 graduation class, and the officers are interested in estimating the mean income of this entire class of 835 members. Begin by identifying the population of interest and the parameter of interest. To estimate the mean income of all 835 class members they selected a simple random sample of 41 class members, and the mean income of these 41 people was $36,659 with a standard deviation of $1,482. If appropriate, use this information to calculate and interpret a 90% confidence interval for the mean income of all 835 members of this 2000 graduating class.

C.   Tests of Significance

Recall that a statistical hypothesis is a statement (or conjecture) about a population parameter. In this chapter the population parameter is the population mean μ, and hence we need to test statements about the population mean μ. More specifically, we want to test the null hypothesis that the population mean μ equals some specified value μ_0 (H_0: $\mu = \mu_0$) versus the alternative hypothesis that μ is greater than the specified value μ_0 (H_A: $\mu > \mu_0$), μ is less than the specified value μ_0 (H_A: $\mu < \mu_0$), or μ is not equal to the specified value μ_0 (H_A: $\mu \neq \mu_0$).

The second and third examples provided at the beginning of this chapter involve statistical tests about the population mean μ.

(2). It is conjectured that the mean cost of all women's swimwear purchased in 2009 was $60, and of interest is to test this conjecture versus the alternative that the mean cost of all women's swimwear purchased in 2009 was actually greater than $60. In this situation the population consists of all sales of women's swimwear in 2009, and the parameter of interest is μ = the mean cost of all women's swimwear purchased in 2009. The null hypothesis would be $H_0 : \mu = 60$ and since we want to test to see if the mean cost of all swimwear purchased in 2009 is actually greater than $60, the alternative hypothesis is $H_A : \mu > 60$, representing an upper one-sided test.

(3). General Motors advertises that the 2010 Chevy Equinox averages 32 miles per gallon when driven on the highway. Of interest is to test this claim versus the alternative that the mean miles per gallon when driven on the highway for all 2010 Chevy Equinox vehicles is different from 32 miles per gallon. In this situation the population consists of all 2010 Chevy Equinox vehicles driven on the highway, and the parameter of is μ = the mean miles per gallon of all 2010 Chevy Equinox vehicles when driven on the highway. The null hypothesis would be $H_0 : \mu = 32$ and since we want to test to see if the mean miles per gallon when driven on the highway for all 2010 Chevy Equinox vehicles is different from 32 miles per gallon, the alternative hypothesis is $H_A : \mu \neq 32$, representing a two-sided test.

As we did for confidence intervals, in this chapter we will learn how to test such hypotheses when the population standard deviation σ is known, and then when the σ is unknown.

1. Significance Test for μ When the Population Standard Deviation σ is Known

In Moore: Read Chapter 14 (pages 378 – 384) and Chapter 15 (page 400 – 403)

Our goal is to make and test statistical hypotheses about the population mean μ. More specifically, we want to test the null hypothesis that the population mean μ equals some specified value μ_0 (H_0: $\mu = \mu_0$) versus the alternative hypothesis that μ is greater than the specified value μ_0 (H_A: $\mu > \mu_0$), μ is less than the specified value μ_0 (H_A: $\mu < \mu_0$), or μ is not equal to the specified value μ_0 (H_A: $\mu \neq \mu_0$). To test these hypotheses we must collect data and use the data to calculate the test statistic. Then either the test statistic is used to calculate the p-value of the test and the p-value compared to the significance level to make a decision and conclusion (as in examples 57 and 59), or the significance level is used to define the rejection region and the test statistic compared to the rejection region to make a decision and conclusion (as in examples 61 and 62). In this section we are assuming that the population standard deviation σ is **known**.

Recall that the point estimate of the population mean μ is the sample mean $\overline{X}$. The test statistic formula is derived from the sampling distribution of $\overline{X}$, which means the same two assumptions required for confidence intervals, namely (1) a simple random sample is selected from the population and (2) either the population distribution is known to be normal or the sample size is large enough for the central limit theorem to apply, must be satisfied.

With these assumptions, the sampling distribution of the sample mean $\overline{X}$ is normal with mean $\mu_{\overline{X}} = \mu$ and standard deviation $\sigma_{\overline{X}} = \sigma/\sqrt{n}$ $\left(\overline{X} \sim N(\mu, \sigma/\sqrt{n})\right)$, and using a Z-score transformation a candidate for the test statistic is $Z = \dfrac{\overline{X} - \mu}{\sigma/\sqrt{n}}$. The problem is that the population mean μ is unknown.

If we substitute the point estimate $\overline{X}$ into the formula for μ, $Z = \dfrac{\overline{X} - \mu}{\sigma/\sqrt{n}} = \dfrac{\overline{X} - \overline{X}}{\sigma/\sqrt{n}} = \dfrac{0}{\sigma/\sqrt{n}} = 0$ and the result is always 0. To solve this problem we use the fact that we carry out the test assuming the null hypothesis H_0: $\mu = \mu_0$ is true, and hence we can replace μ with the hypothesized value μ_0 to generate the test statistic. Hence when (1) we have a simple random sample from the population and (2) either the population distribution is known to be normal or the sample size is large enough for the central limit theorem to apply, and the population standard deviation σ is known, the test statistic is:

$$Z = \frac{\overline{X} - \mu_0}{\sigma/\sqrt{n}}$$

Example 90

A regional airline claims that the mean delay time on all of their flights is 15 minutes, with a standard deviation of 8 minutes. Due to some long delays, the regional airline indicates that the distribution of delay times is skewed heavily to the right. A disgruntled passenger who had a fairly long delay disputes the claim that the mean delay time is 15 minutes and wants to test to determine if the mean delay time is actually longer than 15 minutes. Begin by stating the population of interest, the parameter of interest, and the hypotheses that should be tested. To test the hypotheses, a simple random sample of 25 passengers is selected, and the delay time for each of their flights determined. The mean delay time for this sample of 25 passengers is 21.2 minutes. If appropriate, use this data to test the hypotheses at the $\alpha = .05$ level of significance.

Example 91

The mean mileage of a particular type of tire is 45,000 miles, with a standard deviation of 2,000 miles. A tire manufacturer claims that they have produced a new tire that has an improved mean mileage with the same standard deviation. Begin by stating the population of interest, the parameter of interest, and the hypotheses that should be tested. To test these hypotheses, an independent tire firm tested a simple random sample of 100 of the new tires and found the mean mileage of this sample of 100 tires to be 45,500 miles. If appropriate, use this data to test the hypotheses at the $\alpha = .01$ level of significance.

Example 92

The label on a brand of canned pineapple slices states that the mean carbohydrate content per serving of canned pineapple is 50 grams. It may be assumed that the standard deviation of the carbohydrate content of all servings of canned pineapple slices is 4 grams. A test is to be conducted to determine if the mean carbohydrate content per serving of canned pineapple is as stated on the label, or whether it is different from that printed on the label. Begin by stating the population of interest, the parameter of interest, and the hypotheses that should be tested. A simple random sample of twenty-five servings has a mean carbohydrate content of 51.3 grams and contained no obvious outlier values. Does this sample provide sufficient evidence that the mean carbohydrate content per serving is different from that printed on the label? If appropriate, use this data to test the hypotheses at the $\alpha = .05$ level of significance.

2. Significance Test for μ When the Population Standard Deviation σ is Unknown

In Moore: Read pages 449 – 453

Again our goal is to test the null hypothesis that the population mean μ equals some specified value μ_0 (H_0: $\mu = \mu_0$) versus the alternative hypothesis that μ is greater than μ_0 (H_A: $\mu > \mu_0$), μ is less than μ_0 (H_A: $\mu < \mu_0$), or μ is not equal to μ_0 (H_A: $\mu \neq \mu_0$). To test these hypotheses we must collect data and use the data to calculate the test statistic. Then either the test statistic is used to calculate the p-value of the test and the p-value compared to the significance level to make a decision and conclusion (as in examples 58 and 60), or the significance level is used to define the rejection region and the test statistic compared to the rejection region to make a decision and conclusion (as in examples 63 and 64). In this section we are assuming that the population standard deviation σ is **unknown**, and therefore instead of using the standard normal (Z) distribution to create a test statistic we will use the t-distribution with n – 1 degrees of freedom.

The point estimate of the population mean μ is the sample mean $\overline{X}$, and the assumptions that must be satisfied remain the same, namely (1) a simple random sample is selected from the population and (2) either the population distribution is known to be normal or the sample size is large enough for the central limit theorem to apply.

With these assumptions, the sampling distribution of the sample mean $\overline{X}$ is normal with mean $\mu_{\overline{X}} = \mu$ and standard deviation $\sigma_{\overline{X}} = \sigma / \sqrt{n}$ $\left(\overline{X} \sim N(\mu, \sigma / \sqrt{n}) \right)$, and using a Z-score transformation a candidate for the test statistic is $Z = \dfrac{\overline{X} - \mu}{\sigma / \sqrt{n}}$. Obviously if the population standard deviation σ is unknown then this statistic cannot be computed. Therefore, in this case we must compute the sample standard deviation s, and when (1) we have a simple random sample from the population and (2) either the population distribution is known to be normal or the sample size is large enough for the central limit theorem to apply, and the population standard deviation σ is unknown, the test statistic is:

$$t = \frac{\overline{X} - \mu_0}{s / \sqrt{n}}$$

This statistic follows a t-distribution with n – 1 degrees of freedom, and the calculation of the p-value (or the rejection region) is dependent on this.

Example 93

Officials in a large city claim that a call to the 911 police emergency number will bring an ambulance in an average (mean) of 4.8 minutes. The city recently installed a new computer system, and officials of the EMS claim that ambulance response time has improved since the installation of this new computer system. Begin by stating the population of interest, the parameter of interest, and the hypotheses that should be tested. In a simple random sample of twenty calls for an ambulance after the new computer system was installed, the mean response time was 4.6 minutes with a standard deviation of 1.2 minutes. A stem-and- leaf plot of the sample of 20 response times shows no obvious outliers. Does this data provide sufficient evidence that the computer system has improved the speed of service? If appropriate, use this data to test the hypotheses at the $\alpha = .01$ level of significance.

Example 94

The Federal Trade Commission (FTC) has received a number of complaints about a hamburger chain that is selling hamburgers promoted as weighing 1/4 lb. prior to cooking. Consumers complained that the weight of the hamburger is less than a 1/4 lb. (or .25 lb). Begin by stating the population of interest, the parameter of interest, and the hypotheses that should be tested. Before formally opening an investigation, the FTC took a simple random sample of 100 such hamburgers. The mean weight before cooking was .238 lb. with a standard deviation of 0.09 lb. If appropriate, use this data to test at significance level α = .05 to determine if the mean weight of the hamburgers is less than .25 lb., thus warranting further investigation.

Example 95

It is conjectured that the mean cost of all women's swimwear purchased in 2009 was $60, and of interest is to test this conjecture versus the alternative that the mean cost of all women's swimwear purchased in 2009 was actually greater than $60. In this situation the population consists of all sales of women's swimwear in 2009, and the parameter of interest is μ = the <u>mean</u> cost of all women's swimwear purchased in 2009. The null hypothesis would be $H_0 : \mu = 60$ and since we want to test to see if the mean cost of all swimwear purchased in 2009 is actually greater than $60, the alternative hypothesis is $H_A : \mu > 60$, representing an upper one-sided test. Due to some very expensive swimwear sold by such retailers as Victoria's Secret, the distribution of women's swimwear costs is skewed heavily to the right. To test the hypotheses above, a simple random sample of 22 women's swimwear purchases is selected, and the mean cost of the swimwear in this sample was $189 with a standard deviation of $32.50. If appropriate, use this data to test the hypotheses at significance level α = .05.

Additional Reading and Examples

1.   Sampling distributions are theoretical concepts that require that the population parameters (μ and σ in the case of $\overline{X}$) are known. In real inference problems these parameters are unknown and our goal is to either estimate the parameters or test hypotheses about the parameters. The sampling distributions are key components in deriving the formulas used to make the inferences.

2.   The assumptions necessary to make inferences about population means are: (1) we must have a simple random sample from the population and (2) the population distribution must be normal or the sample is "large enough" for the central limit theorem. For problems involving means the sample size n is large enough if n is 15 or larger, unless there are outliers creating heavy skewness, in which case the sample size n should be at least 40. In cases in which the population is not normal, the normal approximation used to describe the shape of the sampling distribution gets better and better as the sample size increases. In cases in which the sample size is not large enough for the central limit theorem to apply the shape of the distribution is not necessarily normal but <u>it can still be described.</u> However, this description depends on knowledge of the real population distribution and in most cases is beyond the difficulty level of this book.

3.   The population distribution of the gripping strengths of industrial workers is known to have a mean of 110 grams and a standard deviation of 10 grams. A simple random sample of 75 workers is selected, and the mean strength of these 75 workers is 112 grams. Find the probability that the mean gripping strength of the sample of 75 workers will be 112 or more.

   The random variable X is the gripping strength, which has a mean $\mu = 110$ and a standard deviation $\sigma = 10$. We want to find the probability that the sample mean $\overline{X}$ will be 112 or more: $P(\overline{X} \geq 112)$.

   We begin by describing the sampling distribution. Since we have a simple random sample:

   Mean: $\qquad\qquad\qquad \mu_{\overline{X}} = \mu = 110$

   Standard deviation: $\qquad \sigma_{\overline{X}} = \dfrac{\sigma}{\sqrt{n}} = \dfrac{10}{\sqrt{75}} = 1.1547$

   Shape: $\qquad\qquad\qquad$ The shape of the population is not known. However, the sample size of 75 is large enough for the central limit theorem to apply, so $\overline{X} \sim N\,(110, 1.1547)$.

   Then $P\,(\overline{X} \geq 112) = P\left(Z \geq \dfrac{112\text{-}110}{1.1547} \right) = P(Z \geq 1.73) = 1\text{-}P(Z<1.73) = 1\text{-}.9582 = .0418$.

   Therefore, the probability that the sample mean will be as high as or higher than the value observed in this sample is only .0418, a low probability.

4. The purpose of a confidence interval is to estimate an unknown population parameter with an indication of how accurate the estimate is and how confident we are that the result is correct. If the sample is representative of the population then the point estimate should be close to the unknown parameter, although it is likely not equal to it exactly. If the sample size is small and the population is not normal, the true confidence level will be different from the value used in computing the interval. For this reason you should examine your data carefully (possibly using a stem-and-leaf plot or histogram) for skewness and other signs of nonnormally. The confidence interval relies only on the sampling distribution of the sample mean $\overline{X}$, which even for quite small samples is much closer to normal than the individual observations. When the sample size is 15 or more the confidence level is not greatly disturbed by non-normal populations unless extreme outliers or quite strong skewness are present.

5. The margin of error and hence the width of the interval (**width = twice the margin of error**) are affected by the degree of confidence and the sample size. For a given sample, the margin of error and interval width increase if the degree of confidence is increased and they both decrease if the degree of confidence is decreased. If the sample size is increased the margin of error and hence the width of the interval will decrease. However, if the sample size is decreased the margin of error and hence the width of the interval will increase. Obviously increasing the sample size means changing the actual sample, and hence the sample mean $\overline{X}$ (which is the point estimate) will also likely change.

6. Killer bees do not appear very different from ordinary honeybees. Without observing their behavior, we need careful statistical analysis of many different measurements to distinguish one kind from the other. Identifying dead killer bees can help track their spread to new territories.

One characteristic used to identify killer bees is the width of the wings. It is known that the standard deviation of the width of the wings of all killer bees is 0.06 millimeters. Our goal is to estimate the mean wing width using a 95% confidence interval.

First, how large of a sample of killer bees must be selected in order to produce a 95% confidence interval with margin of error that does not exceed 0.02 millimeters?

To answer this question we must compute the sample size. We know that $\sigma = 0.06$ and that $m = 0.02$. For a 95% confidence interval $z^* = 1.960$. So the required sample size is

$$n = \left(\frac{z^*\sigma}{m} \right)^2 = \left(\frac{(1.960)(0.06)}{0.02} \right)^2 = 34.5744$$

Hence we need a sample of at least 35 killer bees.

Now we obtain a simple random sample of 35 killer bees and determine the wing width for each bee. The data is as follows (given in millimeters).

2.88	2.94	2.83	2.91	2.86	2.79	2.90	2.83	2.80	2.88	2.91	2.88
2.83	2.91	2.97	2.80	2.77	2.80	2.88	2.81	2.82	2.83	2.80	2.86
2.86	2.88	2.77	2.89	2.87	2.84	2.84	2.90	2.80	2.91	2.85	

The mean of this sample is $\bar{x} = 2.8543$. Since (1) we have a simple random sample, (2) there is no indication of any outliers, implying the sample of size 35 is "large enough" for the central limit theorem to apply, and (3) σ is <u>known</u>, then the assumptions are satisfied and the confidence interval will be based on the standard normal (Z) distribuiton. So the 95% confidence interval is

$$\bar{x} \pm z^* \left(\frac{\sigma}{\sqrt{n}} \right) = 2.8543 \pm 1.960 \left(\frac{0.06}{\sqrt{35}} \right) = 2.8543 \pm 0.0199 = (2.8344, 2.8742).$$

Therefore, we have 95% confidence that the mean wing width of all killer bees is between 2.8344 mm and 2.8742 mm. If we observe a group of bees with mean wing width outside this range that presents evidence that they may be a different type of bee. Also note that the calculated margin of error (0.0199) is less than 0.02.

7. A real estate developer is interested in estimating the mean income of all the residents in an apartment complex. The complex is very large, so contacting each resident is not feasible. Therefore, the developer obtains a list of the names of the complex residents and chooses a simple random sample of 64 of these residents. The mean income of this sample of 64 residents is $30,191. From historical records it is known that the standard deviation of the incomes of all residents in this type of complex is $4,000.

It is likely that the developer doesn't require high confidence in the estimate, and therefore an 80% confidence interval will be calculated. Since the developer selected a large simple random sample from the population and since the population standard deviation is known, the use of the Z procedure is appropriate. For an 80% confidence interval the appropriate critical value is $z^* = 1.282$.

With $n = 64$, $\bar{x} = 30191$, and $\sigma = 4000$, the 80% confidence interval is

$$\bar{x} \pm z^* \left(\frac{\sigma}{\sqrt{n}} \right) = 30191 \pm 1.282 \left(\frac{4000}{\sqrt{64}} \right) = 30191 \pm 641 = (29550, 30832).$$

Therefore the developer can have 80% confidence that the mean income of all residents in this apartment complex is between $29,550 and $30,832.

8. An ice cream manufacturer states that cartons of chocolate ice cream are supposed to weigh exactly 1 pound, but this cannot be controlled perfectly. To test their production machinery, they selected a simple random sample of 18 cartons of chocolate ice cream produced one day. The mean and standard deviation of the weights of this sample of 18 cartons were 1.21 and 0.09, respectively.

This type is problem is referred to as a <u>quality control</u> procedure. The company is attempting to assure the quality of their product – in this case that the cartons are containing the correct amount of ice cream. If the company finds that their stated value of 1 pound is not accurate, then the process will be adjusted to bring production in line with what is advertised.

A 95% confidence interval can be used to make this determination. With 18 observations, n - 1 = 18 − 1 = 17 and hence we use the t distribution with 17 degrees of freedom. From the t-table, $t^* = 2.110$. From the sample n = 18, $\bar{x}$ = 1.21, and s = 0.09. Assuming the distribution of weights of chocolate ice cream is not heavily skewed, then the 95% confidence interval for the mean contents of all cartons of chocolate ice cream produced that day is:

$$\bar{X} \pm t^* \left(\frac{s}{\sqrt{n}} \right) = 1.21 \pm 2.110 \left(\frac{0.09}{\sqrt{18}} \right) = 1.21 \pm 2.110(.0212) = 1.21 \pm .0448 = (1.1652, 1.2548)$$

Therefore the company can be 95% confident that the mean content of all cartons of chocolate ice cream produced by this process is between 1.1652 pounds and 1.2548 pounds. Since 1 is not in this interval, then the interval provides significant evidence at the 5% significance level that the mean contents of all cartons of chocolate ice cream is different from 1 pound and hence the process should be adjusted.

9. Congressmen in a southern state are interested in the opinions that their constituents have about a new tax proposal made by the President. The IRS reports that the current mean tax burden among all American citizens is $12,000 with a standard deviation of $3,500. The congressmen from this state believe the mean figure is higher in their state and they would like to perform a test to determine the accuracy of their claim. They agree to conduct the test at the 5% significance level.

Hence they want to test null hypothesis H_0: μ = $12,000 versus the alternative H_a: μ > $12,000.

To test these hypotheses they created a toll-free 1-800 number that people can use to indicate how much they pay in taxes each year. Over a two-hour period 225 people call in, with the mean amount these 225 people report having paid in taxes last year being $12,149.45. Does this data provide significant evidence in favor of the claim made by the congressmen?

Since $12,149.45 is greater than $12,000 this data does provide some evidence that the alternative hypothesis is true. To determine if it is significant evidence a significance test involving a test statistic must be performed.

However, because the data was generated from a <u>volunteer response sample</u> and not a simple random sample, the procedures described in this chapter are not valid. So we cannot statistically determine if this data provides significant evidence or not without using a more complicated inference procedure.

10. Suppose that a psychological questionnaire has a series of questions about what makes you angry and how often you get angry. The number of YES answers is added up to get an "anger score." The test has been given to many teenagers, and it is known that for American teenagers as a group the distribution is fairly symmetric with a mean score of 10 and a standard deviation of 4. The test is going to be given to a simple random sample of 16 clients of the Division of Juvenile Rehabilitation to see whether they show more anger than teenagers in general, while assuming that the standard deviation is unchanged from that of the larger group. The scores of the sample are as follows and they want to test at the $\alpha = .01$ significance level.

    13 18 10 12 15 8 14 13 15 16 11 13 9 10 15 16

    (1) We want to test $H_0: \mu = 10$ versus $H_A: \mu > 10$.

    (2) Since we have a simple random sample of size 16 and the population is roughly symmetric, then the assumptions are satisfied. The population standard deviation is $\sigma = 4$. The mean of the sample is

    $$\bar{x} = \frac{13+18+10+12+15+8+14+13+15+16+11+13+9+10+15+16}{16} = 13.$$

    Then the observed test statistic is $Z = \dfrac{\bar{X} - \mu_0}{\sigma/\sqrt{n}} = \dfrac{13 - 10}{4/\sqrt{16}} = \dfrac{3}{1} = 3.00$.

    (3) P-value: We have an upper one-sided test, so the p-value is
    p-value $= P(Z \geq 3.00) = 1 - P(Z < 3.00) = 1 - .9987 = .0013$.

    Rejection region: Find $\alpha = .01$ in the top row of the table, critical value is $z^* = 2.326$. So the rejection region is reject H_0 if $z_{obs} \geq 2.326$.

    (4) Using p-value: Since the p-value $< .01$, we reject the null hypothesis in favor of the alternative.
    Using rejection region: Since $z_{obs} = 3.00$ is greater than 2.326, we reject the null hypothesis.

    (5) Therefore, there is sufficient evidence that the mean anger level, as measured by this test, is higher in Division of Juvenile Rehabilitation teenagers than in the general population. There is sufficient evidence that the mean anger level is greater than 10.

11. The two senators from a particular state are interested in the opinions that their constituents have about a new tax proposal made by the President. In particular they believe the mean amount of money that their constituents pay in taxes each year exceeds $10,000. To test this claim, they create a toll-free 1-800 number that people can use to indicate how much they pay in taxes each year and whether they support the proposal.

Over a two-hour period 225 people call in, with the mean and standard deviation of the amount these people report having paid in taxes being $12,149.45 and $3,492.14, respectively.

The senators want to test the null hypothesis H_0: $\mu = 10000$ versus the alternative hypothesis H_A: $\mu > 10000$. Unfortunately the data the senators collected is of little use because the constituents voluntarily called in and gave the information – a simple random sample was not selected. For this reason the t procedures described in this section are not valid. Those who called in likely have strong feelings about the proposal, probably because they have the most to lose if the proposal is passed. This likely means that those who call are in an upper income bracket and therefore the mean income of the sample overestimates the mean income of all constituents.

12. A company plans to market a gasoline additive by claiming that it increases the gas mileage and will therefore save the customer money. In fact, the company completed a study of a simple random sample of 20 cars that showed a mean improvement of 2.6 miles per gallon. They report these figures as being strong evidence that the gasoline additive is beneficial.

In the fine print of the report the company reports that the standard error of the mean is 1.7 miles per gallon, and that the test is done at the 5% significance level. Being experienced statisticians we should question the claim made by the company. In fact, we can even test to see if the data does provide strong evidence that the gasoline additive is beneficial.

We want to test H_0: $\mu = 0$ versus H_A: $\mu > 0$. Since the sample mean $\overline{X} = 2.6$ and standard error $s/\sqrt{n} = 1.7$ are given in the report, the test statistic is calculated to be $t = \dfrac{\overline{X} - \mu_0}{s/\sqrt{n}} = \dfrac{2.6 - 0}{1.7} = 1.529$. This test statistic follows a t distribution with 19 degrees of freedom.

P-value: with 19 degrees of freedom, p-value = P ($t_{19} \geq 1.529$), which falls between .05 and .10.
Rejection region: upper one-sided test, $\alpha = .05$, and df = 19, reject the null hypothesis if $t_{obs} \geq 1.729$.

At significance level $\alpha = .05$, the p-value is greater than .05 and hence we would fail to reject the null hypothesis. Likewise, using the rejection region, since the observed test statistic value of 1.529 is not greater than the critical value of 1.729, we would fail to reject the null hypothesis.

Since we fail to reject the null hypothesis, then there is insufficient evidence that the mean improvement in mileage is greater than 0, and hence there actually is <u>not</u> statistical evidence that the additive is beneficial.

TI-83/84 Calculator

The TI-83/84 calculator can be used to conduct any of the inferences on population means described in this chapter. To do so, the user needs to identify whether the inference requires a confidence interval or a test, and whether the population standard deviation σ is known or unknown. To access the four procedures, press **STAT** and use the right-arrow button to scroll over to **TESTS**. Once the list of inference procedures appears, there are four that apply to the topics of this chapter, as follows.

1: Z-Test – this conducts a statistical test of hypotheses, assuming the population standard deviation σ is <u>known</u>.

2: T-Test – this conducts a statistical test of hypotheses, assuming the population standard deviation σ is <u>unknown</u>

7: ZInterval – this computes a confidence interval, assuming the population standard deviation σ is <u>known</u>.

8: TInterval – this computes a confidence interval, assuming the population standard deviation σ is <u>unknown</u>.

For each of the above, there are two options for entering information. If you have the actual data, then the data is entered into a list as described on page 8 (for example, suppose the data is entered into list L1), and then the **Data** option is chosen. If you do not have the actual data, or even if you do have the actual data but also you have the summary statistics (sample mean $\overline{X}$ and sample standard deviation s for the inferences based on t), then you can choose **Stats**. For each of the four functions listed above, complete the following.

1: Z-Test – regardless of whether you choose **DATA** or **STATS**, the value μ_0 is the hypothesized value in the null hypothesis, and you must enter the value of the population standard deviation σ. You must also choose the appropriate sign in the alternative hypothesis ($\neq \mu_0$, $< \mu_0$, or $> \mu_0$). If you choose **DATA**, beside **LIST** you must give the list the data is in (for example, as described above it would be L1), and set the frequency (**Freq**) equal to 1. Move the cursor down to **Calculate** and press **ENTER**. The calculator gives you the value of the test statistic (Z) and the p-value (p), and in addition you also get values of the sample mean ($\overline{X}$), the sample standard deviation (S_x), and the sample size (n). If you choose **STATS**, then in addition to the items listed above you must enter the sample mean $\overline{X}$ and the sample size n, then move the cursor down to **Calculate** and press **ENTER**. Once again you get the values of the test statistic (Z) and the p-value (p).

2: T-Test – regardless of whether you choose **DATA** or **STATS**, the value μ_0 is the hypothesized value in the null hypothesis, and you must also choose the appropriate sign in the alternative hypothesis ($\neq \mu_0$, $< \mu_0$, or $> \mu_0$). If you choose **DATA**, beside **LIST** you must give the list the data is in (for example, as described above it would be L1), and set the frequency (**Freq**) equal to 1. Move the cursor down to **Calculate** and press **ENTER**. The calculator gives you the value of the test statistic (t) and the p-value (p), and in addition you also get values of the sample mean ($\overline{X}$), the sample standard deviation (S_x), and the sample size (n). If you choose **STATS**, then in addition to the hypothesized mean and sign of the alternative hypothesis you must enter the sample mean $\overline{X}$, the sample standard deviation S_x and the sample size n, then move the cursor down to **Calculate** and press **ENTER**. Once again you get the values of the test statistic (t) and the p-value (p).

7: ZInterval – regardless of whether you choose **DATA** or **STATS**, you must enter the value of the population standard deviation σ and next to **C-Level** you must enter the confidence level as a proportion (such as .90, .95, .98 or .99). If you choose **DATA**, beside **LIST** you must give the list the data is in (for example, as described above it would be L1), and set the frequency (**Freq**) equal to 1. Move the cursor down to **Calculate** and press **ENTER**. The calculator gives you the confidence interval, and in addition you also get values of the sample mean ($\overline{X}$), the sample standard deviation (S_x), and the sample size (n). If you choose **STATS**, then in addition to the population standard deviation and the confidence level you must enter the sample mean $\overline{X}$ and the sample size n, then move the cursor down to **Calculate** and press **ENTER**. Once again you get the confidence interval and the values of the sample mean $\overline{X}$ and the sample size n.

8: TInterval – regardless of whether you choose **DATA** or **STATS**, next to **C-Level** you must enter the confidence level as a proportion (such as .90, .95, .98 or .99). If you choose **DATA**, beside **LIST** you must give the list the data is in (for example, as described above it would be L1), and set the frequency (**Freq**) equal to 1. Move the cursor down to **Calculate** and press **ENTER**. The calculator gives you the confidence interval, and in addition you also get values of the sample mean ($\overline{X}$), the sample standard deviation (S_x), and the sample size (n). If you choose **STATS**, then in addition to the confidence level you must enter the sample mean $\overline{X}$, the sample standard deviation S_x and the sample size n, then move the cursor down to **Calculate** and press **ENTER**. Once again you get the confidence interval and the values of the sample mean $\overline{X}$, the sample standard deviation S_x and the sample size n.

Practice Problems:

IX.1. The current salaries of a 1990 college graduation class are heavily skewed to the right due to a few individuals with large salaries, with a mean salary of $95,000 and a standard deviation of $22,450.

(a). Suppose a simple random sample of 100 graduates of this class are selected. Describe completely the sampling distribution of the resulting mean salary of this sample of 100 graduates.

(b). Determine the probability that the mean salary of a sample of 100 graduates will be $100,000 or greater.

IX.2. The ages of college athletes are known to be approximately normally distributed with mean $\mu = 20.5$ years and standard deviation $\sigma = 0.75$ years.

(a). What is the probability that a randomly chosen athlete will be 21 years of age or older?

(b). Suppose a simple random sample of 90 college athletes is selected and their ages averaged. What is the sampling distribution of this sample mean $\overline{X}$?

(c). Find the probability that the mean age of the simple random sample of 90 college athletes will be 20 years or less.

IX.3. The amount of weight that men can dynamically lift overhead has a mean of 120 pounds and a standard deviation of 11.4 pounds. Due to some extremely strong men, the distribution is skewed fairly heavily to the right.

(a). If a simple random sample of 45 men is selected and the mean amount that these men can dynamically lift overhead determined, what is the sampling distribution of this sample mean?

(b). What is the probability that the mean amount that the sample of 45 men can dynamically lift overhead is between 116 and 125 pounds?

IX.4. A company that owns and services a fleet of cars for its sales force has found that the service lifetime of disc brake pads varies from car to car according to a normal distribution with mean $\mu = 55,000$ miles and standard deviation $\sigma = 4,500$ miles. The company installs a new brand of brake pads on a simple random sample of 8 cars.

(a). If the new brand has the same lifetime distribution as the previous type, what is the distribution of the sample mean lifetime for the 8 cars?

(b). The average life of the pads on these 8 cars turns out to be $\overline{x} = 51,800$ miles. What is the probability that the sample mean lifetime is 51,800 miles or less if the lifetime distribution is unchanged? The company takes this probability as evidence that the average lifetime of the new brand of pads is less than 55,000 miles.

IX.5. The 19th season of The Oprah Winfrey Show debuted on Monday, September 13, 2004, and on the show Oprah gave new Pontiac G6 cars to everyone in the audience. Suppose that after the first month of driving, the miles per gallon for the new Pontiac G6's that Oprah gave away on her September 13 show have a normal distribution with mean 26.3 mpg and standard deviation 3.6 mpg.

(a). Suppose a simple random sample of 20 Pontiac G6's is selected and the miles per gallon after the first month of ownership determined. Describe completely the sampling distribution of the resulting mean miles per gallon for this sample of 20 Pontiac G6's.

(b). Suppose a simple random sample of 20 Pontiac G6's is selected and the miles per gallon after the first month of ownership determined. Based on the distribution described above, what is the probability that the **mean** miles per gallon for this sample of 20 Pontiac G6's is greater than 27 miles per gallon?

IX. 6. Scientists are interested in finding biological indicators of water quality. One such indicator is the Virginia freshwater snail Cone Vertigo (*Vertigo oralis*). After collecting data on hundreds of snails, biologist have determined that the width of the Cone Vertigo, measured at its widest point, follows an approximate normal distribution with mean 46 mm with a standard deviation of 16 mm.

(a). What is the probability that the width of a Cone Vertigo will be between 45 and 50 mm?

(b). A simple random sample of 60 Cone Vertigoes is selected and the width of each snail is measured. What is the probability that the <u>mean</u> width of the sample of 60 snails is between 45 and 50 mm?

IX. 7. The summer classes program at a large urban university works under a different operating budget than during the fall and spring semesters. Instructor pay comes from a special fund reserved just for summer classes, and other expenses are often split over two fiscal years (a new fiscal year begins July 1). Therefore, for the summer program to be self-supporting, the number of students per course must meet a certain limit. Our goal is to estimate the mean number of students per summer class. To estimate this mean a simple random sample of 45 summer 2010 classes was selected, and the mean number of students per class in this sample of 45 classes is 33.8 students. The standard deviation of the number of students per class for all summer 2010 classes is 11.2 students. If appropriate, calculate and interpret a 95% confidence interval for the mean number of students in all summer 2010 classes.

IX. 8. Northern Pest Control is interested in estimating the mean amount of solution used during all their sprayings for insects.

(a). Suppose that Northern Pest Control knows that the standard deviation of the amount of solution used during all sprayings for insects is 54 ounces. What is the minimum sample size necessary that will give Northern Pest Control a 95% confidence interval with margin of error no larger than 13 ounces?

(b). Northern Pest Control recorded the amount of solution used during a simple random sample of 72 sprayings. The mean amount of solution used in this sample of 72 sprayings was 312 ounces. If appropriate, use this information to calculate and interpret a 95% confidence interval for the mean amount of solution used during all their sprayings for insects. What is the margin of error of your confidence interval?

IX. 9. Of interest is to estimate the critical dimension of auto engine crankshafts. The data come from a production process that is known to have standard deviation $\sigma = 0.075$ millimeters. The process mean is supposed to be $\mu = 224$ millimeters but can drift away from this target value during production. How large of a sample of crankshafts produced by this process would be needed to estimate the mean critical dimension within plus or minus 0.025 millimeters with 90% confidence?

IX. 10. "*Upward Basketball* is one of the most exciting evangelistic sports ministries in the country. The great sport of basketball is used to reach children and their families for Christ. Designed for first to eighth grade boys and girls, *Upward Basketball* seeks to develop the self-esteem of each participant, while teaching respect for authority, sportsmanship, character, and basketball skills." [Source: http://www.fbcsuffolk.org/upward_basketball.htm].

In a particular city there are 20 churches participating in the *Upward Basketball* program. Of interest is to estimate the mean number of Sundays per year that all children participating in these 20 *Upward Basketball* programs attend church. Assume that it is known that the standard deviation of the number of Sundays per year that all children participating in these 20 *Upward Basketball* programs attend church is 6.7 Sundays. The distribution is also bimodal in shape, as there are many children who regularly attend church, while many other children rarely attend church.

(a). To estimate the mean number of Sundays per year that all children participating in these 20 *Upward Basketball* programs attend church, you are asked to compute a 98% confidence interval estimate. *Upward Basketball* leaders want you to be very specific with the estimate by creating an interval whose <u>width</u> does not exceed 5 Sundays. How large of a sample of *Upward Basketball* participants (children) would you have to select in order for a 98% confidence interval estimate to achieve this?

(b). Upon seeing the answer computed in part (a) and acknowledging that the population distribution is bimodal, a simple random sample of 40 *Upward Basketball* participants was selected and the number of Sundays that each attended church over the past year determined. The mean number of Sundays that this sample of 40 *Upward Basketball* participants attended church over the past year was calculated to be 24.3. If appropriate, use this information to calculate a 98% confidence interval estimate for the mean number of Sundays per year that all children participating in these 20 *Upward Basketball* programs attend church.

(c). Interpret the interval you calculated in part (b).

(d). Is the mean number of Sundays per year that all children participating in these 20 *Upward Basketball* programs attend church in your interval? Explain.

(e). What would happen to the confidence interval if the number of *Upward Basketball* participants sampled were increased to 80? Answer this question in terms of both the point estimate <u>and</u> the margin of error (or width).

IX. 11. The Census Bureau reports that in 2000 households spent an average of 31% of their total spending on housing. A homebuilders association in Cleveland believes that the current mean is lower in their area. They interviewed a simple random sample of 40 homeowners in the Cleveland metropolitan area to learn what percent of their spending goes toward housing. Take µ to be the mean percent of spending devoted to housing among all Cleveland households. We want to test the null hypotheses H_0: $\mu = 31\%$ versus the alternative H_a: $\mu < 31\%$. The population standard deviation is $\sigma = 9.6\%$.

(a). Assuming that the null hypothesis is true, what is the sampling distribution of the mean percent $\overline{X}$ that the sample spends on housing? Sketch the density curve of this sampling distribution.

(b). Suppose that the study finds $\overline{X} = 30.2\%$ for the 40 households in the sample. Mark this point on the axis in your sketch. Then suppose that an independent study gives $\overline{X} = 27.6\%$. Mark this point on your sketch. Referring to your sketch, explain why one result is good evidence that average Cleveland spending on housing is less than 31% and the other result is not.

(c). Calculate the p-values for both $\overline{X} = 30.2\%$ and $\overline{X} = 27.6\%$. Compare the values and relate them to the answer made in part (b).

IX. 12. The Virginia Standards of Learning (SOL) tests have come under harsh criticism as being inappropriate assessments of a student's learning. The Virginia Department of Education disagrees, and states that a student who will be a successful contributor to society should do well on the test. They claim that the mean score for these students should be 80, with a standard deviation of 10. The distribution of SOL test scores is skewed <u>slightly</u> to the left.

(a). A parental group disagrees with the claim of the Virginia Department of Education, and instead claims that the test is too difficult and the mean score will be lower than 80. To assess this claim, an independent simple random sample of 20 adults (who were not a part of the parental group making the claim) was selected and each completed the SOL test. Their scores on the test are given below.

86 68 77 75 82 91 75 75 66 78 78 67 72 83 78 **32** 88 66 70 77

If appropriate, use this data to test at significance level $\alpha = .05$ to determine if the mean score of all people on the SQL test is less than 80 points.

(b). Upon further review of the data the Virginia Department of Education learned that the adult who scored 32 on the SOL test has a severe reading disability that would exempt them from taking the regular SOL test. Hence the Virginia Department of Education wants to repeat the analysis with this observation removed. If appropriate, repeat the test based on the remaining simple random sample of 19 SOL test scores.

(c). Use the results above to explain what effect an outlier can have on the decision of a significance test.

IX. 13. The American Vehicle Satisfaction Score (AVSS) consists of a series of questions asked to purchasers of new vehicles in the United States that assess their satisfaction with the new vehicle that they have purchased. Scores on the AVSS are scaled such that the mean score is 50, with a standard deviation of 10. The distribution of the scores (for the population) is slightly skewed to the right. General Motors is advertising the Hummer H3 sports utility truck (SUT), and they believe that the mean AVSS score for all 2006 Hummer H3 purchasers is greater than 50. To test this claim, they selected a simple random sample of

27 purchasers of 2006 Hummer H3 SUTs. The AVSS scores three months following the purchase are given below.

47 56 57 44 48 51 52 48 59 58 44 50 53 57 48 46 49 57 51 56 46 50 58 58 49 57 52

If appropriate, use this data to test at significance level $\alpha = .10$ to determine if the mean AVSS score for all purchasers of 2006 Hummer H3 SUTs is greater than 50,

IX. 14. A national grocery store chain reports that the mean amount spent on groceries per trip by all of its customers is $75.45 with a standard deviation of $15.00. The chain recently opened stores in the Richmond, Virginia area and claim that the mean amount spent on groceries per trip by customers in their stores is less than the national mean. To test this claim a simple random sample of 200 Richmond area customers is selected and the amount spent on groceries during their last national grocery store chain shopping trip determined. The mean amount spent by this sample of customers is $71.89.

(a). The statistical procedures in this section are valid when several assumptions are met. What are these assumptions and are they met in this problem?

(b). If appropriate, use the results of this sample to test at significance level $\alpha = .01$ the claim that the mean amount spent on groceries per trip by customers in Richmond, Virginia stores is less than the national mean.

IX. 15. An ice cream manufacturer states that cartons of chocolate ice cream are supposed to weigh exactly one pound, but this cannot be controlled perfectly. When the machinery is working properly, the weights of the cartons of chocolate ice cream vary with a standard deviation of 0.09 pounds. To test their production machinery, they selected a simple random sample of 18 cartons of chocolate ice cream produced one day. The weights of the 18 cartons are as follows (in pounds).

1.23 1.17 1.30 1.18 1.22 1.09 1.24 1.18 1.27 1.20 1.17 1.16 1.04 1.23 1.25 1.18 1.24 1.07

(a). Graph the data and comment on the appropriateness of using inference procedures based on Z.

(b). If appropriate, calculate and interpret a 95% confidence interval for the mean weight of all cartons of chocolate ice cream produced that day.

(c). At significance level $\alpha = .05$, if appropriate test to determine if the mean weight of all cartons of chocolate ice cream produced that day is different from 1 pound.

(d). Compare your results in parts (b) and (c). How do they relate?

255

IX. 16. Universities often sign long-term food service contracts with companies. A large urban university signed a 20-year contract with McDonald's Corporation. Many faculty members and students at this university believe that the length of this contract is too long. They believe that the mean length of all food service contracts between universities and food service companies is less than 20 years. There is also evidence that the standard deviation of the lengths of all such food service contracts is 10.6 years. To test their claim a concerned group of faculty members selected a simple random sample of 55 universities with food service contracts. The mean of the contract lengths in this sample is 19 years. If appropriate, use this data to test at significance level $\alpha = .01$ to determine if the mean length of all food service contracts between universities and food service companies is less than 20 years.

IX. 17. The November 2, 2004 episode of The Montel Williams Show featured amazing pets and their lucky owners. The show featured stories about pets that had aided their owners in various ways. For this problem the population of interest is all pet owners, and the November 2, 2004 Montel Show reported that the mean length of time that pet owners have owned their pets is 7.2 years. The standard deviation of the times that all pet owners have owned their pets is 1.8 years. Of interest is to conduct a test to determine if the mean is 7.2 years, or if the mean length of time that pet owners have owned their pets is actually less than 7.2 years. A simple random sample of 400 pets was selected, and the time that they had been owned by their owners determined. In the sample the mean amount of time the pets had been owned by their owners was 6.8 years. State the hypotheses of interest, and if appropriate, use this data to test these hypotheses at significance level $\alpha = .10$.

IX. 18. A rhizome is an elongated horizontal subterranean plant stem that produces shoots above and roots below and is responsible for the reproduction of many types of plants. A biologist is interested in *Phagmites australis*, or common reed, a grass that reproduces by rhizomes. It is reported that a one-meter long rhizome of *Phagmites australis* produces, on average, 7 aboveground shoots. The biologist acquired a simple random sample of 50 one-meter long *Phagmites australis* rhizomes, planted these in well- nourished soil, and counted the number of aboveground shoots on each over a two month period. The mean number of aboveground shoots over the two-month period for the sample of 50 rhizomes was 6.45, with a standard deviation of 1.7 shoots. If appropriate, use this data to test at significance level $\alpha = .05$ to determine if the mean number of shoots per rhizome for all *Phagmites australis* rhizomes is equal to 7 or is different from 7.

IX. 19. A pharmaceutical manufacturer does a chemical analysis to check the potency of products. The standard release potency for cephalothin crystals is 910. A simple random sample of 16 crystals gives the following potency data:

897   914   913   906   916   918   905   921   918   906   895   893   908   906   907   901

(a). Check the data for outliers or strong skewness that might threaten the validity of the statistical procedures that can be used to make inferences. A graph may be most helpful to do this.

(b). If appropriate, calculate and interpret a 95% confidence interval for the mean potency of all cephalothin crystals.

(c). If appropriate, use this data to test at significance level $\alpha = .05$ to determine if the mean potency is different from the standard release potency.

IX. 20. In an attempt to determine the appropriate methods of publicizing the Annual Giving campaign, YMCA officials are obtaining demographic information about the potential contributors. One of these demographic characteristics is the age of the contributor. The mean age of all adults in the surrounding area is known to be 48.3 years. The YMCA selected a simple random sample of 29 contributors to the YMCA Annual Giving campaign and determined the age of each. The mean age of this sample of 29 contributors was 45.4 years with a standard deviation of 6.2 years. If appropriate, use this information to test at significance level $\alpha = .10$ to determine if the mean age of all contributors is different from the reported mean age of 48.3 years for all adults living in the surrounding area.

IX. 21. Critics of the ABC television show "Who Wants to be a Millionaire" claimed that initial questions were too trivial (easy) and that later questions focus on obscure knowledge. They claimed that most high school students could get most of the initial questions correct, but that they would get very few of the later questions correct. To analyze this, they created a test that contained 40 questions that were used for the $125,000, $250,000, $500,000, and $1,000,000 questions. This test was given to a simple random sample of 30 high school students. The number of questions that each of these students got correct is recorded below.

12	14	9	15	10	16	10	13	8	12	19	11	7	9	14
15	9	12	8	14	10	13	12	7	14	11	18	12	11	15

(a). If appropriate, use the data above to estimate the mean number of questions that all high school students would get correct on this test using a 90% confidence interval. Interpret the interval you calculate.

(b). Since each question has four potential choices, a student who is guessing should still get, on average, 10 questions correct. If appropriate, test at level $\alpha = .10$ to see if the mean number of questions that all high school students would get correct on this test is different from 10.

(c). Relate your decision and conclusion in part (b) to the confidence interval calculated in part (a). Do they in essence give you the same information?

IX. 22. According to the U.S. Department of Transportation's Air Travel Consumer Report, the nation's 12 largest airlines recorded an on-time arrival percentage of 77.4% during 2001. Of interest is to estimate the mean delay time for the 22.6% of all flights that did not arrive on time during 2001. A simple random sample of 35 late arriving flights was selected, and the mean delay time of this sample of 35 flights was 14.2 minutes, with a standard deviation of 6.4 minutes. The distribution of the delay times in the sample of late flights was slightly skewed to the right.

(a). Identify the population of interest.

(b). If appropriate, use this information to calculate and interpret a 90% confidence interval for the mean delay time for all flights that did not arrive on time during 2001.

(c). A Congressional subgroup studying airline efficiency wants to determine if the mean delay time is less than 15 minutes. If appropriate, use the data above to test at significance level $\alpha = .10$ to determine if the mean delay time of all delayed flights in 2001 was less than 15 minutes.

IX. 23. As elected officials, Congresspersons are always in the public eye and reelection often depends on public perception of the job they are doing and the type of person that they are. For this reason most Congresspersons make contributions to several religious and charitable organizations. Of interest is to estimate the mean number of religious and charitable organizations to which the members of Congress make contributions. A simple random sample of 30 members of Congress was selected, and the number of religious and charitable organizations to which a contribution was made in 2009 determined. This data is recorded below. The mean and standard deviation of this sample are 17 and 7.405, respectively.

10	25	22	13	6	14	31	20	9	14	19	19	23	4	13	28	21	19
22	33	10	17	24	20	8	15	19	16	5	11						

(a). If appropriate, use the data above to estimate the mean number of religious and charitable organizations to which all members of Congress have made contributions using a 99% confidence interval. Interpret the interval you calculate.

(b). A Congressional clerk claims that the mean number of religious or charitable organizations that all members of Congress contribute to is 20. If appropriate, use the data above to test at significance level $\alpha = .01$ to determine if the mean number of religious or charitable organizations that all members of Congress contribute to is different from 20.

(c). Relate your decision and conclusion in part (b) to the confidence interval calculated in part (a). Do they in essence give you the same information?

IX. 24. According to the Butterball website, Butterball turkeys typically range from 10 to 25 pounds. Of interest is to estimate the mean weight of all Butterball turkeys that were sold for Thanksgiving 2009. To estimate this, a simple random sample of 51 Butterball turkeys sold between November 1 and November 25, 2009 were selected and their weights recorded. The mean weight of this sample of 51 Butterball turkeys was 18.7

pounds, with a standard deviation of 2.4 pounds. Using this data a 95% confidence interval for the mean weight of all Butterball turkeys sold for Thanksgiving 2009 is calculated to be (18.025, 19.375).

(a). Verify the assumptions for the inference procedures described in this chapter.

(b). Perform the calculations to confirm that the above confidence interval is correct.

(c). For each of the following identify if the statement is a correct interpretation of the confidence interval and/or the definition of confidence.

    (i). Butterball has 95% confidence that the mean weight of all Butterball turkeys that were sold for Thanksgiving 2009 is between 18.025 and 19.375 pounds.

    (ii). 95% of all Butterball turkeys that were sold for Thanksgiving 2009 weighed between 18.025 and 19.375 pounds.

    (iii). If repeated simple random samples of 51 Butterball turkeys are selected and a 95% confidence interval computed for each sample, then 95% of the sample means would be contained between 18.025 and 19.375.

    (iv). The mean weight of all Butterball turkeys that were sold for Thanksgiving 2009 is equal to exactly 18.7 pounds.

    (v). If repeated simple random samples of 51 Butterball turkeys are selected and a 95% confidence interval computed for each sample, then the mean weight of all Butterball turkeys that were sold for Thanksgiving 2009 will be contained in 95% of the confidence intervals.

    (vi). The probability that the mean weight of all Butterball turkeys that were sold for Thanksgiving 2009 is between 18.025 and 19.375 pounds is .95.

(d). A local store indicates that the mean weight of the Butterball turkeys that it sold for Thanksgiving 2009 was 20 pounds. If a test were to be conducted to determine if this claim were correct, versus the alternative that the mean is actually different from 20 pounds, state the hypotheses of interest and use the confidence interval above to test at significance level $\alpha = .05$ to make a decision and conclusion regarding these hypotheses.

IX. 25. Ground transportation in and out of the Richmond International Raceway complex for the NASCAR race on Saturday, May 14, 2005 was very slow. Of interest is to estimate the mean amount of time that it took fans to park once they were within one mile of the RIR complex. A simple random sample of 31 fans was selected, and the mean amount of time that it took this sample of 31 fans to park once they were within one mile of the RIR complex was 69 minutes, with a standard deviation of 11.4 minutes. The distribution of the times in the sample was slightly skewed to the left. If appropriate, use this information to calculate and interpret a 98% confidence interval for the mean amount of time that it took all fans to park once they were within one mile of the RIR complex.

IX. 26. General Motors claims that the mean miles per gallon in their Hummer H3 sport utility truck is 18 mpg on the highway. To test this claim, an independent automobile club obtained a simple random sample of 20 new Hummer H3 SUTs, put exactly one gallon of gasoline in each, and ran the vehicles on a closed track until they ran out of gas. The number of miles that each Hummer H3 ran (rounded to the nearest tenth of a mile) is given below. The mean and standard deviation of this data are 17.84 mpg and 0.29 mpg, respectively. If appropriate, use the data to test at significance level $\alpha = .05$ if there is significant evidence that the mean miles per gallon in all such new Hummer H3 SUTs differs from the stated 18 mpg.

| 17.8 | 17.6 | 18.1 | 18.2 | 18.0 | 17.4 | 17.8 | 18.2 | 17.7 | 17.3 |
| 18.2 | 17.9 | 18.3 | 17.8 | 18.0 | 17.5 | 17.6 | 17.7 | 18.1 | 17.6 |

X. Inferences for Comparing Two Population Means

In Moore: Read Chapter 18 (pages 471 – 485)

Statistical inference involves using statistics computed from a sample to make statements about unknown population parameters. In the previous chapters we have selected a simple random sample from a population and used the resulting sample statistics to make statements about the population mean μ or the population proportion π. Now suppose we have two populations with population means μ_1 and μ_2, respectively and standard deviations σ_1 and σ_2, respectively, and our current interest involves making inferences about the <u>difference</u> between the population means, $\mu_1 - \mu_2$. Consider the following examples.

1. It is of interest to estimate the difference in the mean IQ of all male students at this university and the mean IQ of all female students at this university. Then the populations of interest are all male students at this university and all female students at this university, and the parameter of interest is $\mu_1 - \mu_2$ = the difference between the mean IQ of all male students (μ_1) and the mean IQ of all female students (μ_2).

2. The economic downturn of 2008 and 2009 did not affect all people equally. It is conjectured that the mean loss in investments among all people who live in urban settings was different from the mean loss in investments among all people who live in rural settings. Then the populations of interest are all people who live in urban settings and all people who live in rural settings, and the parameter of interest is $\mu_1 - \mu_2$ = the difference between the mean loss in investments among all people who live in urban settings (μ_1) and the mean loss in investments among all people who live in rural settings (μ_2).

Once the populations and the parameter are identified, then samples must be selected from each population and data collected for the individuals in the samples. The samples can be selected <u>independently</u> of each other, or there could be a <u>dependency</u> between the two samples. From the sample selected from the first population the sample mean $\overline{X}_1$ is calculated, and from the sample selected from the second population the sample mean $\overline{X}_2$ is calculated. The difference between these two sample means, $\overline{X}_1 - \overline{X}_2$, is then the **point estimate** of the difference between the population means $\mu_1 - \mu_2$.

In the remainder of this chapter we begin with the sampling distribution of the difference between the sample means $\overline{X}_1 - \overline{X}_2$ in the case where the samples are independent. Then this sampling distribution is used to make inferences, both confidence intervals and tests of significance, for $\mu_1 - \mu_2$ in cases in which the samples are independent. Finally, the concept of a paired t-test is considered to conduct tests of significance about $\mu_1 - \mu_2$ when the two samples are dependent (paired).

A. Sampling Distribution of $\overline{X}_1 - \overline{X}_2$

We have two populations, the first population has mean μ_1 and standard deviation σ_1, the second population has mean μ_2 and standard deviation σ_2, and of interest is to make inferences about the difference in the population means, $\mu_1 - \mu_2$. A simple random sample of n_1 subjects is selected from the first population and the mean of this sample, $\overline{X}_1$, is calculated. Likewise, a simple random sample of n_2 subjects is selected from the second population and the mean of this sample, $\overline{X}_2$, is calculated. In this section and in sections B and C of this chapter, we are assuming that the two samples are <u>independent</u> of each other, implying that the two samples are selected separately from each other. Then we can compute the difference in the sample means, $\overline{X}_1 - \overline{X}_2$. This difference is the <u>point estimate</u> of the difference in the population means $\mu_1 - \mu_2$ and we need the sampling distribution of $\overline{X}_1 - \overline{X}_2$.

The assumptions are similar to those in the last two chapters, namely (1) that both samples are <u>simple random samples</u> from the respective populations (and that they are <u>independent</u> of each other) and (2) that either both population distributions are <u>normal</u> or both sample sizes are "large enough" for the <u>central limit theorem</u> to apply. Since this chapter involves means, we return to our rules of Chapter IX, so the sample size is large enough for the central limit theorem to apply if it is 15 or greater unless the population is <u>heavily skewed</u>, and if the population is <u>heavily skewed due to outliers</u> the sample size must be 40 or greater.

If these assumptions are satisfied, and if the populations means μ_1 and μ_2 and the population standard deviations σ_1 and σ_2 are all known, then the sampling distribution of $\overline{X}_1 - \overline{X}_2$ is as follows.

(1) Center: the mean of the sampling distribution of $\overline{X}_1 - \overline{X}_2$ is $\mu_{\overline{x}_1 - \overline{x}_2} = \mu_1 - \mu_2$.

(2) Spread: the standard deviation of sampling distribution of $\overline{X}_1 - \overline{X}_2$ is $\sigma_{\overline{x}_1 - \overline{x}_2} = \sqrt{\dfrac{\sigma_1^2}{n_1} + \dfrac{\sigma_2^2}{n_2}}$.

(3) Shape: the shape of the sampling distribution will be normal.

(4) Unusual features: since the shape will be normal, then there are no unusual features in the sampling distribution.

We can summarize the sampling distribution by writing it as: $\overline{X}_1 - \overline{X}_2 \sim N\left(\mu_1 - \mu_2, \sqrt{\dfrac{\sigma_1^2}{n_1} + \dfrac{\sigma_2^2}{n_2}} \right)$.

Using the Z-score transformation, we can create the statistic $Z = \dfrac{(\overline{X}_1 - \overline{X}_2) - (\mu_1 - \mu_2)}{\sqrt{\dfrac{\sigma_1^2}{n_1} + \dfrac{\sigma_2^2}{n_2}}}$ that has a standard normal distribution. Confidence interval and test statistic formulas that can be used to make inferences about $\mu_1 - \mu_2$ can be derived from this statistic.

Example 96

The mean delay time for all flights leaving Washington National Airport is 8 minutes with a standard deviation of 3 minutes. The mean delay time of all flights leaving Dulles International Airport is 11 minutes with a standard deviation of 4 minutes. Suppose a simple random sample of 40 flights from Washington National Airport and an independent simple random sample of 50 flights from Dulles International Airport are chosen. The mean delay times for the flights in each sample are computed. If appropriate, describe the sampling distribution of the difference between the sample means, $\overline{X}_1 - \overline{X}_2$.

Example 97

The mean classroom size for all classrooms at University T is 56 with a standard deviation of 7.5, and the mean class size for all classrooms at University W is 53 with a standard deviation of 6.8. Suppose a simple random sample of 71 classrooms from University T and an independent simple random sample of 65 classrooms from University W are chosen and the mean classroom size for the classrooms in each sample determined. If appropriate, describe the sampling distribution of the difference between the sample means, $\overline{X}_1 - \overline{X}_2$.

In the next two sections the sampling distribution will be used to make inferences about the difference in the population means, $\mu_1 - \mu_2$. However, as for means and proportions, the sampling distribution theory can also be used together with the Table of Standard Normal Probabilities on pages 338 and 339 to make probability statements about $\overline{X}_1 - \overline{X}_2$. Since a Z-score transformation involves subtracting the mean from the statistic and then dividing by the standard deviation, then the Z-score transformation involved with $\overline{X}_1 - \overline{X}_2$ is as follows:

$$Z = \frac{(\overline{X}_1 - \overline{X}_2) - (\mu_1 - \mu_2)}{\sqrt{\dfrac{\sigma_1^2}{n_1} + \dfrac{\sigma_2^2}{n_2}}}.$$

Example 98

The mean delay time for all flights leaving Washington National Airport is 8 minutes with a standard deviation of 3 minutes. The mean delay time of all flights leaving Dulles International Airport is 11 minutes with a standard deviation of 4 minutes. Suppose a simple random sample of 40 flights from Washington National Airport and an independent simple random sample of 50 flights from Dulles International Airport are chosen. The mean delay times for the flights in each sample are computed. If appropriate, use the sampling distribution determined in example 96 to determine the probability that the difference in the mean delays times for the flights in the two samples ($\overline{X}_1 - \overline{X}_2$) is greater than 0.

Example 99

The mean classroom size for all classrooms at University T is 56 with a standard deviation of 7.5, and the mean class size for all classrooms at University W is 53 with a standard deviation of 6.8. Suppose a simple random sample of 71 classrooms from University T and an independent simple random sample of 65 classrooms from University W are chosen and the mean classroom size for the classrooms in each sample determined. If appropriate, use the sampling distribution determined in example 97 to determine the probability that the difference in the mean classroom sizes for the classrooms in the two samples ($\overline{X}_1 - \overline{X}_2$) is less than 0.

B. Confidence Intervals

Of interest is to estimate the difference between two population means. For example, consider the first example at the beginning of this chapter.

(1) It is of interest to estimate the difference in the mean IQ of all male students at this university and the mean IQ of all female students at this university. Then the populations of interest are all male students at this university and all female students at this university, and the parameter of interest is $\mu_1 - \mu_2 =$ the difference between the mean IQ of all male students (μ_1) and the mean IQ of all female students (μ_2).

Since the mean IQ of all male students and the mean IQ of all female students are both unknown, then this mean difference must be estimated. Hence a simple random sample is chosen from each population, and the sample mean is computed for each sample. The difference in the sample means, $\overline{X}_1 - \overline{X}_2$, is the **point estimate** of the difference in the population means, $\mu_1 - \mu_2$. The sampling distribution of $\overline{X}_1 - \overline{X}_2$ discussed in the previous section is used to determine a margin of error, and hence a confidence interval formula is derived. In the two subsections below this is done first when the population standard deviations σ_1 and σ_2 are known, and then repeated when they are unknown.

1. Confidence Interval for $\mu_1 - \mu_2$: Population Standard Deviations Known

With the assumptions (1) that both samples are <u>simple random samples</u> from the respective populations (and that they are <u>independent</u> of each other) and (2) that either both population distributions are <u>normal</u> or both sample sizes are "large enough" for the <u>central limit theorem</u> to apply, and in this section assuming the population standard deviations σ_1 and σ_2 are known, the sampling distribution of $\overline{X}_1 - \overline{X}_2$ is as follows:

$$\overline{X}_1 - \overline{X}_2 \sim N\left(\mu_1 - \mu_2, \sqrt{\frac{\sigma_1^2}{n_1} + \frac{\sigma_2^2}{n_2}}\right) . \text{ Then } Z = \frac{(\overline{X}_1 - \overline{X}_2) - (\mu_1 - \mu_2)}{\sqrt{\frac{\sigma_1^2}{n_1} + \frac{\sigma_2^2}{n_2}}} , \text{ and solving for } \mu_1 - \mu_2 \text{ a}$$

$100*C\%$ confidence interval for $\mu_1 - \mu_2$ is:

$$(\overline{X}_1 - \overline{X}_2) \pm Z^* \sqrt{\frac{\sigma_1^2}{n_1} + \frac{\sigma_2^2}{n_2}}$$

Since this chapter involves means, we return to our rules of Chapter IX, so the sample size is large enough for the central limit theorem to apply if it is 15 or greater unless the population is <u>heavily skewed</u>, and if the population is <u>heavily skewed due to outliers</u> the sample size must be 40 or greater.

The value of Z* can be determined from the bottom two rows of the t-Table on page 340 as before, and the interpretation and properties of the interval are the same as for the other cases considered.

Example 100

A NCAA official is interested in determining the difference in the mean number of points scored in all small college (Division III) football games and the mean number of points scored in all large college (Division I) football games. Begin by identifying the populations of interest and the parameter of interest. It is known that the standard deviation of points scored in all small college games is 12.65 and the standard deviation of points scored in all large college games is 15.69. To estimate this difference, he selected a simple random sample of 50 small college games and an independent simple random sample of 50 large college games and found the number of points scored in the games. The results are: for small college, $\overline{X}_1 =$ 47.32, and for large college, $\overline{X}_2 = 40.64$. If appropriate, use this data to calculate and interpret a 95% confidence interval for the difference between the mean number of points scored in small college and large college football games.

Example 101

Economists in Richmond, Virginia are interested in determining the difference in the mean amount of money spent per shopping trip by customers at Kroger and the mean amount of money spent per shopping trip by customers at Martin's. Begin by identifying the populations of interest and the parameter of interest. It is known that the standard deviation of the amount of money spent per shopping trip by all customers at Kroger is $16.25 and that the standard deviation of the amount of money spent per shopping trip by all customers at Martin's is $13.72. An economist visited a local Kroger store and collected information from the first 28 customers who would respond. The mean amount of money spent by this sample of 28 Kroger customers was $97.37. A different economist visited a local Martin's store and collected information from the first 28 customers who would respond. The mean amount of money spent by this sample of 28 Martin's customers was $92.18. If appropriate, use this data to calculate and interpret a 99% confidence interval for the difference between the mean amount of money spent per shopping trip by customers at Kroger and the mean amount of money spent per shopping trip by customers at Martin's.

2. Confidence Intervals for $\mu_1 - \mu_2$: Population Standard Deviations Unknown

Suppose we have two <u>independent</u> simple random samples of sizes n_1 and n_2 from two populations. We continue to assume that either both populations are normal or that both sample sizes are large enough for the central limit theorem to apply. We want to find a 100*C% confidence interval for the difference between population means $\mu_1 - \mu_2$ when population standard deviations σ_1 and σ_2 are <u>unknown</u>.

If the population standard deviations σ_1 and σ_2 are unknown, the standard normal statistic $Z = \dfrac{(\overline{X}_1 - \overline{X}_2) - (\mu_1 - \mu_2)}{\sqrt{\dfrac{\sigma_1^2}{n_1} + \dfrac{\sigma_2^2}{n_2}}}$ is no longer appropriate. Instead we must use a statistic that follows a t distribution that uses the sample standard deviations s_1 and s_2 instead of the population standard deviations σ_1 and σ_2.

Such a t-statistic is $t = \dfrac{(\overline{X}_1 - \overline{X}_2) - (\mu_1 - \mu_2)}{\sqrt{\dfrac{s_1^2}{n_1} + \dfrac{s_2^2}{n_2}}}$, which follows a t distribution with degrees of freedom equal to the <u>smaller</u> of $n_1 - 1$ and $n_2 - 1$.

Then using a little algebra, a 100*C% confidence interval for $\mu_1 - \mu_2$ is:

$$(\overline{X}_1 - \overline{X}_2) \pm t^* \sqrt{\dfrac{s_1^2}{n_1} + \dfrac{s_2^2}{n_2}}$$

The t* value can be found in the t-Table on page 340 with degrees of freedom equal to the <u>smaller</u> of $n_1 - 1$ and $n_2 - 1$. Again the interpretation and properties of the intervals are the same as in all other cases considered.

269

Example 102

At a large university a sociologist is interested in the difference between the mean amount of money that all male students spend on snack food per week versus the mean amount of money that all female students spend on snack food per week. Begin by indentifying the populations of interest and the parameter of interest. The sociologist selects a simple random sample of 82 male students from the registrar's records. She then selects an independent simple random sample of 81 female students from the registrar's records. She finds that the mean amount of money spent on snack food per week by the 82 male students is $20 with a standard deviation of $12. For the 81 female students, the mean amount of money spent on snack food per week is $9 with a standard deviation of $3. If appropriate, calculate and interpret a 99% confidence interval for the difference in the mean amount of money spent on snack food per week by all male and female students.

Example 103

In May 2009 new fuel efficiency standards for vehicles were issued by the Transportation Department and the Environmental Protection Agency following a deal with the auto industry. Of interest is to estimate the difference in the mean miles per gallon in all vehicles produced in the two years prior to the new standards and the mean miles per gallon in all vehicles produced since the new standards went into place. Begin by identifying the populations of interest and the parameter of interest. A simple random sample of 57 vehicles produced in the two years prior to the new standards going into place was selected, the mean miles per gallon of this sample of 57 vehicles was 23.1 with a standard deviation of 6.3. An independent simple random sample of 51 vehicles produced after the new standards went into place was selected, the mean miles per gallon of this sample of 51 vehicles was 25.2 with a standard deviation of 6.5. If appropriate, use this data to calculate and interpret a 90% confidence interval for the difference in the mean miles per gallon in all vehicles produced in the two years prior to the new standards and the mean miles per gallon in all vehicles produced since the new standards went into place

C.   Tests of Significance

Now suppose we want to test hypotheses about the difference in two population means $\mu_1 - \mu_2$. Specifically, the null hypothesis is that the difference in the population means $\mu_1 - \mu_2$ equals some specified value μ_0 ($H_0 : \mu_1 - \mu_2 = \mu_0$). This null hypothesis is tested versus the alternative hypothesis that $\mu_1 - \mu_2$ is greater than μ_0 (H_A: $\mu_1 - \mu_2 > \mu_0$), that $\mu_1 - \mu_2$ is less than μ_0 (H_A: $\mu_1 - \mu_2 < \mu_0$), or the two-sided hypothesis that $\mu_1 - \mu_2$ is not equal to μ_0 (H_A: $\mu_1 - \mu_2 \neq \mu_0$). In most practical problems the hypothesized value μ_0 is 0, and in this case the hypotheses simply to testing null hypothesis H_0: $\mu_1 = \mu_2$ versus alternative hypothesis H_A: $\mu_1 > \mu_2$, H_A: $\mu_1 < \mu_2$, or $H_A : \mu_1 \neq \mu_2$. For example, consider the second example introduced at the beginning of this chapter.

(2).   The economic downturn of 2008 and 2009 did not affect all people equally. It is conjectured that the mean loss in investments among all people who live in urban settings was different from the mean loss in investments among all people who live in rural settings. Then the populations of interest are all people who live in urban settings and all people who live in rural settings, and the parameter of interest is $\mu_1 - \mu_2$ = the difference between the mean loss in investments among all people who live in urban settings (μ_1) and the mean loss in investments among all people who live in rural settings (μ_2). The null hypothesis would be that the mean loss for all people who live in urban settings and rural settings is the same (H_0: $\mu_1 = \mu_2$) and the alternative hypothesis would be that the mean loss of all people who live in urban settings is different from the mean loss of all people who live in rural settings ($H_A : \mu_1 \neq \mu_2$).

We need to determine a formula for a test statistic that can be used to test such hypotheses. As was done for confidence intervals, we assume that (1) that both samples are simple random samples from the respective populations (and that they are independent of each other) and (2) that either both population distributions are normal or both sample sizes are "large enough" for the central limit theorem to apply. We will first give a test statistic formula when the population standard deviations σ_1 and σ_2 are known, and then will give a similar test statistic formula for the more practical situation in which the population standard deviations σ_1 and σ_2 are unknown.

1. Significance Test for $\mu_1 - \mu_2$: Population Standard Deviations Known

Suppose that (1) we have two independent simple random samples, that (2) <u>both</u> populations are normally distributed: $X_1 \sim N(\mu_1, \sigma_1)$ and $X_2 \sim N(\mu_2, \sigma_2)$ or <u>both</u> sample sizes are large enough such that the central limit theorem applies, and that (3) both population standard deviations σ_1 and σ_2 are known.

Then the standard normal statistic $Z = \dfrac{(\overline{X}_1 - \overline{X}_2) - (\mu_1 - \mu_2)}{\sqrt{\dfrac{\sigma_1^2}{n_1} + \dfrac{\sigma_2^2}{n_2}}}$ derived from the sampling distribution of

$\overline{X}_1 - \overline{X}_2$ is a candidate for the test statistic. However, $\mu_1 - \mu_2$ is unknown and must be estimated. Since we carry out the test assuming the null hypothesis $H_0 : \mu_1 - \mu_2 = \mu_0$ is true, then the test statistic for such a test is:

$$Z = \frac{(\overline{X}_1 - \overline{X}_2) - \mu_0}{\sqrt{\dfrac{\sigma_1^2}{n_1} + \dfrac{\sigma_2^2}{n_2}}}$$

The p-value, decision and conclusion are completed as for the other cases we have considered.

Example 104

A NCAA official is interested in determining the difference in the mean number of points scored in all small college (Division III) football games and the mean number of points scored in all large college (Division I) football games. In example 100 we estimated this difference using a 95% confidence interval. Now suppose we want to conduct a test to determine if the mean number of points scored in all small college (Division III) football games is different from the mean number of points scored in all large college (Division I) football games. Begin by stating the hypotheses of interest. Using the same information as in example 100, it is known that the standard deviation of points scored in all small college games is 12.65 and the standard deviation of points scored in all large college games is 15.69. In a simple random sample of 50 small college games the mean number of points scored per game was 47.32 and an independent simple random sample of 50 large college games the mean number of points scored per game was 40.64. If appropriate, use this data to test the hypotheses at the $\alpha = .05$ significance level.

2. Significance Test on $\mu_1 - \mu_2$: Population Standard Deviations Unknown

Once again we want to test the null hypothesis that the difference in the population means $\mu_1 - \mu_2$ equals some specified value μ_0 ($H_0: \mu_1 - \mu_2 = \mu_0$) versus the alternative hypothesis that $\mu_1 - \mu_2$ is greater than μ_0 ($H_A: \mu_1 - \mu_2 > \mu_0$), that $\mu_1 - \mu_2$ is less than μ_0 ($H_A: \mu_1 - \mu_2 < \mu_0$), or the two-sided hypothesis that $\mu_1 - \mu_2$ is not equal to μ_0 ($H_A: \mu_1 - \mu_2 \neq \mu_0$). In most practical problems the hypothesized value μ_0 is 0, and in this case the hypotheses simply to testing null hypothesis $H_0: \mu_1 = \mu_2$ versus alternative hypothesis $H_A: \mu_1 > \mu_2$, $H_A: \mu_1 < \mu_2$, or $H_A: \mu_1 \neq \mu_2$.

We continue to assume that (1) we have two <u>independent</u> simple random samples of sizes n_1 and n_2 from two populations, and (2) that either the two populations are normally distributed or that the sample sizes are large enough for the central limit theorem to apply. However, now the population standard deviations σ_1 and σ_2 are <u>unknown</u>.

Since the population standard deviations σ_1 and σ_2 are not known the Z test statistic in the last section is not appropriate, and instead we must consider using the t statistic $t = \dfrac{(\overline{X}_1 - \overline{X}_2) - (\mu_1 - \mu_2)}{\sqrt{\dfrac{s_1^2}{n_1} + \dfrac{s_2^2}{n_2}}}$. This is a candidate for the test statistic, but cannot be used because the population means μ_1 and μ_2 are not known. Since the test is carried out assuming the null hypothesis $H_0: \mu_1 - \mu_2 = \mu_0$ is true, the test statistic is as follows:

$$t = \frac{(\overline{X}_1 - \overline{X}_2) - \mu_0}{\sqrt{\dfrac{s_1^2}{n_1} + \dfrac{s_2^2}{n_2}}}$$

This test statistic follows a t distribution with degrees of freedom equal to the <u>smaller</u> of $n_1 - 1$ and $n_2 - 1$. Again the p-value, decision, and conclusion are completed as in previous sections.

Example 105

The U. S. Department of Agriculture compiles information on acreage, production, and value of potatoes and publishes its findings in *Agricultural Statistics*. Potato yield is measured in hundreds of pounds (cwt) per acre. It is conjectured that the mean potato yield in Nevada is higher than the mean potato yield in Idaho. Begin by identifying the populations of interest, the parameter of interest, and the hypotheses that should be tested. To test these hypotheses independent simple random samples of forty 1-acre plots of potatoes from Idaho and thirty-two 1-acre plots of potatoes from Nevada gave the following yields.

Idaho:	299	337	396	379	301	414	380	328	386	311	288	354	381	399
	324	287	369	336	334	334	360	368	375	314	373	369	378	
	330	274	361	312	385	316	392	363	353	351	337	382	355	

Nevada:	353	324	398	362	385	406	448	384	382	398	342	377	418
	303	424	470	411	383	379	378	410	370	386	338	329	346
	341	432	410	409	370	403							

This data was first presented in example 10 on page 52 in which a back-to-back stem-and-leaf plot was constructed. If appropriate, use the data to test at the $\alpha = .01$ significance level to determine if the mean potato yield in Nevada is higher than the mean potato yield in Idaho.

Example 106

The economic downturn of 2008 and 2009 did not affect all people equally. It is conjectured that the mean loss in investments among all people who lived in urban settings was different from the mean loss in investments among all people who lived in rural settings. The populations of interest are all people who lived in urban settings and all people who lived in rural settings, and the parameter of interest is $\mu_1 - \mu_2 =$ the difference between the mean loss in investments among all people who lived in urban settings (μ_1) and the mean loss in investments among all people who lived in rural settings (μ_2). The null hypothesis would be that the mean loss for all people who lived in urban settings and rural settings is the same (H_0: $\mu_1 = \mu_2$) and the alternative hypothesis would be that the mean loss of all people who lived in urban settings is different from the mean loss of all people who lived in rural settings ($H_A : \mu_1 \neq \mu_2$). To test these hypotheses a simple random sample of 100 people who lived in urban settings and an independent simple random sample of 100 people who lived in rural settings were selected. For those who lived in the urban settings the mean loss for the 100 people in the sample was $26,048 with a standard deviation of $21,219; for those who lived in the rural settings the mean loss for the 100 people in the sample was $31,295 with a standard deviation of $18,365. If appropriate, use this data to test the hypotheses at the $\alpha = .10$ significance level.

D. Paired t-Test

This chapter has involved making inferences about the difference in two population means, $\mu_1 - \mu_2$, and the previous three sections (sampling distribution, confidence interval and test of significance) have assumed that **independent** simple random samples have been selected from the two populations. There are situations, however, where the samples are not selected independently of each other but are instead dependent or **paired**. For example consider the following situation.

To determine the level of learning in a college physics course, all students in attendance the first day were given a 25-question test that covered the topics that would be discussed in the course. At the end of the semester, students present the last day were given the 25-question test again. A simple random sample of 60 students who completed both the pre-test (test on the first day) and the post-test (test on the last day) were selected and the results used to test to see if the mean performance on the post-test was better than the mean performance on the pre-test. In this case the population is all students who took the pre-test and the post-test, and the parameter of interest is $\mu_1 - \mu_2$ where μ_1 is the mean number of questions correct on the pre-test and μ_2 is the mean number of questions correct on the post-test. Of interest is to test null hypothesis H_0: $\mu_1 - \mu_2 = 0$ versus alternative hypothesis H_A: $\mu_1 - \mu_2 < 0$.

The above problem is different from others in this chapter because the data are <u>paired</u>: the samples are not two independent samples of 60 students, meaning a total of 120 students with one observation per student, but instead there is only one sample of 60 students and two measurements (pre-test and post-test) are made on each. For situations such as this with paired data the test statistic used to test the hypothesis is called a **paired t-test** and is different from that in the previous section.

For each of the n subjects in the sample, the difference between the two measurements is determined. In the example, the difference would be the pre-test score minus the post-test score. This generates a data set with n differences, and the paired t-test is simply a t-test as described in chapter IX on these differences. The test statistic is:

$$t = \frac{\overline{X}_d - \mu_0}{s_d / \sqrt{n}}$$

In this formula $\overline{X}_d$ is the mean of n <u>differences</u> in the sample, and s_d is the standard deviation of these <u>differences</u>. This statistic follows a t-distribution with $n - 1$ degrees of freedom. The assumptions for this t-test are that (1) a <u>simple random sample</u> is selected, with two measurements on each individual in the sample and (2) that the differences are normally distributed or the sample size is large enough for the <u>central limit theorem</u> to apply.

Example 107

It is conjectured that among students who take the math SAT test twice, the mean score is higher the second time that is taken. Begin by identifying the population of interest, the parameter of interest and the hypotheses that should be tested. To test these hypotheses a simple random sample of 20 students who took that math SAT test twice was selected and the scores are as follows. If appropriate, use this data to test the hypotheses at the α = .05 level of significance.

Student	1	2	3	4	5	6	7	8	9	10	11	12	13	14	15	16	17	18	19	20
First score	320	340	255	480	500	560	600	420	780	720	645	660	395	660	590	310	365	585	725	560
Second score	340	335	280	470	520	570	680	450	800	705	660	695	400	640	590	325	380	600	750	550

Example 108

To determine the level of learning in a college physics course, all students in attendance the first day were given a 25-question test that covered the topics that would be discussed in the course. At the end of the semester, students present the last day were given the 25-question test again. A simple random sample of 60 students who completed both the pre-test (test on the first day) and the post-test (test on the last day) were selected and the results used to test to see if the mean performance on the post-test was better than the mean performance on the pre-test. In this case the population is all students who took the pre-test and the post-test, and the parameter of interest is $\mu_1 - \mu_2$ where μ_1 is the mean number of questions correct on the pre-test and μ_2 is the mean number of questions correct on the post-test. Of interest is to test null hypothesis H_0: $\mu_1 - \mu_2 = 0$ versus alternative hypothesis H_A: $\mu_1 - \mu_2 < 0$. For the simple random sample of 60 students, the scores on the pre-test and post-test were determined, and the differences determined. Since the expectation was that students would do better on the post-test, most of the differences were negative and the mean difference in the sample of 60 students was $\overline{X}_d = -8.5$ with a standard deviation of $s_d = 4.1$. If appropriate, use this information to test the hypotheses at the $\alpha = .10$ significance level.

Additional Reading and Examples

1. The inference procedures in this chapter are only valid if the assumptions are satisfied. Violations of these assumptions should cause one to question the conclusions drawn from the data. As for the inference procedures in previous chapters, the assumptions are <u>independent</u> simple random samples from the two populations, and either that both populations are (approximately) normally distributed or both sample sizes are large enough for the central limit theorem to apply. The decision to use the Z or t procedures is based on whether the population standard deviations are known (not usually the case, use Z) or unknown (use t). If the samples are <u>dependent</u> (<u>paired</u>) then the paired t-test of the last section can be considered.

2. Most inference procedures that deal with two population means involve determining if the means are the same or if they are significantly different. In the significance tests this is equivalent to setting the hypothesized value μ_0 equal to 0. At significance level α, if 0 is contained within the $(1-\alpha)\times100\%$ confidence interval for the mean difference, then we declare that there is <u>insufficient</u> evidence that there is a difference between the two means. However, if 0 is <u>not</u> in the interval that there is <u>sufficient</u> evidence that the two means are different.

3. To understand the effect of a dirty air filter on gasoline mileage, a simple random sample of 10 cars is selected and a clean air filter installed in each car. A second simple random sample of 10 cars is selected and an old dirty air filter of the same type is installed in each car. The gasoline mileage of each car is measured, with the data given in the table below.

Clean Filters					Dirty Filters				
19.0	22.0	24.0	24.5	25.0	16.0	20.0	21.0	21.5	23.0
25.0	25.5	26.0	28.0	31.0	21.0	22.5	25.0	25.0	27.0

Graphical displays of this data show fairly symmetric distributions with no outliers, even though the clean filters' distribution has fairly long tails. Of particular interest is in the difference between the mean mileage of the two groups, which would give information about any mileage difference due to the condition of the air filter. The question "How much effect does a dirty air filter have on gasoline mileage?" corresponds to the following question stated in statistical terms: "What is the difference between the population mean mileage when a clean air filter is used as compared to when a dirty air filter is used?" Calculating a 99% confidence interval would be one method of attempting to answer the question. From the data we have the following.

Clean filters	n = 10	$\overline{X} = 25.0$	s = 3.21
Dirty filters	n = 10	$\overline{X} = 22.2$	s = 3.09

Since the population standard deviations are not known the t procedures must be used. The degrees of freedom is 9 (the minimum of $10 - 1 = 9$ and $10 - 1 = 9$), so from the t-Table on page 340, $t_9^* = 3.250$. Then the 99% confidence interval is:

$$(\overline{X}_1 - \overline{X}_2) \pm t^* \sqrt{\frac{s_1^2}{n_1} + \frac{s_2^2}{n_2}} = (25.0 - 22.2) \pm 3.250 \sqrt{\frac{3.21^2}{10} + \frac{3.09^2}{10}} = 2.80 \pm 3.250(1.409) = 2.80 \pm 4.579$$

$$= (-1.779, 7.379).$$

In interpreting this interval, we have 99% confidence that the difference between the mean gas mileage for clean filters and dirty filters is between -1.179 and 7.379.

If we wanted to test H_0: $\mu_1 - \mu_2 = 0$ versus H_A: $\mu_1 - \mu_2 \neq 0$ at significance level $\alpha = .01$, we can use the above confidence interval to help make a decision and conclusion (only because this is a two-sided test). Since 0 is contained in this interval, then 0 is a reasonable value and hence we would not want to reject the null hypothesis that the mean difference is 0. Hence we conclude that there is insufficient evidence at the 1% significance level that there is a difference in the mean gas mileage using the clean and dirty air filters.

4. Consider the situation above, but now suppose only one simple random sample of 10 cars was selected. Each of these 10 cars was first driven after a clean air filter was installed, and then the same 10 cars were driven after a dirty air filter was installed. Now the data is paired because the two samples are dependent. If the same data exists, but is now listed to reflect the pairs, a paired t-test can be used to test H_0: $\mu_1 - \mu_2 = 0$ versus H_A: $\mu_1 - \mu_2 \neq 0$ at significance level $\alpha = .01$.

Car	1	2	3	4	5	6	7	8	9	10
Clean filter	19.0	22.0	24.0	24.5	25.0	25.0	25.5	26.0	28.0	31.0
Dirty filter	16.0	20.0	21.0	21.5	23.0	21.0	22.5	25.0	25.0	27.0
Difference	3.0	2.0	3.0	3.0	2.0	4.0	3.0	1.0	3.0	4.0

The mean of these 10 differences is $\overline{X}_d = 2.8$ and the standard deviation is $s_d = .9189$. Since the differences are fairly symmetric (close to normal) the sample size is large enough for the central limit theorem to apply and the paired t-test can be conducted.

$$t = \frac{\overline{X}_d - \mu_0}{s_d / \sqrt{n}} = \frac{2.8 - 0}{.9189 / \sqrt{10}} = \frac{2.8}{.2906} = 9.635$$

p-value = 2 P(t$_9$ $\geq$ 9.635). From the t-table, P(t$_9$ $\geq$ 9.635) < .0005, so p-value < .001.

Rejection region: with α = .01, α/2 = .005 so reject H$_0$ if |t$_{obs}$| $\geq$ 3.250.

p-value: Since p-value < .01 we reject the null hypothesis.

Rejection region: since t = 9.635 > 3.250, we reject the null hypothesis.

So there is sufficient evidence that the mean difference between cars using clean air filters and dirty air filters is different from 0.

5. An attempt was made to verify whether women are being discriminated against, as far as wages are concerned, in a certain industry. To study this claim, a court-appointed researcher obtained a simple random sample of 55 female employees with 8 or more years' experience and with a history of regular employment during that time. The mean wage per hour of this sample was $12.80, with a standard deviation of $0.90. The court-appointed researcher obtained an independent simple random sample of 72 male employees with 8 or more years' experience and with a history of regular employment during that time. The mean wage of this sample was $13.40 per hour, with a standard deviation of $1.10.

This data can be used to test whether the mean wage of all female workers with 8 or more years of experience and with a history of regular employment in the industry during that time is lower than the mean wage of all male workers with 8 or more years of experience and with a history of regular employment in the industry during that time. Defining μ_1 to be the mean wage for all female workers and μ_2 to be the mean wage for all male workers, the hypotheses to test are H$_0$: $\mu_1 = \mu_2$ versus alternative hypothesis H$_a$: $\mu_1 < \mu_2$. We have two large, _independent,_ simple random samples, and since the population standard deviations are not known the test statistic will follow a t distribution.

$$t = \frac{(\overline{X}_1 - \overline{X}_2) - \mu_o}{\sqrt{\frac{s_1^2}{n_1} + \frac{s_2^2}{n_2}}} = \frac{(12.80 - 13.40) - 0}{\sqrt{\frac{.90^2}{55} + \frac{1.10^2}{72}}} = \frac{-0.60}{.17757} = -3.379$$

The degrees of freedom is the smaller of 55 – 1 = 54 and 72 – 1 = 71, which is 54. In the t-table on page 340, df = 60 will be used.

Then the p-value is p-value = P(t$_{60}$ $\leq$ -3.379) = P(t$_{60}$ > 3.379). Therefore, .0005 < p-value < .001.

With such a small p-value the test is highly significant and we reject the null hypothesis. Therefore, there is sufficient evidence that the mean wage per hour of all female workers with 8 or more years of experience and with a history of regular employment in the industry during that time is lower than the mean wage per hour of their male counterparts.

TI-83/84 Calculator

To make inferences about the difference between two population means when two <u>independent</u> simple random samples of data are collected the following choices are made.

3:2-SampZTest – significance test for $\mu_1 - \mu_2$ when the population standard deviations σ_1 and σ_2 are known

4:2-SampTTest – significance test for $\mu_1 - \mu_2$ when the population standard deviations σ_1 and σ_2 are unknown

9:2-SampZInt – confidence interval for $\mu_1 - \mu_2$ when the population standard deviations σ_1 and σ_2 are known

0:2-SampTInt – confidence interval for $\mu_1 - \mu_2$ when the population standard deviations σ_1 and σ_2 are unknown

If the actual data exists, then the data can be entered into two lists and the **DATA** option chosen as your input method. In what follows, suppose the first sample of data is entered into list L1, and the second sample of data is entered into list L2. If you have the summary statistics (means, standard deviations and sample sizes) then the **STATS** input method can be chosen. Details for each follow.

1. To get a confidence interval for $\mu_1 - \mu_2$ when the population standard deviations σ_1 and σ_2 are known. Press **STAT**, use the right-arrow button to scroll over to **TESTS**, and use the down-arrow button to scroll down to **9:2-SampZInt** and then press **ENTER**. Select **DATA** as your input method. Then enter the values of the population standard deviations σ_1 and σ_2. Then give the lists that contain the data (for example L1 and L2) and set the **FREQ1** and **FREQ2** each to 1. Finally, next to **C-Level** give the confidence level, scroll down to **Calculate**, and press **ENTER**. To enter the summary statistics, select **STATS** as your input method. Then enter the values of the population standard deviations σ_1 and σ_2, the sample means and sample sizes $\overline{X}_1$, n_1, $\overline{X}_2$ and n_2, enter the confidence level next to **C-Level**, scroll down to **Calculate**, and press **ENTER**.

   Regarding the output, in addition to the confidence interval you also receive the sample means, the sample standard deviations, and the sample sizes.

2. For a significance test for $\mu_1 - \mu_2$ when the population standard deviations σ_1 and σ_2 are known. Press **STAT**, use the right-arrow button to scroll over to **TESTS**, and use the down-arrow button to scroll down to **3:2-SampZTest** and then press **ENTER**. Select **DATA** as your input method. Then enter the values of the population standard deviations σ_1 and σ_2. Next give the lists that contain the data (for example L1 and L2) and set the **FREQ1** and **FREQ2** each to 1. Then choose whether the test is a two-sided test, lower one-sided test, or upper one-sided test, scroll down to **Calculate**, and press **ENTER**. To enter the summary statistics, select **STATS** as your input method. Then enter the values of the population standard deviations σ_1 and σ_2, the sample means and sample sizes $\overline{X}_1$, n_1, $\overline{X}_2$ and n_2, choose whether the test is a two-sided test, lower one-sided test, or upper one-sided test, scroll down to **Calculate**, and press **ENTER**.

284

Regarding the output, you receive the value of the Z test statistic and the corresponding p-value. Additionally, you receive the sample means, the sample standard deviations, and the sample sizes.

3. To get a confidence interval for $\mu_1 - \mu_2$ when the population standard deviations σ_1 and σ_2 are unknown. Press **STAT**, use the right-arrow button to scroll over to **TESTS**, and use the down-arrow button to scroll down to **0:2-SampTInt** and then press **ENTER**. Select **DATA** as your input method. Then give the lists that contain the data (for example L1 and L2) and set the **FREQ1** and **FREQ2** each to 1. Next to **C-Level** give the confidence level, next to **Pooled** choose **No**, and then scroll down to **Calculate** and press **ENTER**. To enter the summary statistics, select **STATS** as your input method. Then enter the values of the sample means, sample standard deviations and sample sizes $\overline{X}_1$, Sx_1, n_1, $\overline{X}_2$, Sx_2 and n_2, enter the confidence level next to **C-Level**, next to **Pooled** choose **No**, scroll down to **Calculate**, and press **ENTER**.

Regarding the output, in addition to the confidence interval you also receive the calculated degrees of freedom, the sample means, the sample standard deviations, and the sample sizes. The degrees of freedom used by the calculator is usually different from the minimum of $n_1 - 1$ and $n_2 - 1$. However, the overall results are usually very similar to those calculated using the formula presented in this chapter.

4. For a significance test for $\mu_1 - \mu_2$ when the population standard deviations σ_1 and σ_2 are unknown. Press **STAT**, use the right-arrow button to scroll over to **TESTS**, and use the down-arrow button to scroll down to **4:2-SampTTest** and then press **ENTER**. Select **DATA** as your input method. Then give the lists that contain the data (for example L1 and L2) and set the **FREQ1** and **FREQ2** each to 1. Choose whether the test is a two-sided test, lower one-sided test, or upper one-sided test, next to **Pooled** choose **No**, and then scroll down to **Calculate**, and press **ENTER**. To enter the summary statistics, select **STATS** as your input method. Then enter the values of the sample means, sample standard deviations and sample sizes $\overline{X}_1$, Sx_1, n_1, $\overline{X}_2$, Sx_2 and n_2. Choose whether the test is a two-sided test, lower one-sided test, or upper one-sided test, next to **Pooled** choose **No**, scroll down to **Calculate**, and press **ENTER**.

Regarding the output, you receive the value of the t test statistic and the corresponding p-value, along with the degrees of freedom that are calculated. Additionally, you receive the sample means, the sample standard deviations, and the sample sizes.

If the data is dependent (paired), then begin by getting the differences between the pairs. Once the differences are determined, then **2: T-Test** can be used as described in Chapter IX. The steps for this procedure are repeated below. Recall that the "data" referenced below are the differences.

2: T-Test – regardless of whether you choose **DATA** or **STATS**, the value μ_0 is the hypothesized value in the null hypothesis, and you must also choose the appropriate sign in the alternative hypothesis ($\neq \mu_0$, $< \mu_0$, or $> \mu_0$). If you choose **DATA**, beside **LIST** you must give the list the data is in (for example, as described above it would be L1), and set the frequency (**Freq**) equal to 1. Move the cursor down to **Calculate** and press **ENTER**. The calculator gives you the value of the test statistic (t) and the p-value (p), and in addition you also get values of the sample mean ($\overline{X}$), the sample standard deviation (S_x), and the sample size (n). If you choose **STATS**, then in addition to the hypothesized mean and sign of the alternative hypothesis you must enter the sample mean $\overline{X}$, the sample standard deviation S_x and the sample size n, then move the cursor down to **Calculate** and press **ENTER**. Once again you get the values of the test statistic (t) and the p-value (p).

Practice Problems:

X.1.   A large city is served by two community college, Community College R and Community College T. For Community College R the mean grade point average (GPA) of all students is 2.85 with a standard deviation of 0.63. For Community College T the mean grade point average (GPA) of all students is 2.91 with a standard deviation of 0.58. A simple random sample of 37 students from Community College R is selected and an independent simple random sample of 42 students from Community College T is selected.

(a).   If appropriate, use this information to describe the sampling distribution of the difference in the sample mean GPA's, $\overline{X}_1 - \overline{X}_2$.

(b).   If appropriate, find the probability that the difference in the sample mean GPA's, $\overline{X}_1 - \overline{X}_2$, is greater than 0.

X. 2.   Two large book publishers are competing to sell their introductory level books at a large college. For the first book company, the mean cost for all of its introductory level books is $121.25 with a standard deviation of $32.89. For the second book company, the mean cost for all of its introductory level books is $118.32 with a standard deviation of $38.15. A simple random sample of 43 introductory level books from the first book company is selected and an independent simple random sample of 50 introductory level books from the second book company is selected.

(a).   If appropriate, use this information to describe the sampling distribution of the difference in the sample mean book costs, $\overline{X}_1 - \overline{X}_2$.

(b).   If appropriate, find the probability that the difference in the sample mean book costs, $\overline{X}_1 - \overline{X}_2$, is between $5 and $10.

X. 3.   A political scientist believes that the mean age of all voters in Florida is higher than the mean age of all voters in the rest of the country. To test this claim, a simple random sample of 29 Florida voters was selected and the mean age of this sample was 47.9 years. A simple random sample of 267 voters from the other 49 states was selected, and the mean age of this sample was 47.5 years. It is known that the distribution of all voting age Americans is only slightly skewed to the right, that the standard deviation of all voting age residents of Florida is 11.4 years, and that the standard deviation of all voting age residents in the rest of the country is 12.7 years. If appropriate, use this data to test at significance level $\alpha = .05$ to determine if the mean age of all voters in Florida is higher than the mean age of all voters in the rest of the country.

X. 4.   A study of iron deficiency in infants compared samples of infants whose mothers chose different ways of feeding them. One group contained breast-fed infants. The children in another group were fed a standard baby formula without any iron supplements. Here are the summary results on blood hemoglobin levels at 12 months of age.

| Breast-fed | n = 23 | $\overline{X}$ = 13.3 | s = 1.7 |
| Formula | n = 19 | $\overline{X}$ = 12.4 | s = 1.8 |

(a).   Is this a controlled experiment? Explain why or why not and how this affects the conclusions that can be drawn from the study.

(b).   Is there significant evidence that the mean hemoglobin level is different among breast-fed infants than formula infants? If appropriate, conduct a test and state a conclusion.

(c).   If appropriate, calculate and interpret a 95% confidence interval for the mean difference in hemoglobin level between the two populations of infants.

X. 5.   A study was conducted to determine whether teacher expectation can improve student performance. The experimental group involves all students in classes in which the teachers were told that their students would show large IQ gains during the test semester. A simple random sample of 100 students was selected from this experimental group, and the mean and standard deviation of the IQ gains for this sample of 100 students are 16.5 and 14.2, respectively. The control group involves all students in classes in which the teachers were told nothing regarding improved student performance. A simple random sample of 100 students was selected from the control group, and the mean and standard deviation of the IQ gains for this sample of 100 students are 7.0 and 13.1, respectively.

(a).   If appropriate, calculate and interpret a 90% confidence interval for the difference in the mean IQ gain for all students in the experimental group and the mean IQ gain for all students in the control group.

(b).   Is the difference between the mean IQ gain of all students in the experimental group and the mean IQ gain of all students in the control group in the confidence interval above? Explain.

X. 6. Visitors to Disney's Magic Kingdom are interested in comparing the mean wait time to ride Space Mountain using the regular stand-by line or using FASTPASS. Disney selected a simple random sample of 73 people as they first stepped into the stand-by line to get onto Space Mountain and determined how long it took for each of these people to get on the ride. The mean and standard deviation of the wait times of this sample were 84 minutes and 17 minutes, respectively. Disney then selected an independent simple random sample of 41 people who were in the FASTPASS line. The mean wait time for this sample was 9.5 minutes, with a standard deviation of 3 minutes. If appropriate, use this information to calculate and interpret a 95% confidence interval for the difference in the mean wait times of stand-by line visitors and FASTPASS line visitors waiting to get on Space Mountain.

X. 7. A traffic safety report states that the mean number of traffic violations (speeding, driving under the influence of alcohol, reckless driving, etc) for men is similar to the mean number of traffic violations for women. To test this hypothesis versus the alternative that the mean number of traffic violations for men and women are not the same, a researcher selected a simple random sample of 61 men and an independent simple random sample of 65 women. In the sample of 61 men, the mean number of traffic violations per man was 8.4 with a standard deviation of 3.9. In the sample of 65 women, the mean number of traffic violations per woman was 6.8 with a standard deviation of 3.7. If appropriate, use this information to test at significance level $\alpha = .05$ to determine if the mean number of traffic violations for men and women are different.

X. 8. Nestled in the valleyed northwestern section of St. Croix, is the Laurence Rockefeller built, Robert Trent Jones-designed Carambola Golf Course. Since opening thirty years ago, the Carambola has been awarded a gold medal by GOLF magazine for being one of the finest golf resorts in the world and has been given a four-star rating by Golf Digest. In St. Thomas, the Tom Fazio-designed Mahogany Run Golf Course overlooks the Atlantic Ocean with a view of the neighboring British Virgin Islands beyond. Both golf courses are 18-hole, par 70 courses, and of interest is to estimate the difference in the mean number of strokes that golfers take to complete the courses. A simple random sample of 70 golfers at Carambola Golf Course had a mean of 79.4 shots to complete the course, with a standard deviation of 7.2 shots. An independent simple random sample of 41 golfers at the Mahogany Run Golf Course had a mean of 83.2 shots to complete the course, with a standard deviation of 6.8 shots. If appropriate, use this data to calculate and interpret a 95% confidence interval for the difference in the mean number of shots for all golfers to complete the Carambola Golf Course and the mean number of shots for all golfers to complete the Mahogany Run Golf Course.

X. 9. A study was commissioned to compare the typical credit card debt for American male adults and American female adults. The study originated following claims that the mean credit card debt for American female adults is greater than the mean credit card debt for American male adults. The study involved selecting a simple random sample of 66 American adult males with credit cards. The mean credit card debt for this sample of males was $3,254, with a standard deviation of $893. An independent simple random sample of 41

American female adults with credit cards was also selected. The mean credit card debt for this sample of females was $3,667, with a standard deviation of $917. If appropriate, use this data to test at significance level $\alpha = .05$ the claim that the mean credit card debt for all American female adults is greater than the mean credit card debt for all American male adults.

X. 10. At Virginia Commonwealth University, STAT 208 is designed for students who likely will take no further statistics or quantitative courses once the course is completed (for example, students majoring in history or English). STAT 210 is designed for students who likely will take an additional statistics or quantitative course once the course is completed (for example, students majoring in biology or psychology). Of interest is to estimate the difference in the mean verbal SAT scores for all students taking STAT 208 and for all students taking STAT 210. A simple random sample of 41 students taking STAT 208 is selected, and the mean verbal SAT score for this sample of students is 515 with a standard deviation of 33. An independent simple random sample of 77 students taking STAT 210 is selected, and the mean verbal SAT score for this sample of students is 506 with a standard deviation of 28.

(a). If appropriate, use this data to calculate and interpret a 90% confidence interval for the difference in the mean verbal SAT scores for all students taking STAT 208 and for all students taking STAT 210.

(b). Administrators want to determine if there is a difference between the mean verbal SAT score for all students taking STAT 208 and the mean verbal SAT score for all students taking STAT 210. State the hypotheses that they want to test, and if appropriate use the confidence interval in part (a) to test these hypotheses at level $\alpha = .10$.

X. 11. A study was sponsored to determine if the mean retirement age of white-collar workers is lower than the mean retirement age of blue-collar workers. A simple random sample of 30 retired white-collar workers was selected and the mean retirement age of these 30 people was 57.2 years, with a standard deviation of 4.9 years. An independent simple random sample of 34 blue-collared workers was selected, and the mean retirement age of these 34 people was 61.4 years, with a standard deviation of 4.6 years. If appropriate, use this information to test at level $\alpha = .05$ to determine if the mean retirement age of white-collar workers is lower than the mean retirement age of blue-collar workers.

X.12. On Wednesday, April 12, 2006, both the University of Virginia (UVA) and Virginia Commonwealth University (VCU) signed agreements with the Virginia Community College system to guarantee admission to gifted graduates of the state's community colleges. Of interest is to test to determine if the mean grade point average (CPA) of graduating community college students who will be attending UVA is different from the mean grade point average (CPA) of graduating community college students who will be attending VCU. In a simple random sample of 11 community college graduates who will be attending UVA, the mean GPA is 3.41 with a standard deviation of 0.53. In an independent simple random sample of 9 community college graduates who will be attending VCU, the mean CPA is 3.17 with a standard deviation of 0.59. State the hypotheses of interest, and if appropriate, use this data to test these hypotheses at significance level a = .10.

X. 13. Makers of generic drugs must show that they do not differ much from the "name" drugs that they are equivalent to. One characteristic in which the generic and "name" drugs should be similar is their absorption in the blood. A simple random sample of 20 healthy nonsmoking males was selected. Each person was given each drug, with a period of time in between so that the first drug had disappeared from the blood before the second drug was given. To avoid bias, 10 of the 20 males was administered the generic drug first and the other 10 were administered the "name" drug first. The data below give the absorption extent for the two drugs. The absorption for the drug that was taken first is in bold.

Subject	"Name" drug	Generic drug	Subject	"Name" drug	Generic drug
1	**4108**	1755	11	2344	**2738**
2	2526	**1138**	12	**1864**	2302
3	2779	**1613**	13	1022	**1284**
4	**3852**	2254	14	2256	**3052**
5	**1833**	1310	15	938	**1287**
6	2463	**2120**	16	1339	**1930**
7	**2059**	1851	17	**1262**	1964
8	**1709**	1878	18	**1438**	2549
9	**1829**	1682	19	1735	**3340**
10	2594	**2613**	20	**1020**	3050

(a). What is the population of interest in this study? Might this change once the characteristics of the sample are known?

(b). This is a matched-pairs experiment. Would you consider this a controlled experiment or an observational study? What is the treatment? What is the response?

(c). Using the data above, if appropriate, conduct a paired t-test at significance level α = .10 to determine if the mean absorption for the two drugs is different.

X. 14. What type of batteries, Duracell or Energizer, have the longest life expectancy in TI-83 calculators? To answer this question, a simple random sample of 40 TI-83 calculators were acquired. Each calculator was hooked to a machine that simulated calculator use, and in each calculator a set of Duracell batteries was used and a set of Energizer batteries was used. The order of the battery use was randomized. For each calculator the number of simulated days of battery use was determined using each type of batteries, and the difference between the Duracell and Energizer batteries determined. A negative difference implies that the Energizer batteries lasted longer and a positive difference implies that the Duracell batteries lasted longer. The mean difference for this sample of 40 calculators was 5.8 days, with a standard deviation of 24.6 days. If appropriate, use this data to test at significance level $\alpha = .05$ to determine if the mean number of days using Duracell batteries and the mean number of days using Energizer batteries are different.

Practice Problem Solutions

I.1. Population – all residents of the city

Parameter – percentage of all city residents who favor spending the money necessary to finance the renovation of the city's sports arena.

Sample – a random sample of 250 city residents.

Statistic – percentage of the 250 sampled residents who favor spending the money necessary to finance the renovation of the city's sports arena.

Inference – the percentage in the sample of 250 residents can be used to estimate the percentage of all city residents who favor spending the money necessary to finance the renovation of the city's sports arena.

I.2. (a). qualitative variable – can name illness
    (b). continuous quantitative variable – all rates are continuous
    (c). discrete quantitative variable – can count number of pets
    (d). continuous quantitative variable – measurable quantity
    (e). qualitative variable – can state status
    (f). continuous quantitative variable – measure the temperature

I.3. The population consists of the 318 church congregation members. Any characteristic of all 318 church congregation members is a parameter. The sample consists of the 30 "roof committee" members. Any numerical characteristic of this sample is a statistic.

    (a). Statistic – sample size
    (b). Statistic – sample percentage
    (c). Parameter – population mean
    (d). Statistic – sample mean
    (e). Parameter – population size
    (f). Parameter – population total contribution
    (g). Discrete quantitative variable – countable number
    (h). Qualitative variable – can name Sunday school class
    (i). Continuous quantitative variable – all percentages are continuous
    (j). Continuous quantitative variable – all averages are continuous
    (k). Discrete quantitative variable – countable number

I.4. (a). σ – standard deviation of $15.00 belongs to the population
    (b). s – standard deviation of the sample
    (c). s – standard deviation of the sample
    (d). σ – standard deviation of the all scores, belongs to the population

I.5. The population consists of the 535 members of Congress. Any characteristic of all 435 Congress members is a parameter. The sample consists of the 20 members randomly selected. Any numerical characteristic of this sample is a statistic.

    (a). Statistic – sample size
    (b). Parameter – population size
    (c). Parameter – population percentage in attendance
    (d). Statistic – sample percentage that gave a positive rating
    (e). Statistic – number of Democrats in the sample
    (f). Statistic – mean age of the sample
    (g). Continuous quantitative variable – all percentages are continuous
    (h). Qualitative variable – can name the state from which a Congress person was elected
    (i). Discrete quantitative variable – can count number of Democrats attending each meeting

II.1. This is a volunteer response sample - only those with strong enough opinions to spend the time and 50 cents to make the call are going to respond to the advertisement.

II.2. Number the managers from 01 (Althouse) to 28 (Yuan). In the Table of Random Digits, line 139, we choose 6 two-digit numbers between 01 and 28. They are: 40, 71, 99, **16**, 46, 91, 92, **11**, 86, 29, 38, **14**, **08**, 34, 73, 42, 55, 97, **10**, **13**. These numbers correspond to 16 = Mitchell, 11 = Hylton, 14 = Mendoza, 08 = Green, 10 = Haroon, and 13 = Jean-Richard.

II.3. The accounts receivable are broken up into three groups (strata). 100 out of the 5000 or 2% are in amounts over $50,000, so we need to randomly sample 100(.02) = 2 such large accounts. 500 out of the 5000 or 10% are in amounts between $1,000 and $50,000, so we need to randomly 100(.10) = 10 such midsize accounts. Finally, 4400 out of the 5000 or 88% are in amounts under $1,000, so we need to randomly sample 100(.88) = 88 such small accounts.

Label the 100 large accounts from 01 to 00 (with 00 representing 100). Beginning at line 115, the two randomly chosen large accounts are 08 and 70.

Label the 500 midsize accounts from 001 to 500. Beginning at line 125, the first 5 three-digit numbers between 001 and 500 are 189, 251, 085, 465, and 036.

Label the 4400 small accounts from 0001 to 4400. Beginning at line 135, the first 5 four-digit numbers between 0001 and 4400 are 4150, 1181, 3457, 0475, and 4328.

II.4. (a). Haphazard sample because the selection was done by convenience instead of randomization.
(b). Stratified random sample because a sample was chosen from each continent.
(c). Simple random sample because each observation was listed in alphabetical order and a random sample was then selected.

II.5. (a). Haphazard sample because the selection was done by convenience instead of randomization.
(b). Stratified random sample because even though the people were divided into two groups, a random sample was taken from each.
(c). Simple random sample because each person had an equal opportunity to be chosen and they were randomly selected by the numbered tickets.

II.6. (a). Simple random sample because each person had an equal opportunity to be chosen and they were randomly selected by their V-number.
(b). Haphazard sample because no randomization was used. Not everyone attended the VCU Homecoming Blood Drive therefore the survey created undercoverage.
(c). Stratified random sample because a sample was taken from each list.

II.7. (a). The experimental units are the package liners.
(b). The treatment factor is the heat applied (temperature), at levels 250, 275, 300, and 325 degrees Fahrenheit.
(c). The response variable is the force required to open the package.
(d). With 4 different sealing temperatures, they can make a comparison. So there must be a random assignment of the pairs of package liners to the four temperatures, thus imposing the treatments.

II.8. (a). If the drug is only administered to one group then there is nothing to which the results can be compared. Hence we cannot determine if the new pain relief medication really is beneficial.
(b). Randomly assign 20 patients to each of three groups: Group 1: the placebo group; Group 2: the aspirin group; Group 3: the new medication group. After treating the patients in each group, ask them how much pain they feel, and then compare the mean pain relief experienced by each group.
(c). No. The patients should not be told which drug they are using, because if they know which group they are in then this could affect their response. The experiment should be blind. The experiment should also be double-blind to prevent the person administering the medication from influencing the subjects into giving responses that support the conclusion.

II.9. (a). For each of the 40 men record their blood pressure. Then randomly divide them into two groups. Group 1 receives the calcium supplement, Group 2 receives the placebo. After a sufficient amount of time has passed, measure the blood pressure again and observe any change. We can then compare the mean blood pressure change in the two groups.

(b). Number the individuals for 01 to 40 down the columns and in the Table of Random Digits, line 119, read the first 20 two-digit numbers between 01 and 40. This is Group 1, which becomes 01 = Alomar, 06 = Clemente, 12 = Farouk, 38 = Underwood, (continuing on line 120) 33 = Rosen, 40 = Zhang, 23 = Krushchev, 30 = Ogle, 34 = Solomon, 20 = Imrani, 19 = Hruska, 15 = Green, (continuing on line 121) 03 = Bennett, 18 = Howard, 32 = Rodriguez, 16 = Guillen, (continuing on line 122) 09 = Denman, 27 = Marsden, 02 = Asihiro, and 29 = O'Brian. The rest are Group 2.

II.10. (a). Treatment is the type of fertilizer and the response is the number of tomatoes produced per plot. This is a controlled experiment because fertilizers (treatments) are randomly assigned to the plots and the yields of tomatoes are compared.

(b). Treatment is the university that the student attended and the response is the score on the 40-question mathematics test. This is an observational study because students determined which university they attended and hence no treatment was imposed by the experimenters.

(c). Treatment is the party preference of the people and the responses are the answers given to the questions regarding support of the abortion law. This is an observational study because the analysts cannot control to which group the people (experimental units) are in – they observe them as they are. No treatment is applied.

(d). Treatment is the method for treating poison ivy and the response is the number of days until the poison ivy is cleared up. This is a controlled experiment because the physicians decided which of the three methods of treating poison ivy each person received, and a comparison was made.

(e). Treatment is the party who wrote the statement that is being read, either Republican or Democratic; response is the opinion of the citizen regarding the confirmation of Judge Alito. This is a controlled experiment because the citizens without prior opinion are randomly assigned to read one of the two statements (imposition of the treatment) and then the results are compared.

(f). Treatment is the method for preparing burritos and response is the rating of the quality of the burrito. This is a controlled experiment because which burrito the customer receives is determined randomly. Hence a treatment is imposed and the results of the questionnaire compared.

(g). Treatment is a statistics preparation short course that the student participates in and the response is the grade at the end of the course. This is a controlled experiment because students are randomly assigned to the 3 groups, implying a treatment is imposed, and grades were compared at the end.

II.11. This would generate a nonresponse bias if the customers who refuse to respond are different from those who do respond.

III.1. There is one possible outlier (243). The center is between 150 and 180. The distribution is bimodal and for the most part relatively symmetrical. The data ranges from 96 to 243.

09	6
10	5
11	4,8
12	3,9,1,3,2
13	2,4,7
14	3,1
15	3
16	7
17	9,3,8
18	7,3,9,4
19	8,2,5,3,0
20	7,1,4
21	8
22	1,5
23	
24	3

where 20|7 = 207 pounds

III.2. The back-to-back stem-and-leaf plot is to the right. The Ruth distribution is fairly symmetric and 60 does not appear to be an outlier. For McGwire the distribution has two long tails, with the record 70 home runs in 1998 probably not being an outlier but the 9 home runs in 1993 and 1994 possibly being outliers. Babe Ruth is the more consistent home run hitter.

Ruth		McGwire
	0	9, 9
	1	
5, 2	2	2
5, 4	3	2, 2, 3, 9, 9
1, 6, 7, 6, 9, 6, 1	4	9, 2
4, 9, 4	5	2, 8
0	6	5
	7	0 where 7 | 0 = 70

III.3. (a). Treatment = length of commercial; response = responses to short list of questions. The data range from 1.3 to 5.8. An extended stem-and-lead plot with stems = ones and leaves = tenths is preferred.
(c). The data range is skewed to the left with an outlier of 1.3. The center is in the 4.0's, and the data ranges from 1.3 to 5.8.

1	3
1	
2	0 where 1 | 3 = 13
2	6, 9, 7
3	0, 3, 1
3	7, 5, 7, 9
4	2, 0, 4, 4
4	8, 6, 9, 6
5	0, 3, 0, 2, 1, 4, 3, 0
5	8, 5

III.4. The data range from 23 to 98. A standard stem-and-leaf plot with stems = tens and leaves = ones is appropriate.

The distribution is slightly skewed to the right due to the outlier of 98. The data ranges from 23 to 98, with a center around 50.

2	3
3	0,5,3,6,1,7,9
4	4,1,8,4,3,7,0,6,7
5	1,6,4,0,3,4,9
6	3,7,0,4,5,6
7	2,6
8	
9	8 where 7 | 2 = 72

III.5. The data ranges from 0.32 to 5.23. An extended stem-and-leaf plot is preferred.

The distribution is skewed to the right due to the outlier of 5.23. Without the outlier the distribution is fairly symmetric. The center is around 2, and the data ranges from 0.32 to 5.23.

0	32,45
0	99,71,82
1	23,27,08,10
1	99,54,63,72,81,88
2	24,08,12,24
2	76,83,89
3	21,42
3	78
4	
4	
5	
5	23 where 2 | 76 = 2.76

III.6. The stem-and-leaf plot is to the right. The distribution is skewed to the right, with a center between 250 and 300. The data ranges from 172 to 523 and there are no obvious outliers.

1	
1	98,72,98,93
2	14,13,33,38,10,41,10,38
2	95,52,52,54,50,90
3	07,40,17,29
3	52,52,50
4	
4	62,87
5	23,19,23 where 5 | 23 = 523

III.7. The distribution is skewed to the right due to the outlier of 48. The data ranges from 4 to 48, with a center between 10 and 20.

```
0 | 4, 4
0 | 9, 9, 9, 5, 6, 6, 5, 6, 9, 6
1 | 1, 3, 2, 0, 4, 4, 3
1 | 8, 6, 6, 6, 6, 8
2 | 0, 2, 4,
2 | 5
3 |
3 |
4 |
4 | 8                     where 4 | 8 = 48
```

III.8. (1) $n = 72$ $\sqrt{72} = 8.485$ Use 9 intervals

(2) Range = 598 – 43 = 555

(3) Class width = $\dfrac{555}{9} = 61.666$ Use 60——

(4) Multiples of 60 are: 0, 60, 120,...
The smallest observation is 43
The lower limit of first interval is 0

(5-7)

Interval	Frequency	Relative Frequency
0 – 60	7	7/72 * 100 = 9.72%
60 – 120	37	51.39%
120 – 180	15	20.83%
180 – 240	5	6.94%
240 – 300	2	2.78%
300 – 360	1	1.39%
360 – 420	2	2.78%
420 – 480	0	0%
480 – 540	2	2.78%
540 – 600	1	1.39%
	72	100%

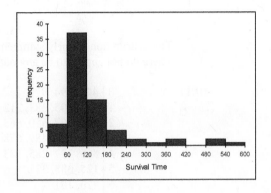

The distribution is highly skewed to the right. Due to the skewness, the center is close to 200. From the histogram we determine that the data ranges from 0 to 600.

III.9 (1) $n = 25$ $\sqrt{25} = 5$ Use 5 intervals

(2) Range = 92 - 14 = 78

(3) Class width = 78/5 = 15.6   Use 16

(4) Multiples of 16 are: 0, 16, 32, 48, 64, 80, …
The smallest observation is 14
The lower limit of first interval is 0

(5-7)

Interval	Frequency	Relative Frequency
0 – 16	1	1/25 * 100 = 4.00%
16 – 32	12	48.00%
32 – 48	9	36.00%
48 – 64	2	8.00%
64 – 80	0	0%
80 – 96	1	4.00%
	35	100%

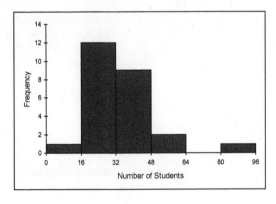

The distribution is skewed to the right, with a center in the interval 16-32 and a spread from 14 to 92. There is one outlier at 92.

III.10. (1) $n = 35$ $\sqrt{35} = 5.916$ Use 6 intervals

(2)   Range = 65 - 20 = 45

(3)   Class width = $\dfrac{45}{6} = 7.5$ Use 8

(4)   Multiples of 8 are: 0, 8, 16, 24, 32, 40, …
The smallest observation is 20
The lower limit of first interval is 16

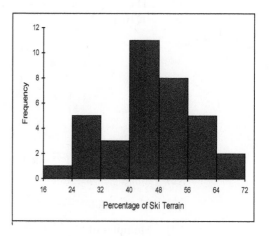

(5-7) Interval	Frequency	Relative Frequency
16 – 24	1	1/35 * 100 = 2.86%
24 – 32	5	14.29%
32 – 40	3	8.57%
40 – 48	11	31.43%
48 – 56	8	22.86%
56 – 64	5	14.29%
64 – 72	2	5.71%
	35	100%

The distribution is fairly symmetrical, with a center in the 40's and a spread from 16 to 72.
There do not appear to be any outliers.

III.11

```
0 | 442, 794, 979
1 | 689, 405, 683, 212, 790, 129, 490, 945
2 | 790, 107, 650, 665, 100, 970, 354, 053, 238, 857
3 | 106, 560, 489, 678, 456, 575, 875, 344
4 | 895, 337, 285, 103
5 | 125, 688, 337
6 | 326, 101
7 | 327
8 | 002                     where 5 | 688 = 5688
```

The distribution is fairly skewed to the right, with a center of 2547.5. The data ranges from 442 to 8002 with no obvious outliers.

III.12

```
10 | 25,
10 | 66, 94, 85, 84, 92
11 | 24, 33, 12, 36, 45, 24
11 | 76, 62, 53, 55, 54
12 | 12, 49, 12,
12 | 68, 55
13 | 26
13 | 62
14 |
14 | 99                     where 12 | 68 = 12.68
```

The distribution is fairly skewed to the right, with a center of 11.53. The data ranges from 10.25 to 14.99 with an outlier at 14.99.

III.13 (a).

0	5225
1	6354, 2682, 5761, 0884, 3833, 2046, 4076, 9984
2	0859, 6677, 2190, 6286
3	1818, 6934, 4067, 6997
4	2695, 5899, 0293, 9303
5	5284, 7994
6	2495, 8414, 5794, 3280
7	0971, 4910
8	
9	4208 where 9	4208 = 94,208

(b). 1. $\sqrt{30}$ = 5.48 implies use 6 intervals (if they use 5 that is ok)
   2. Range = 94,208 – 5,225 = 88,983

   3. Class width = $\dfrac{\text{range}}{\text{\# intervals}}$ = $\dfrac{88,983}{6}$ = 14,831
   Rounding up, use an equal class width of 15,000.
   4. Multiples of 15,000 are 0, 15,000, 30,000, 45,000, …
   The smallest observation is 5,225, so we chose the lower
   limit of the first interval to be 0.

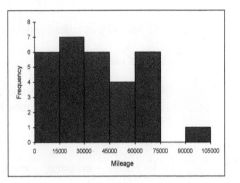

Interval	Frequency	Relative Frequency
0 – 15,000	6	6/30 * 100 = 20.0%
15,000 – 30,000	7	23.3%
30,000 – 45,000	6	20.0%
45,000 – 60,000	4	13.3%
60,000 – 75,000	6	20.0%
75,000 – 90,000	0	0%
90,000 – 105,000	1	3.3%
	30	99.9%

(c). The distribution is slightly skewed to the right, with a center between 30,000 – 40,000 (mean = 38,274, median = 35,501). The data ranges from 5,225 to 94,208 (or 0 to 105,000 if looking at the histogram). The vehicle with mileage of 94,208 is an outlier.

IV.1. (a). $\overline{X}$ = $\dfrac{154+109+137+...+129+200+148}{18}$ = $\dfrac{2539}{18}$ = 141.06

(b). $\overline{X}$ = $\dfrac{154+109+137+...+129+148}{17}$ = $\dfrac{2339}{17}$ = 137.59
Removing the large outlier decreases the mean by 3.5 points.

(c). Ordered data: 101, 103, 109, 115, 126, 126, 129, 137, *137*, **140**, 148, 152, 154, 154, 165, 165, 178, 200

n = 18, so median location = (n + 1)/2 = 19/2 = 9.5
So the median is (137 + 140)/2 = 138.5

When the outlier of 200 is removed, n = 17 so median location = (n + 1)/2 = 18/2 = 9
So the median is 137, only a 1.5 decrease. The median is more resistant than the mean.

IV.2. (a). The median would remain 38 because the two newly added numbers, 30 and 43, come before and after the median, respectively, when you order the numbers from smallest to largest. Therefore, 38 would still remain the middle number, or the median.

(b). n = 7 students: $\overline{X} = \dfrac{\sum x}{n} = 38$ minutes, therefore $\sum x = 38\,(7) = 266$

n = 9 students: $\overline{X} = \dfrac{\sum x}{n} = \dfrac{266 + 30 + 43}{9} = 37.67$ minutes

IV. 3. Measure of central location resistant to outliers = median

To calculate the <u>median</u>:

a. Order numbers from smallest to largest:

500, 640, 650, 685, **700**, 720, 725, 750, **775, 800**, 825, 850, 900, **950**, 1000, 1125, 1200, 1800

b. Determine median location:

(n +1)/2= (18 +1)/2= 9.5; Median= (775 + 800)/2 = 787.5

Measure of spread resistant to outliers = IQR

To calculate <u>IQR</u>:

Q_1 = median of the nine smallest numbers = 700
Q_3 = median of the nine largest numbers = 950

IQR= Q_3 - Q_1 = 950 – 700 = 250

IV.4. Range = maximum – minimum = 44 – 24 = 20

Mean= $\overline{X} = \dfrac{37+28+36+33+37+43+41+28+24+44+27+24}{12} = 33.5$

Standard Deviation:

x	x - $\overline{X}$	$(x - \overline{X})^2$
37	37 - 33.5 = 3.5	$(3.5)^2 = 12.25$
28	28 - 33.5 = -5.5	$(-5.5)^2 = 30.25$
36	36 - 33.5 = 2.5	$(2.5)^2 = 6.25$
33	33 - 33.5 = -0.5	$(-.5)^2 = 0.25$
37	37 - 33.5 = 3.5	$(3.5)^2 = 12.25$
43	43 - 33.5 = 9.5	$(9.5)^2 = 90.25$
41	41 - 33.5 = 7.5	$(7.5)^2 = 56.25$
28	28 - 33.5 = -5.5	$(-5.5)^2 = 30.25$
24	24 - 33.5 = -9.5	$(-9.5)^2 = 90.25$
44	44 - 33.5 = 10.5	$(10.5)^2 = 110.25$
27	27 - 33.5 = -6.5	$(-6.5)^2 = 42.25$
24	24 - 33.5 = -9.5	$(-9.5)^2 = 90.25$

$\dfrac{\sum\limits_{i=1}^{n}(x_i - \overline{x})^2}{n-1} = \dfrac{12.25 + 30.25 + 6.25 + \ldots + 42.25 + 90.25}{12 - 1} = \dfrac{571}{11} = 51.9091$

Standard deviation = s = $\sqrt{\dfrac{\sum\limits_{i=1}^{n}(x_i - \overline{x})^2}{n-1}} = \sqrt{51.9091} = 7.2048$

For the IQR, first we order the data: 24, 24, **27, 28**, 28, **33, 36**, 37, **37, 41**, 43, 44

n = 12, so median location = (12 + 1)/2 = 6.5
Then the median = (33 + 36)/2 = 34.5

Q_1 = median of the six smallest observations = (27 + 28)/2 = 27.5
Q_3 = median of the six largest observations = (37 + 41)/2 = 39.
So IQR = 39 – 27.5 = 11.5

The standard deviation and IQR measure spread around a central value and both are in the units of the original data. Since there are no outliers, either would be a reasonable measure of dispersion for this data. Most often the standard deviation would be reported.

IV.5. The following extended stem-and-leaf plot graphically displays the distribution. It could be replaced by a boxplot or histogram.

```
1 •   |
1 *   | 8
2 •   | 4
2 *   | 8, 7
3 •   | 1, 2
3 *   | 7, 7, 9. 5
4 •   | 1, 2, 0
4 *   |
5 •   | 4
5 *   | 5, 8, 5, 6
6 •   | 2
6 *   |                        where 2 | 4 = 24 sit-ups
```

n = 19, so median location = (19+1)/2 = 10. Hence the median is 39.
Q_1 = median of the nine smallest observations = 31
Q_3 = median of the nine largest observations = 55
So the interquartile range is 55 – 31 = 24.

The mean and standard deviation are: $\overline{X}$ = 40.5789   s = 12.803
With the distribution being both bimodal and skewed left, the distribution is difficult to describe. The mean is slightly larger than the median, reflecting the skewness of the distribution, but there are no outliers in the distribution. The data ranges from 18 to 62, and the large IQR results because of the bimodal distribution.

IV.6. The following extended stem-and-leaf plot graphically displays the distribution.

(a)
```
00|  7
01|
02|
03|  9
04|  2
05|  2
06|  4,9
07|  0,9
08|  7
09|  0,4,6        where 09 | 0 = 90
10|  0,5
```

The distribution is skewed to the left. The center is at approx. 70. There is an outlier at 7. The data ranges from 7 to 105.

(b). The mean and median are: $\overline{X} = 71$ M= 74.5

(c). Range: maximum – minimum= 105 –7 = 98

Standard Deviation: s = 28.02

IQR: $Q_3 - Q_1 =$ 94 – 52 = 42

Since the distribution is skewed to the left, the IQR is the preferred measurement of spread – it is resistant to the outlier value of 7.

IV.7. The distribution is skewed to the right due to the outlier value of approximately 148. Even without the outlier there is still a slight skew to the right. The data ranges from 30 to 148, and the interquartile range is 88 – 58 = 30. The median is approximately 67.

IV.8. The distribution is skewed to the right due to the outlier values of 87 and 97. Without the outliers the distribution is fairly symmetric. The median is 57, with an interquartile range of 66 – 52 = 14. The data ranges from 38 to 97.

IV.9. Ruth's ordered home run totals: 22 25 34 **35** 41 41 46 **46** 46 47 49 **54** 54 59 60

$$\frac{n+1}{2} = \frac{15+1}{2} = 8$$

The median is the 8th ordered observation = 46

Q_1 = median of the seven smallest observations = 35

Q_3 = median of the seven largest observations = 54

Five number summary: Min = 22 Q_1 = 35 M = 46 Q_3 = 54 Max = 60

IQR = 54 – 35 = 19

Lower Fence = Q_1 - 1.5 IQR = 35 - 1.5 (19) = 6.5

Upper Fence = Q_3 + 1.5 IQR = 54 + 1.5 (19) = 82.5

There are no observations less than 6.5 and no observations greater than 82.5, so there are no outliers.

Lower Adjacent Value = Smallest remaining observation = 22

Upper Adjacent Value = Largest remaining observation = 60

Maris's ordered home runs: 8 13 **14** 16 **23** **26** 28 **33** 39 61

$$\frac{n+1}{2} = \frac{10+1}{2} = 5.5$$

The median is the average of the 5th and 6th ordered observations = (23 + 26)/2 = 24.5

Q_1 = median of the five smallest observations = 14

Q_3 = median of the five largest observations = 33

Five number summary: Min = 8 Q_1 = 14 M = 24.5 Q_3 = 33 Max = 61

IQR = 33 - 14 = 19

Lower Fence = Q_1 - 1.5 IQR = 14 - 1.5 (19) = -14.5

Upper Fence = Q_3 + 1.5 IQR = 33 + 1.5 (19) = 61.5

There are no observations less than –14.5 and no observations greater than 61.5, so there are no outliers.

Lower Adjacent Value = Smallest remaining observation = 8

Upper Adjacent Value = Largest remaining observation = 61

McGwire's ordered home runs: 9 9 22 **32** 32 33 **39** 39 42 49 **52** 58 65 70

$$\frac{n+1}{2} = \frac{14+1}{2} = 7.5$$

The median is the average of the 7th and 8th ordered observations = (39+39)/2 = 39

Q_1 = median of the seven smallest observations = 32

Q_3 = median of the seven largest observations = 52

Five number summary: Min = 9 Q1 = 32 M = 39 Q_3 = 52 Max = 70

IQR = 52 – 32 = 20
Lower Fence = Q_1 - 1.5 IQR = 32 - 1.5 (20) = 2
Upper Fence = Q_3 + 1.5 IQR = 52 + 1.5 (20) = 82
There are no observations less than 2 and no observations greater than 82, so there are no outliers.
Lower Adjacent Value = Smallest remaining observation = 9
Upper Adjacent Value = Largest remaining observation = 70

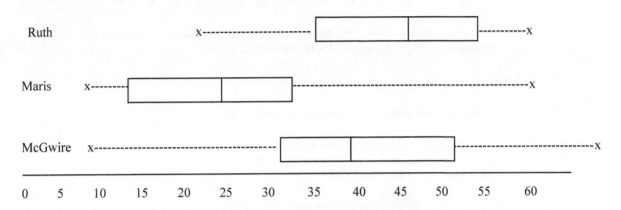

There are no outliers in any of the three distributions. Clearly McGwire has the most variability in his home run totals (highest IQR and range). However, Ruth appeared to be the most consistent home run hitter, possessing the highest median. While the value was not an outlier, it is clear that Maris's 61 home runs in 1961 is much more unusual from him than was Ruth's former record of 60 or McGwire's 70.

IV.10. Ordered data:
442, 794, 979, 1129, 1212, 1405, 1490, 1683, 1689, **1790, 1945**, 2053, 2100, 2107, 2238, 2354, 2650, 2665, 2790, **2857, 2970**, 3106, 3344, 3345, 3489, 3560, 3575, 3678, 3875, **4103, 4285**, 4337, 4895, 5125, 5337, 5688, 6101, 6326, 7327, 8002

$$\frac{n+1}{2} = \frac{40+1}{2} = 20.5$$
The median is the average of the 20th and 21st ordered observations = (2857+2970)/2 = 2913.5

Q_1 = median of the 20 smallest observations = (1790+1945)/2 = 1867.5
Q_3 = median of the 20 largest observations = (4103+4285)/2 = 4194
Five number summary: Min = 442, Q_1 = 1867.5, Median = 2913.5, Q_3 = 4194, Max = 8002

IQR = $Q_3 - Q_1$ = 4194 – 1867.5 = 2326.5
Lower fence = Q_1 – 1.5(IQR) = 1867.5 – 1.5(2326.5) = -1622.25
Upper fence = Q_3 + 1.5(IQR) = 4194 + 1.5(2326.5) = 7683.75
The only observation outside the two fence values is 8002, so 8002 is an outlier.
Lower adjacent value = smallest remaining observation = 442
Upper adjacent value = largest remaining observation = 7327

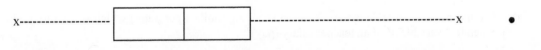

The distribution is skewed to the right due to the outlier at 8,002. The median is 2,913.5. The IQR is 2,326.5.

IV.11

(a).

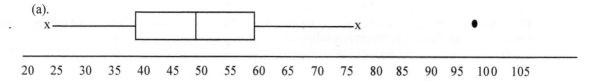

| 20 | 25 | 30 | 35 | 40 | 45 | 50 | 55 | 60 | 65 | 70 | 75 | 80 | 85 | 90 | 95 | 100 | 105 |

(b). The distribution is skewed to the right. Hence, we calculate the median and interquartile range as measures of center and spread. There is an outlier at 98.

$$n = 33, \frac{n+1}{2} = \frac{33+1}{2} = 17$$

So the median is at the 17th ordered observations = 48

Q_1 = median of the 16 smallest observations = 39.5
Q_3 = median of the 16 largest observations = 59.5
IQR = $Q_3 - Q_1$ = 59.5 – 39.5 = 20

(c). Mean = $\overline{X} = \dfrac{30 + 45 + 51 + ... + 39 + 47 + 59}{33} = \dfrac{1664}{33} = 50.42$

Standard Deviation = s = 15.26

IV.12.

(a).

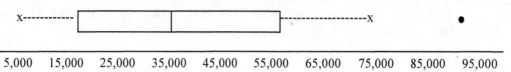

| 5,000 | 15,000 | 25,000 | 35,000 | 45,000 | 55,000 | 65,000 | 75,000 | 85,000 | 95,000 |

(b). The distribution is slightly skewed to the right. Therefore, the median and IQR should be calculated for the measures of central location and spread. There is an outlier at 94,208.

Median: 35,500.5
IQR: Q3 – Q1 = 57994 -16354 = 41640

(c). The descriptions are very similar. All the descriptions described the shape as being slightly skewed with an outlier at 94,208. The descriptions of center and spread were also similar.

V.1. Both height at age 6 and height at age 16 are both (continuous) quantitative variables. We want to use height at age 6 to predict height at age at 16, so height at age 6 is the explanatory variable and height at age 16 is the response variable.

V.2. (a). The independent variable is the education spending (dollars per pupil) which is used to predict the dependent variable, median teacher salary (pay).

(b).

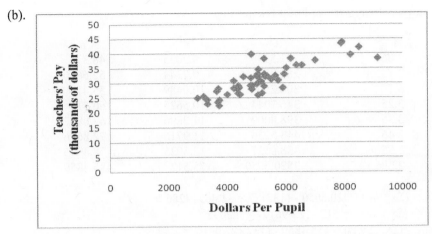

(c). There is a positive linear relationship. The strength is fairly good with a r = .79656 or .80. This positive association makes sense because money spent for teacher salaries is part of the education budget.

(d). The state of California, which spends $4,826 per pupil and has a median teacher salary of $39,600 could be considered an outlier. If a least squared regression line were drawn, it would be the furthest away from the line and hence have the largest residual.

V.3. (a). A correlation coefficient of −0.93 implies a strong, negative relationship between the two variables. A correlation near 0 implies a weak relationship. As stated in part (b), the correlation is actually −0.093, not −0.93.

(b). The coefficient of determination is $r^2 = (-0.093)^2 = .008649$. Hence the length of the trip explains approximately 0.86% of the variation in miles per gallon on the trip.

(c). An intercept of 31.2 implies that if the length of the trip is 0 miles, then the predicted miles per gallon on the trip is 31.2. The slope value of −0.03 implies that if the length of the trip increases by 1 mile, the miles per gallon decreases by 0.03.

(d). There is not a strong linear relationship between the two variables, so the line is not going to be very useful for predicting at any point. At least 200 miles is in the range of the original data, so predicting at this point is at least valid – it will just not be very useful. Predicting at 1200 miles is extrapolation and the resulting value will likely be completely useless.

V.4. (a).

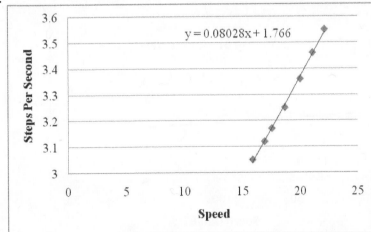

(b). There is a <u>very</u> strong positive linear relationship.

X	Y	X²	Y²	XY
15.86	3.05	251.5396	9.3025	48.373
16.88	3.12	284.9344	9.7344	52.6656
17.50	3.17	306.2500	10.0489	55.475
18.62	3.25	346.7044	10.5625	60.515
19.97	3.36	398.8009	11.2896	67.0992
21.06	3.46	443.5236	11.9716	72.8676
22.11	3.55	488.8521	12.6025	78.4905
132	22.96	2520.6050	75.512	435.4859

$S_{xx} = \Sigma x_i^2 - (\Sigma x_i)^2/n = 2520.6050 - (132)^2/7 = 31.46214286$
$S_{yy} = \Sigma y_i^2 - (\Sigma y_i)^2/n = 75.512 - (22.96)^2/7 = 0.2032$
$S_{xy} = \Sigma x_i y_i - (\Sigma x_i)(\Sigma y_i)/n = 435.4859 - (132)(22.96)/7 = 2.5259$

$$r = \frac{S_{xy}}{\sqrt{S_{xx} \bullet S_{yy}}} = \frac{2.5259}{\sqrt{31.46214286 \bullet 0.2032}} = 0.999$$

The correlation coefficient is r = .999. This value corresponds to the relationship illustrated on the scatterplot.

(c). $\text{slope} = \frac{s_{xy}}{s_{xx}} = \frac{2.53}{31.46} = .08028$ $\text{intercept} = \overline{Y} - \text{slope}(\overline{X}) = 3.28 - .08028(18.857) = 1.766$

The regression line is $\hat{y} = 1.766 + .08028\, X$

(d). $r^2 = (.9990)^2 = .998$. Running speed explains 99.8% of the variation in steps per second.

(e). We would have to draw a new scatterplot and regression line. The new scatterplot would use steps per second as the x variable and speed as the y variable. However, the correlation coefficient r and the coefficient of determination r^2 would <u>not</u> change.

V.5. (a). A strong linear relationship is a correlation coefficient value near -1 or near +1. Variable X_2 = the student's age with r = -0.75 has the value closest to -1 or +1.

(b). A weak linear relationship is a correlation coefficient value near 0. Variable X_4 = the student's score on the midterm exam has the value closest to 0.

V.6. (a).

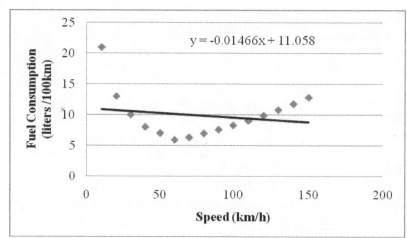

(b). The data does not have a linear trend; therefore, the line is not a good predictor of the data.

(c). The predicted values and residuals for each observation are:

X	Y	$\hat{Y}$	Residual
10	21	10.91	10.09
20	13	10.76	2.34
30	10	10.62	-0.62
40	8	10.47	-2.47
50	7	10.33	-3.33
60	5.9	10.18	-4.28
70	6.3	10.03	-3.73
80	6.95	9.89	-2.94
90	7.57	9.74	-2.17
100	8.27	9.59	-1.32
110	9.03	9.45	-0.42
120	9.87	9.30	0.57
130	10.79	9.15	1.64
140	11.77	9.01	2.76
150	12.83	8.86	3.97

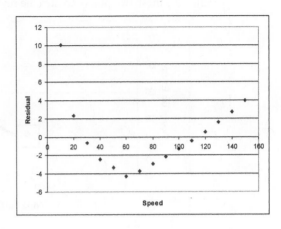

Note that the residuals sum to –0.01, very close to 0.

(d). The residual plot shows the same quadratic pattern shown in the scatterplot. This suggests that a quadratic regression model would do a better job of predicting fuel consumption than the linear regression model given in the problem.

V.7.

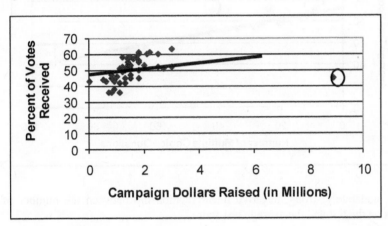

(a). See scatterplot above.

(b). The intercept of 47.5 means that if no money is spent on the campaign the predicted percentage of votes received is 47.5 percent. The slope of 1.48 means that if the campaign dollars raised increases by one million dollars, then the percent of votes received will increase by 1.48 percent.

(c). The circled observation is an influential observation that changes the position of the regression line.

(d). $\hat{y} = 47.5 + 1.48(5) = 47.5 + 7.4 = 54.9\%$

This value falls within the range of the X data, so it is not extrapolation. However, due to the influential observation the regression line does not explain a high percentage of the variation in the Y data.

(e). $\hat{y} = 47.5 + 1.48(12) = 47.5 + 17.76 = 65.26\%$

Since 12 is outside the range of the original data this is an example of extrapolation and the prediction is not reliable.

V.8. (a). There is a very strong, positive, linear relationship between time to complete the exam and the score on the exam.

(b). One point is (0, -18.2445). If one plugs X = 240 into the regression line equation, the resulting predicted value is $\hat{Y} = -18.2445 + .8821(240) = 193.4595$. So a second point is (240, 193.4595). Connecting these two points creates the regression line.

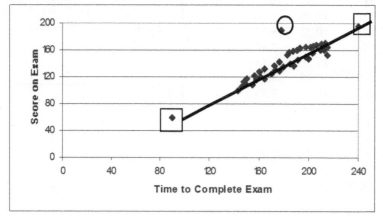

(c). There is one outlier circled on the scatterplot and two influential observations boxed on the scatterplot.

V.9.

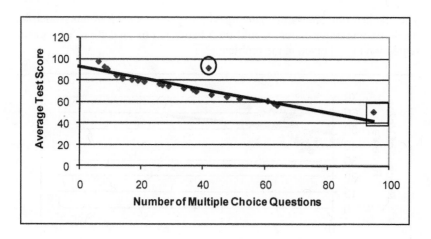

(a). There is moderately strong, negative linear relationship between the number of multiple choice questions on the test and the average test score.
(b). See scatterplot.
(c). See scatterplot. There is one circled outlier and one boxed influential observation.
(d). An intercept value of 91 means that if the number of multiple choice questions is equal to 0, the predicted average test score is equal to 91. A slope value of -.49 means that if the number of multiple choice questions increases by one, the predicted average test score will decrease by .49 points.
(e). The difficulty of the test and the subject matter being covered would be examples of lurking variables because they influence the average test score and hence the relationship between number of multiple choice questions and the average test score.

V.10. (a). There is weak, positive correlation between age and time. The data does not appear to have a linear trend.
(b). See scatterplot.
(c). An intercept of 178.3611 means that if the age of a visitor is 0 years, the amount of time that the visitor remains at Pony Pasture park is equal to 178.3611 minutes. A slope of .421471 means that if age of the visitor increases by one year, the time they remain at the park increases by .421471 minutes.

308

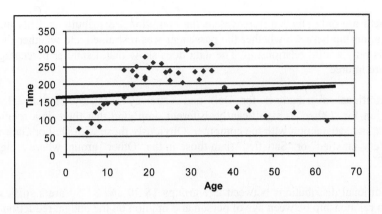

V.11. The explanatory variable is whether or not a student has taken at least two years of foreign language. The response variable is the score on the English achievement test. The lurking variable is the student's command of English: those with good command of English are more likely to take a foreign language and to perform well on the achievement test.

V.12. The overall average for Charlie is $\frac{30+9}{43+17} = \frac{39}{60} = .650$. The overall average for James is $\frac{29+4}{42+8} = \frac{33}{50}$ = .660. Despite Charlie having a higher average in both the regular season and the playoffs, James has a higher overall average. This is an example of Simpson's Paradox, where the lurking variable, whether it is the regular season or playoffs, reverses the direction of the relationship.

V.13. (a). Both parents smoke   Student smokes: $\frac{400}{400+1380} = \frac{400}{1780} = .2247$ (22.47%)

Student does not smoke: $\frac{1380}{400+1380} = \frac{1380}{1780} = .7753$ (77.53%)

One parent smokes   Student smokes: $\frac{416}{416+1823} = \frac{416}{2239} = .1858$ (18.58%)

Student does not smoke: $\frac{1823}{416+1823} = \frac{1823}{2239} = .8142$ (81.42%)

Neither parent smokes   Student smokes: $\frac{188}{188+1168} = \frac{188}{1356} = .1386$ (13.86%)

Student does not smoke: $\frac{1168}{188+1168} = \frac{1168}{1356} = .8614$ (86.14%)

(b). There are differences in the conditional distributions, although the differences are not great. From the above calculations we see that if the parents smoke there is a greater chance that the child will smoke. The percentage of students who smoke decreases as the number of parents who smoke decreases.

V.14. (a). Of the 26,971 passengers, 197+1749 = 1946 were restrained. This is 7.22%.

(b). Restrained   Injured: $\frac{197}{197+1749} = \frac{197}{1946} = .1012$ (10.12%)

Uninjured: $\frac{1749}{197+1749} = \frac{1749}{1946} = .8988$ (89.88%)

Unrestrained   Injured: $\frac{3844}{3844+21181} = \frac{3844}{25025} = .1536$ (15.36%)

Uninjured: $\frac{21181}{3844+21181} = \frac{21181}{25025} = .8464$ (84.64%)

There are only slight differences in the conditional distributions. This indicates that if there is a relationship between whether the passenger was restrained and whether the passenger was injured, it is only a mild relationship. The data does show that a smaller percentage of restrained children were injured.

V.15. The conditional distributions for Dell and Gateway are very similar. However, the conditional distribution for "Other" is significantly different, implying that there is a relationship between type of computer and satisfaction with the computer. Obviously those with Dell or Gateway or much more likely to be "Very satisfied" or "Satisfied" than those in the "Other" group, where a higher percentage are "Not satisfied".

V.16. The conditional distributions between age groups 18-30 and 31-50 are significantly different, implying there is a relationship between age of person and opinion on the budget reduction items.

VI.1.

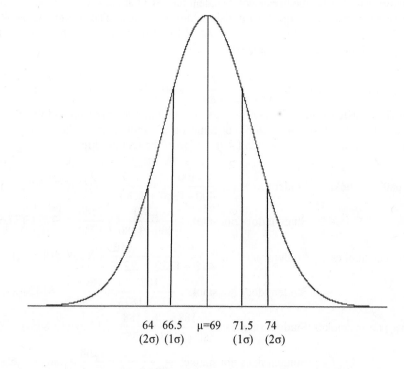

$$\begin{array}{cccccc} 64 & 66.5 & \mu=69 & 71.5 & 74 \\ (2\sigma) & (1\sigma) & & (1\sigma) & (2\sigma) \end{array}$$

VI.2. X = score on Wechsler test, $X \sim N(110, 25)$
    (a). The mean is at the peak of the curve and has 50% of the data less than it and 50% of the data greater than it. So 50% of the data is greater than $\mu = 110$.
    (b). The middle 95% of the data fall between 60 and 160.
    (c). 160 is two standard deviations above the mean. 95% of the data is within two standard deviations of the mean (60 to 160), so 5% of the data is outside this range. Hence 2.5% of the area is above 160.

VI.3. (a). $P(Z < 2.85) = .9978$
    (b). $P(Z > 2.85) = 1 - P(Z < 2.85) = 1 - .9978 = .0022$
    (c). $P(Z > -1.66) = 1 - P(Z < -1.66) = 1 - .0485 = .9515$
    (d). $P(-1.66 < Z < 2.85) = P(Z < 2.85) - P(Z < -1.66) = .9978 - .0485 = .9493$

VI.4. (a). z: $P(Z < z) = .80$ (b). z: $P(Z > z) = .35$
            z = 0.84   z: $P(Z < z) = .65$
                                           z = 0.385

VI.5. Z = (Batting Average - Mean)/ Standard Deviation

1910's (Cobb): $Z = \dfrac{.420 - .266}{.0371} = 4.15$

1940's (Williams): $Z = \dfrac{.406 - .267}{.0326} = 4.26$

1970's (Brett): $Z = \dfrac{.390 - .261}{.0317} = 4.07$

Relative to his peers, Williams did best (although all three did extremely well).

VI.6. X~N(6582, 1732)

(a). $P(X > 7244) = P(Z > \dfrac{7244 - 6582}{1732}) = P(Z > 0.38) = 1 - P(Z < 0.38) = 1 - .6480 = .3520$

(b). z: $P(Z < z) = .1616$
z = -0.99
x = μ + zσ = 6582 + -0.99(1732) = 4,867 copies

VI.7. X ~ N(69, 2.5)

(a). $P(X > 72) = P(Z > \dfrac{72 - 69}{2.5}) = P(Z > 1.20) = 1 - P(Z < 1.20) = 1 - .8849 = .1151$

(b). $P(60 < X < 72) = P(\dfrac{60 - 69}{2.5} < Z < \dfrac{72 - 69}{2.5}) = P(-3.60 < Z < 1.20)$
$= P(Z < 1.20) - P(Z < -3.60)$ = .8849 - .0002 = .8847

(c). z: $P(Z > z) = .10$
z: $P(Z < z) = .90$
z = 1.28
x = μ + zσ = 69 + 1.28(2.5) = 72.2 inches

VI.8. X = score on the examination, X ~ N(40, 6)

(a). $P(X < 45) = P(Z < \dfrac{45 - 40}{6}) = P(Z < 0.83) = .7967 \Rightarrow 79.67\%$

(b). $P(X < 30) = P(Z < \dfrac{30 - 40}{6}) = P(Z < -1.67) = .0475 \Rightarrow 4.75\%$

(c). $P(X > 60) = P(Z > \dfrac{60 - 40}{6}) = P(Z > 3.33) = 1 - P(Z < 3.33) = 1 - .9996 = .0004 \Rightarrow .04\%$

(d). z: $P(Z < z) = .975$
z = 1.960
x = μ + zσ = 40 + 1.96 (6) = 51.76 minutes

VI.9. X = contents of cereal box in ounces, X ~ N(16.09, 0.03)

(a). $P(X < 16) = P(Z < \dfrac{16 - 16.09}{.03}) = P(Z < -3.00) = .0013 \Rightarrow .13\%$

(b). $P(X < 16.05) = P(Z < \dfrac{16.05 - 16.09}{.03}) = P(Z < -1.33) = .0918 \Rightarrow 9.18\%$

(c). $P(X > 16.2) = P(Z > \dfrac{16.2 - 16.09}{.03}) = P(Z > 3.67) = 1 - P(Z < 3.67) = 1 - .9998 = .0002$

(d). $P(16.1 < X < 16.2) = P(\dfrac{16.1 - 16.09}{.03} < Z < \dfrac{16.2 - 16.09}{.03}) = P(0.33 < Z < 3.67)$
$= P(Z < 3.67) - P(Z < 0.33) = .9998 - .6293 = .3705 \Rightarrow 37.05\%$

VI.10. X = number of jobs submitted

$X \sim N(83, 10)$

(a). $P(X < 73) = P\left(Z < \dfrac{73-83}{10}\right) = P(Z < -1.00) = .1587$

(b). $P(X < 93) = P\left(Z < \dfrac{93-83}{10}\right) = P(Z < 1.00) = .8413$

(c). $P(73 < X < 93) = P\left(\dfrac{73-83}{10} < Z < \dfrac{93-83}{10}\right) = P(-1.00 < Z < 1.00) = P(Z < 1.00) - P(Z < -1.00)$

$= .8413 - .1587 = .6826$

VI.11. X = reading speed; $X \sim N(450, 70)$

(a). $P(X > 500) = P\left(Z > \dfrac{500-450}{70}\right) = P(Z > 0.71) = 1 - P(Z < 0.71) = 1 - .7611 = .2389$

(b). $P(X < 375) = P\left(Z < \dfrac{375-450}{70}\right) = P(Z < -1.07) = .1423$

(c). $P(380 < X < 520) = P\left(\dfrac{380-450}{70} < Z < \dfrac{520-450}{70}\right) = P(-1.00 < Z < 1.00)$

$= P(Z < 1.00) - P(Z < -1.00) = .8413 - .1587 = .6826$

(d). z: $P(Z < z) = .10$

z = -1.28

$x = \mu + z\sigma = 450 - 1.28(70) = 360.4$

(e). z: $P(Z > z) = .05$

z: $P(Z < z) = .95$

z = 1.645

$x = \mu + z\sigma = 450 + 1.645(70) = 565.15$

VI.12. X = number of minor imperfections in a size 40-42 t-shirt; $X \sim N(38, 8)$

(a). $P(X > 60) = P\left(Z \geq \dfrac{60-38}{8}\right) = P(Z > 2.75) = 1 - P(Z < 2.75) = 1 - .9970 = .0030$

(b). z: $P(Z < z) = .1120$

z = -1.22 (or z = -1.21)

$x = \mu + z\sigma = 38 + (-1.22)(8) = 38 - 9.76 = 28.24$ imperfections

VI.13. X = width of the Cone Vertigo; $X \sim N(46, 16)$

(a). $P(X > 74) = P\left(Z > \dfrac{74-46}{16}\right) = P(Z > 1.75) = 1 - P(Z < 1.75) = 1 - .9599 = .0401$

(b). z: $P(Z < z) = .18$

z = -0.91

$x = \mu + z\sigma = 46 + -0.91(16) = 31.44$ mm

VI.14. X = length of time that the lab rats sleep; $X \sim N(193, 23)$

(a). $P(X > 240) = P\left(Z > \dfrac{240-193}{23}\right) = P(Z > 2.04) = 1 - P(Z < 2.04) = 1 - .9793 = .0207$

(b). z: $P(Z < z) = .6443$

z = 0.37

$x = \mu + z\sigma = 193 + .37(23) = 201.51$ minutes

(c). z: $P(Z < z) = .25$

z = -0.67

$x = \mu + z\sigma = 193 + -0.67(23) = 177.59$ minutes

z: P(Z < z) = .75
z = 0.67
x = μ + zσ = 193 + 0.67(23) = 208.41 minutes

So the middle 50% of the sleep durations is between 177.59 and 208.41 minutes.

VI.15. X = number of characters per text message sent by all college students; X ~ N(28.5, 7.1)

   (a). $P(26 < X < 31) = P\left(\dfrac{26 - 28.5}{7.1} < Z < \dfrac{31 - 28.5}{7.1}\right) = P(-.35 < Z < .35)$

          $= P(Z < .35) - P(Z < -.35) = .6368 - .3594 = .2774$

   (b). z: P(Z < z) = .1190
       z = -1.18
       x = μ + zσ = 28.5 – 1.18(7.1) = 20.12 characters

   (c). $P(X > 50) = P\left(Z > \dfrac{50 - 28.5}{7.1}\right) = P(Z > 3.03) = 1 - P(Z < 3.03) = 1 - .9988 = .0012$

   (d). z: P(Z < z) = .10
       z = -1.28
       x = μ + zσ = 28.5 + -1.28(7.1) = 19.412 characters

       z: P(Z < z) = .90
       z = 1.28
       x = μ + zσ = 28.5 + 1.28(7.1) = 37.588 characters

       So the middle 80% of the distribution is between 19.412 and 37.588 minutes.

VI.16. (a). 1.330
     (b). 4.029
     (c). Between 2.403 (50 degrees of freedom) and 2.423 (40 degrees of freedom)

VI.17. (a). p = .025
     (b). p = .15
     (c). p = .001

VII.1. (a). The parameter of interest is all the New York City taxi cab drivers. The parameter of interest is μ= the mean income of all New York City taxi cab drivers.

     (b). n= 65, $\overline{X}$ = 32,350, margin of error = 2,250
A 95% confidence interval for the mean income of all New York City taxi cab drivers is equal to $\overline{X}$ ± margin of error which equals 32,350 ± 2,250= (30100,34600)
We have a 95% confidence that the mean income of all New York City taxi cab drivers is between $30,100 and $34,600.

     (c). 32,350 is the mean of the sample, not of the entire population. Although it is likely that the population mean is close to this value, it is very unlikely that it equals this number exactly.

     (d). If we repeat the sampling procedure over and over and compute a confidence interval for each sample, then 95% of the confidence intervals will contain the true population mean and 5% will not.

VII.2. (a). n= 170, $\overline{X}$ = 117.39, margin of error = 3.95
A 99% confidence interval for the mean score on this standard intelligence test for all members of Congress is equal to: $\overline{X}$ ± margin of error which equals 117.39 ± 3.95= (113.44,121.34)
We have a 99% confidence that the mean score on this standard intelligence test for all members of Congress is between 113.44 and 121.34.

     (b). If the degree of confidence were decreased from 99% to 90%, the margin of error and width of the confidence would both decrease.

VII.3. (i).   This is the correct definition of 99% confidence interval.

      (ii).   This is not appropriate- we are making inferences about the population mean, <u>not</u> the sample mean.

     (iii).   This is the correct interpretation of the interval.

     (iv).   When interpreting confidence intervals we should use the term confidence, not the term probability.

     (v).   When interpreting confidence intervals, we should not talk about individual values, but instead about the parameter of interest which is the population mean in this case.

     (vi).   The population mean will likely be close to the sample mean, but it most likely will not be equal exactly to that value.

VII.4. (a).   The parameter of interest is the mean diameter of a spindle in a small motor.
          H_0: $\mu = 5$ H_a: $\mu \neq 5$

     (b).   The parameter of interest is the mean cost of dresses worn by female presenters, entertainers, and/or nominees.
          H_0: $\mu = \$264.32$ H_a: $\mu > \$264.32$

     (c).   The parameter of interest is the mean cost of meals in restaurants in St. Thomas.
          H_0: $\mu = \$17.49$ H_a: $\mu < \$17.49$

VII.5. (a). H_0: $\mu = \$8,425$
          H_a: $\mu < \$8,425$

     (b).   (i) Since p-value < .10, we reject the null hypothesis
         (ii) Since p-value > .10, we fail to reject the null hypothesis
         (iii) Since p-value = .10, we reject the null hypothesis
         (iv) Since p-value < .10, we reject the null hypothesis

     (c).   If $\alpha = .05$
         (i) Since p-value < .05, we reject the null hypothesis
         (ii) Since p-value > .05, we fail to reject the null hypothesis
         (iii) Since p-value > .05, we fail to reject the null hypothesis
         (iv) Since p-value < .05, we reject the null hypothesis

         If $\alpha = .01$
         (i) Since p-value > .01, we fail to reject the null hypothesis
         (ii) Since p-value > .01, we fail to reject the null hypothesis
         (iii) Since p-value > .01, we fail to reject the null hypothesis
         (iv) Since p-value < .01, we reject the null hypothesis

VIII.1.   The population is the 15,000 living alumni, and π is the proportion of these alumni who support the firing of the football coach. The sample proportion of this sample of 200 alumni is $\hat{p} = 76/200 = .38$.

VIII.2. $\mu_{\hat{p}} = \pi = .22$, $\sigma_{\hat{p}} = \sqrt{\dfrac{\pi(1-\pi)}{n}} = \sqrt{\dfrac{.22(1-.22)}{300}} = .0239$, large sample so by the central limit theorem,
        $\hat{p} \sim N(.22, .0239)$.

     (a). $P(\hat{p} > .20) = P\left(Z > \dfrac{.20-.22}{.0239}\right) = P(Z > -0.837) = 1 - P(Z < -0.837) = 1 - .2033 = .7967$

     (b). $P(\hat{p} > .30) = P\left(Z > \dfrac{.30-.22}{.0239}\right) = P(Z > 3.35) = 1 - P(Z < 3.35) = 1 - .9996 = .0004$

VIII.3. $n = 500$ $\pi = .025$

     (a). $\mu_{\hat{p}} = \pi = .025$ $\sigma_{\hat{p}} = \sqrt{\dfrac{\pi(1-\pi)}{n}} = \sqrt{\dfrac{.025(1-.025)}{500}} = .00698$

       $n\pi = 500(.025) = 12.5$, $n(1-\pi) = 500(1-.025) = 487.5$
       Both are greater than or equal to 10, so by the central limit theorem, $\hat{p} \sim N(.025, .00698)$.

(b). $P(\hat{p} < .02) = P(Z < \dfrac{.02 - .025}{.00698}) = P(Z < -0.72) = .2358$

VIII.4.　$n = 300$　$\pi = .125$

(a).　$\mu_{\hat{p}} = \pi = .125$　　　　　$\sigma_{\hat{p}} = \sqrt{\dfrac{\pi(1-\pi)}{n}} = \sqrt{\dfrac{.125(1-.125)}{300}} = .019$

$n\pi = 300(.125) = 37.5,\ \ n(1-\pi) = 300(1 - .125) = 262.5$
Both are greater than or equal to 10, so by the central limit theorem, $\hat{p} \sim N(.125, .019)$.

(b).　$P(\hat{p} \geq .10) = P(Z \geq \dfrac{.10 - .125}{.019}) = P(Z \geq -1.32) = 1 - P(Z < -1.32) = 1 - .0934 = .9066$

VIII.5.　(a).　$n = 200,\ \pi = .06$

$\mu_{\hat{p}} = \pi = .06$　　　　$\sigma_{\hat{p}} = \sqrt{\dfrac{\pi(1-\pi)}{n}} = \sqrt{\dfrac{.06(1-.06)}{200}} = .0168$

Since $n\pi = 200(.06) = 12$ and $n(1-\pi) = 200(1 - .06) = 188$ are both greater than 10, then by the central limit theorem the sampling distribution is approximately normal: $\hat{p} \sim N(.06, .0168)$.

(b).　$P(\hat{p} > .10) = P\left(Z > \dfrac{.10 - .06}{.0168}\right) = P(Z > 2.38) = 1 - P(Z < 2.38) = 1 - .9913 = .0087.$

VIII.6　$n = 500$　$\pi = .25$

(a).　$\mu_{\hat{p}} = \pi = .25$　　　　$\sigma_{\hat{p}} = \sqrt{\dfrac{\pi(1-\pi)}{n}} = \sqrt{\dfrac{.25(1-.25)}{500}} = .0194$

$n\pi = 500(.25) = 12.5,\ \ n(1-\pi) = 500(1 - .25) = 375$
Both are greater than or equal to 10, so by the central limit theorem, $\hat{p} \sim N(.25, .0194)$.

(b).　$P(\hat{p} . < .20) = P(Z < \dfrac{.20 - .25}{.0194}) = P(Z < -2.58) = .0051$

VIII.7.　$n = 500$　$\pi = .67$

(a).　$\mu_{\hat{p}} = \pi = .67$　　　　$\sigma_{\hat{p}} = \sqrt{\dfrac{\pi(1-\pi)}{n}} = \sqrt{\dfrac{.67(1-.67)}{500}} = .0210$

$n\pi = 500(.67) = 335,\ \ n(1-\pi) = 500(1 - .67) = 165$
Both are greater than or equal to 10, so by the central limit theorem, $\hat{p} \sim N(.67, .0210)$.

(b).　$P(.65 < \hat{p} . < .70) = P\left(\dfrac{.65 - .67}{.0210} < Z < \dfrac{.70 - .67}{.0210}\right) = P(-0.952 < Z < 1.43)$

$= P(Z < 1.43) - P(Z < -0.952) = .9236 - .1711 = .7525$

VIII.8.　$n = 950,\ \hat{p} = 627/950 = .66$　　　　　　For a 99% CI, $Z^* = 2.576$

$\hat{p} \pm Z^* \sqrt{\dfrac{\hat{p}(1-\hat{p})}{n}} = .66 \pm 2.576 \sqrt{\dfrac{.66(1-.66)}{950}} = .66 \pm 2.576 \sqrt{.0002} = .66 \pm .0396 = (.6204, .6996)$

We have 99% confidence that the proportion of all Americans who agree with the statement is between .6204 and .6996.

VIII.9.　(a). NO - both $n\pi$ and $n(1 - \pi)$ are equal to 5, which is less than 10.
　　　　(b). NO - $n(1 - \pi) = 200(1 - .99) = 2$ is less than 10, so a sample of size 200 is not "large enough".
　　　　(c). YES - $n\pi$ and $n(1 - \pi)$ are both equal to 10 and we have a simple random sample.
　　　　(d). NO – we have a volunteer response sample, not a simple random sample.

VIII.10. (1) $H_0: \pi = .53$ versus $H_a: \pi > .53$

(2) $n = 88 \quad \hat{p} = 66/88 = .75$

$$Z = \frac{\hat{p} - \pi_0}{\sqrt{\dfrac{\pi_0(1-\pi_0)}{n}}} = \frac{.75 - .53}{\sqrt{\dfrac{.53(1-.53)}{88}}} = \frac{.22}{.0532} = 4.14$$

(3) p-value $= P(Z \geq 4.14) = 1 - P(Z < 4.14) = 1 - .9998 = .0002$

(4) Since p-value $< .05$ we reject H_0

(5) There is sufficient evidence that the proportion of "high risk" students who are retained at University X has increased above .53.

VIII.11. (1) $H_0: \pi = .40$ versus $H_a: \pi < .40$

(2) $n = 400 \quad \hat{p} = 130/400 = .325$

$$Z = \frac{\hat{p} - \pi_0}{\sqrt{\dfrac{\pi_0(1-\pi_0)}{n}}} = \frac{.325 - .40}{\sqrt{\dfrac{.40(1-.40)}{400}}} = \frac{-0.075}{.0245} = -3.06$$

(3) p-value $= P(Z \leq -3.06) = .0011$

(4) Since p-value $< .05$ we reject H_0

(5) There is sufficient evidence that the proportion of all deaths among infants less than 1 year of age in the year 2009 that are due to SIDS is less than .40.

VIII.12. (a). $m = .10$, for a 98% CI we use $Z^* = 2.326$, and we will use $\pi = .50$

$$n = \left(\frac{Z^*}{m}\right)^2 \pi(1-\pi) = \left(\frac{2.326}{.10}\right)^2 (.50)(1-.50) = 135.26$$

We should select a sample of 136 single parents.

(b). $n = 150$, $\hat{p} = 33/150 = .22$, $Z^* = 2.326$

$$\hat{p} \pm Z^* \sqrt{\frac{\hat{p}(1-\hat{p})}{n}} = .22 \pm 2.326 \sqrt{\frac{.22(1-.22)}{150}} = .22 \pm 2.326(.0338) = .22 \pm .079 = (.141, .299)$$

We have 98% confidence that the proportion of all hits to the website that are by single parents in the Pacific time zone is between .141 and .299.

(c). (i) $H_0: \pi = .33$ versus $H_a: \pi \neq .33$

(ii) $\hat{p} = 43/150 = .287$, $n = 150$

$$Z = \frac{\hat{p} - \pi_0}{\sqrt{\dfrac{\pi_0(1-\pi_0)}{n}}} = \frac{.287 - .33}{\sqrt{\dfrac{.33(1-.33)}{150}}} = -1.12$$

(iii) P-value: Two sided test so p-value $= 2P(Z \geq |-1.12|) = 2[1 - P(Z < 1.12)] = 2(1 - .8686)$
$= 2(.1314) = .2628$

(iv) Since p-value $> .05$ we fail to reject the null hypothesis.

(v) There is insufficient evidence that the proportion of all hits to the website that are by single parents in the Central time zone is different from .33.

VIII.13. $n = 150 \quad \hat{p} = 18/150 = .12 \quad$ 90% CI $\Rightarrow Z^* = 1.645$

$$\hat{p} \pm Z^* \sqrt{\frac{\hat{p}(1-\hat{p})}{n}} = .12 \pm 1.645 \sqrt{\frac{.12(1-.12)}{150}} = .12 \pm 1.645(.0265) = .12 \pm .0436 = (.0764, .1636)$$

We have 90% confidence that the proportion of all members and employees who contribute to the YMCA Annual Giving campaign is between .0764 and .1636.

VIII.14. (1) $H_0: \pi = .70$ versus $H_a: \pi > .70$

(2) $\hat{p} = 122/159 = .7673$, n = 159

$$Z = \frac{\hat{p} - \pi_0}{\sqrt{\dfrac{\pi_0(1-\pi_0)}{n}}} = \frac{.7673 - .70}{\sqrt{\dfrac{.70(1-.70)}{159}}} = 1.85$$

(3) P-value: Upper one- sided test so p-value = $P(Z \geq 1.85) = 1 - P(Z < 1.85) = 1 - .9678 = .0322$

(4) Since p-value > .01 we fail to reject the null hypothesis.

(5) There is insufficient evidence that the proportion of all truck drivers who suffer from obstructive sleep apnea is greater than .70.

VIII.15. (a). m = .05, for a 95% CI we use Z* = 1.960, and we will use $\pi = .50$

$$n = \left(\frac{Z^*}{m}\right)^2 \pi(1-\pi) = \left(\frac{1.960}{.05}\right)^2 (.50)(1-.50) = 384.16$$

They should select a sample of 385 attendees.

(b). n = 400, $\hat{p} = 188/400 = .47$, Z* = 1.960

$$\hat{p} \pm Z^* \sqrt{\frac{\hat{p}(1-\hat{p})}{n}} = .47 \pm 1.96 \sqrt{\frac{.47(1-.47)}{400}} = .47 \pm 1.96(.0249) = .47 \pm .0480 = (.422, .518)$$

We have 95% confidence that the proportion of all attendees who live in California is between .422 and .518.

(c). (1) $H_0: \pi = .50$ versus $H_a: \pi > .50$

(2) $\hat{p} = 212/400 = .53$, n = 400

$$Z = \frac{\hat{p} - \pi_0}{\sqrt{\dfrac{\pi_0(1-\pi_0)}{n}}} = \frac{.53 - .50}{\sqrt{\dfrac{.50(1-.50)}{400}}} = \frac{.03}{.025} = 1.20$$

(3) p-value = $P(Z \geq 1.20) = 1 - P(Z < 1.20) = 1 - .8849 = .1151$

(4) Since p-value > .05 we fail to reject the null hypothesis.

(5) There is insufficient evidence that the proportion of all attendees at the 2001 American Music Awards show that were from outside California is higher than .50.

VIII.16. m = .05, for a 95% CI we use Z* = 1.960, and we will use $\pi = .50$

$$n = \left(\frac{Z^*}{m}\right)^2 \pi(1-\pi) = \left(\frac{1.960}{.05}\right)^2 (.50)(1-.50) = 384.16$$

They should select a sample of 385 Americans.

VIII.17. (a). m = .10, for a 95% CI we use Z* = 1.960, and we will use $\pi = .50$

$$n = \left(\frac{Z^*}{m}\right)^2 \pi(1-\pi) = \left(\frac{1.960}{.10}\right)^2 (.50)(1-.50) = 96.04$$

They should select a sample of 97 children.

(b). n = 100, $\hat{p} = 37/100 = .37$, Z* = 1.960

$$\hat{p} \pm Z^* \sqrt{\frac{\hat{p}(1-\hat{p})}{n}} = .37 \pm 1.96 \sqrt{\frac{.37(1-.37)}{100}} = .37 \pm 1.960(.0483) = .37 \pm .095 = (.275, .465)$$

We have 95% confidence that the proportion of all children in the Richmond, Virginia area who snore is between .275 and .465.

VIII.18.   (a). m = .10, for a 99% CI we use Z* = 2.576, and we will use π = .75

$$n = \left(\frac{Z^*}{m}\right)^2 \pi(1-\pi) = \left(\frac{2.576}{.10}\right)^2 (.75)(1-.75) = 124.4208$$

They should select a sample of 125 students.

(b)   n = 200, $\hat{p}$ = 148/200 = .74, Z* = 2.576

$$\hat{p} \pm Z^* \sqrt{\frac{\hat{p}(1-\hat{p})}{n}} = .74 \pm 2.576 \sqrt{\frac{.74(1-.74)}{200}} = .74 \pm 2.576(.0310) = .74 \pm .08 = (.66, .82)$$

We have 99% confidence that the proportion of all medical students enrolled in Virginia universities that have taken the Kaplan MCAT preparatory courses is between .66 and .82.

IX.1.   X = salary of a 1990 college graduate μ = 95000, σ = 22450

(a). n = 100

$$\mu_{\overline{X}} = \mu = 95000 \qquad \sigma_{\overline{X}} = \frac{\sigma}{\sqrt{n}} = \frac{22450}{\sqrt{100}} = 2245$$

Since n = 100 is large by the central limit theorem the distribution of $\overline{X}$ is approximately normal: $\overline{X} \sim N(95000, 2245)$.

(b). $P(\overline{X} \geq 100000) = P\left(Z \geq \frac{100000 - 95000}{2245}\right) = P(Z \geq 2.23) = 1 - P(Z \leq 2.23) = 1 - .9871 = .0129$

IX.2.   X = age of college athletes; X $\sim$ N(20.5, 0.75)

(a). $P(X > 21) = P\left(Z > \frac{21 - 20.5}{0.75}\right) = P(Z > 0.67) = 1 - P(Z < 0.67) = 1 - .7486 = .2514$

(b). n = 90

$$\mu_{\overline{X}} = \mu = 20.5 \qquad\qquad \sigma_{\overline{X}} = \frac{\sigma}{\sqrt{n}} = \frac{0.75}{\sqrt{90}} = 0.079$$

Since the population is normal, then the distribution of $\overline{X}$ is normal: $\overline{X} \sim N(20.5, 0.079)$

(c). $P(\overline{X} \leq 20) = P\left(Z \leq \frac{20 - 20.5}{0.079}\right) = P(Z < -6.32) = .0002$

IX.3.   X = amount of weight that can be dynamically lifted overhead
μ = 120, σ = 11.4, population is skewed heavily to the right

(a). n = 45

$$\mu_{\overline{X}} = \mu = 120 \qquad \sigma_{\overline{X}} = \frac{\sigma}{\sqrt{n}} = \frac{11.4}{\sqrt{45}} = 1.6944$$

Since n = 45 is large, by the central limit theorem the distribution of $\overline{X}$ is approximately normal: $\overline{X} \sim N(120, 1.6944)$.

(b). $P(116 < \overline{X} < 125) = P\left(\frac{116 - 120}{1.6994} < Z < \frac{125 - 120}{1.6994}\right) = P(-2.35 < Z < 2.94)$

$= P(Z < 2.94) - P(Z < -2.35) = .9984 - .0094 = .9890$

IX.4.   X = service lifetime of disc brake pads; X $\sim$ N(μ = 55000, σ = 4500)   n = 8

(a). $\mu_{\overline{x}} = \mu = 55000 \qquad\qquad \sigma_{\overline{x}} = \frac{\sigma}{\sqrt{n}} = \frac{4500}{\sqrt{8}} = 1591$

Since the original population is normal, then the sampling distribution is normal: $\overline{X} \sim N(55000, 1591)$

(b). $P(\overline{X} \leq 51800) = P(Z \leq \dfrac{51800 - 55000}{1591}) = P(Z \leq -2.01) = .0222$

IX.5. X = miles per gallon for the New Pontiac G6's that Oprah gave away, X ~ N(26.3, 3.6)

(a). $\mu_{\overline{X}} = \mu = 26.3$ $\sigma_{\overline{X}} = \dfrac{\sigma}{\sqrt{n}} = \dfrac{3.6}{\sqrt{20}} = 0.805$

Since the original population is normal, the sampling distribution is normal: $\overline{X} \sim N(26.3, .805)$

(b). $P(\overline{X} > 27) = P\left(Z > \dfrac{27 - 26.3}{.805}\right) = P(Z > 0.87) = 1 - P(Z < 0.87) = 1 - .8078 = .1922$

IX.6.   X = width of the Cone Vertigo, X ~ N (46,16)

(a). $P(45 < X < 50) = P\left(\dfrac{45 - 46}{16} < Z < \dfrac{50 - 46}{16}\right) = P(-0.06 < Z < 0.25) = P(Z < .25) - P(Z < -0.06)$

$= .5987 - .4761 = .1226$

(b). $\mu_{\overline{X}} = \mu = 46$ $\sigma_{\overline{X}} = \dfrac{\sigma}{\sqrt{n}} = \dfrac{16}{\sqrt{60}} = 2.0656$

Since the original population is normal, then the sampling distribution is normal:
$\overline{X} \sim N(46, 2.0656)$

Then $P(45 < \overline{X} < 50) = P\left(\dfrac{45 - 46}{2.0656} < Z < \dfrac{50 - 46}{2.0656}\right) = P(-0.48 < Z < 1.94)$

$= P(Z < 1.94) - P(Z < -0.48) = .9738 - .3156 = .6582$

IX.7.   n = 45, $\overline{X} = 33.8$, σ = 11.2

$\overline{X} \pm z* \dfrac{\sigma}{\sqrt{n}} = 33.8 \pm 1.960(\dfrac{11.2}{\sqrt{45}}) = 33.8 \pm 1.960(1.67) = 33.8 \pm 3.27 = (30.53, 37.07)$

We have 95% confidence that the mean number of students in all summer 2010 classes is between 30.53 and 37.07.

IX.8.   (a). σ = 54   m = 13   95% CI implies z* = 1.960

$n = \left(\dfrac{z*\sigma}{m}\right)^2 = \left(\dfrac{1.960(54)}{13}\right)^2 = 66.2846$

So the minimum sample size is n = 67 sprayings.

(b). n = 72, $\overline{X} = 312$, σ = 54

$\overline{X} \pm z* \dfrac{\sigma}{\sqrt{n}} = 312 \pm 1.960(\dfrac{54}{\sqrt{72}}) = 312 \pm 1.960(6.36) = 312 \pm 12.47 = (299.53, 324.47)$

We have 95% confidence that the mean amount of solution used during all their sprayings is between 299.53 and 324.47 ounces.

IX.9.   σ = 0.075   m = 0.025

For a 90% CI, z* = 1.645   So n $= \left(\dfrac{z*\sigma}{m}\right)^2 = \left(\dfrac{1.645(.075)}{.025}\right)^2 = 24.354225$

So a sample of 25 or more crankshafts is needed.

IX.10. (a). $\sigma = 6.7$ $m = 5$ 98% CI implies $z^* = 2.326$

$$n = \left(\frac{z^*\sigma}{m}\right)^2 = \left(\frac{2.326 * 7.6}{5}\right)^2 = 12.4999$$

So the minimum sample size is $n = 13$ children

(b). $n = 40$, $\overline{X} = 24.3$, $\sigma = 6.7$

$$\overline{X} \pm z^* \frac{\sigma}{\sqrt{n}} = 24.3 \pm 2.326(\frac{6.7}{\sqrt{40}}) = 24.3 \pm 2.326(1.06) = 24.3 \pm 2.466 = (21.834, 26.766)$$

(c). We have 98% confidence that the mean number of Sundays per year that all children participating in the 20 *Upward Basketball* programs attend church is between 21.834 and 26.766.

(d). We do not know that the mean number of Sundays per year that all children participating in the 20 *Upward Basketball* programs attend church, so <u>we do not know</u> if it is in the interval or not.

(e). Increasing the sample size decreases the margin of error and interval width because we are dividing by a larger number. The point estimate will be altered as well – it may increase or decrease, depends on the values of the new data that is added.

IX.11. H_0: $\mu = 31\%$ vs. H_a: $\mu < 31\%$
     $\sigma = 9.6\%$ $n = 40$

(a). $\mu_{\overline{X}} = \mu = 31\%$ $\sigma_{\overline{X}} = \frac{\sigma}{\sqrt{n}} = \frac{9.6}{\sqrt{40}} = 1.5179$

Since the sample is fairly large ($n = 40$), the central limit theorem applies and the sampling distribution of $\overline{X}$ is approximately normal with mean $\mu_{\overline{X}} = 31\%$ and standard deviation $\sigma_{\overline{X}} = 1.5179$.

(b). $\overline{X} = 30.2\%$ - very reasonable if H_0: $\mu = 31\%$ is true
$\overline{X} = 27.6\%$ - unreasonable if H_0: $\mu = 31\%$ is true
$\overline{X} = 30.2\%$ is near the peak of the sampling distribution, while 27.6 is in the lower tail and hence casts some doubt as to whether $\mu = 31\%$.

(c). p-value $= P(\overline{X} < 30.2) = P(Z < \frac{30.2 - 31}{1.5179}) = P(Z < -0.53) = .2981$

p-value $= P(\overline{X} < 27.6) = P(Z < \frac{27.6 - 31}{1.5179}) = P(Z < -2.24) = .0125$

The p-value for the value 27.6 is much smaller, implying that this value gives more evidence against H_0: $\mu = 31\%$ in favor of the alternative H_a: $\mu < 31\%$.

IX.12. (a). (i). H_0: $\mu = 80$ vs. H_a: $\mu < 80$ (key word: "less")
(ii). $n = 20$, $\sigma = 10$, $\overline{X} = 74.2$
We have a simple random sample, and since the population is only slightly skewed the sample size is large enough for the central limit theorem to apply.

$$\text{So } Z = \frac{\overline{X} - \mu_o}{\sigma/\sqrt{n}} = \frac{74.2 - 80}{10/\sqrt{20}} = -2.59$$

(iii). p-value $= P(Z < -2.59) = .0048$.
(iv). $\alpha = .05$. Since p-value $< .05$ we reject the null hypothesis.
(v). There is **sufficient** evidence that the mean score of all people on the SOL test is less than 80 points.

(b). (i). H_0: $\mu = 80$ vs. H_a: $\mu < 80$
(ii). $n = 19$, $\sigma = 10$, $\overline{X} = 76.42$
We have a simple random sample, and since the population is only slightly skewed the sample size is large enough for the central limit theorem to apply.

$$\text{So } Z = \frac{\overline{X} - \mu_o}{\sigma/\sqrt{n}} = \frac{76.42 - 80}{10/\sqrt{19}} = -1.56$$

(iii). p-value = $P(Z < -1.56) = .0594$

(iv). $\alpha = .05$. Since p-value $> .05$ we fail to reject the null hypothesis.

(v). There is **insufficient** evidence that the mean score of all people on the SOL test is less than 80 points.

(c). One outlier can have a tremendous effect on the significance test. We know that outliers affect the sample mean. Therefore they also affect the test statistic, the p-value, and can ultimately affect the decision and conclusion of the test, as illustrated above.

IX.13. (i). H_0: $\mu = 50$ vs. H_a: $\mu > 50$

(ii). $n = 27$, $\sigma = 10$, $\overline{X} = 51.89$

We have a simple random sample, and since the population is only slightly skewed the sample size is large enough for the central limit theorem to apply.

$$\text{So } Z = \frac{\overline{X} - \mu_o}{\sigma/\sqrt{n}} = \frac{51.89 - 50}{10/\sqrt{27}} = .982$$

(iii). p-value = $P(Z > 0.982) = 1 - P(Z < 0.982) = 1 - .8365 = .1635$

(iv). $\alpha = .10$ Since p-value $> .10$ we fail to reject the null hypothesis.

(v). There is **insufficient** evidence that the mean AVSS score for all purchasers of 2006 Hummer H3 SUTs is greater than 50.

IX.14. (a). The statistical procedures are valid if we have a simple random sample and if either the population is normally distributed or the sample size is large enough for the central limit theorem to apply. We do have a simple random sample and the population standard deviation is known. The population is not known to be normal, but the sample size of 200 is large enough for the central limit theorem to apply.

(b). (i). H_0: $\mu = 75.45$ vs. H_a: $\mu < 75.45$

(ii). $n = 200$, $\overline{X} = 71.89$, $\sigma = 15$

$$Z = \frac{\overline{X} - \mu_o}{\sigma/\sqrt{n}} = \frac{71.89 - 75.45}{15/\sqrt{200}} = -3.36$$

(iii). p-value = $P(Z \le -3.36) = .0004$

(iv). $\alpha = .01$. Since the p-value $< .01$ we reject the null hypothesis.

(v). Therefore, there is **sufficient** evidence that the mean amount spent on groceries per trip by customers in Richmond, Virginia is less than the national mean.

IX.15. (a).

10●	4
10*	9, 7
11●	
11*	7, 8, 8, 7, 6, 8
12●	3, 2, 4, 0, 3, 4
12*	7, 5
13●	0
13*	

where 13 | 0 = 1.30

The distribution is fairly symmetric with no obvious outliers. Therefore, the sample size of 18 is large enough for the central limit theorem to apply and the Z procedures to be appropriate.

(b). $n = 18$, $\overline{X} = 1.19$, $\sigma = 0.09$

95% CI implies $Z^* = 1.960$

$$\overline{X} \pm Z^* \frac{\sigma}{\sqrt{n}} = 1.19 \pm 1.960 \left(\frac{.09}{\sqrt{18}} \right) = 1.19 \pm 0.04 = (1.15, 1.23)$$

We have 95% confidence that the mean weight of all cartons of chocolate ice cream produced that day is between 1.15 and 1.23 pounds.

(c). (i). $H_0: \mu = 1$ vs. $H_A: \mu \neq 1$ (key word is "different")

(ii). $Z = \dfrac{\overline{X} - \mu_o}{\sigma/\sqrt{n}} = \dfrac{1.19 - 1}{.09/\sqrt{18}} = \dfrac{.19}{.0212} = 8.96$

(iii). p-value $= 2 \times P(Z \geq |8.96|) = 2 \times P(Z \geq 8.96) = 2[1 - P(Z < 8.96) = 2(1 - .9998) = 2(.0002) = .0004$.

(iv). $\alpha = .05$ Since p-value $< \alpha$ we reject the null hypothesis.

(v). There is **sufficient** evidence that the mean weight of all cartons of chocolate ice cream produced that day is different from 1 pound.

(d). Since the hypothesized value under the null hypothesis, 1, is not in the confidence interval, then the result is significant and we would reject the null hypothesis. They do give the same information.

IX.16. (i). $H_0: \mu = 20$ vs. $H_A: \mu < 20$ (key word: "less")

(ii). $n = 55$, $\sigma = 10.6$, $\overline{X} = 19$

We have a simple random sample, and the sample size is large enough for the central limit theorem to apply.

So $Z = \dfrac{\overline{X} - \mu_o}{\sigma/\sqrt{n}} = \dfrac{19 - 20}{10.6/\sqrt{55}} = \dfrac{-1}{1.43} = -0.70$

(iii). p-value $= P(Z < -0.70) = .2420$.

(iv). Since the p-value is greater than .01, the test is not significant. We fail to reject H_0.

(v). There is **insufficient** evidence that the mean length of all food service contracts between universities and food service companies is less than 20 years.

IX.17. (i). $H_0: \mu = 7.2$ vs. $H_A: \mu < 7.2$ (key word: "less")

(ii). $n = 400$, $\sigma = 1.8$, $\overline{X} = 6.8$

We have a simple random sample, and the sample size is large enough for the central limit theorem to apply.

So $Z = \dfrac{\overline{X} - \mu_o}{\sigma/\sqrt{n}} = \dfrac{6.8 - 7.2}{1.8/\sqrt{400}} = -4.44$

(iii). p-value $= P(Z < -4.44) = \; < .0002$

(iv). $\alpha = .10$ Since the p-value is less than .10, the test is not significant. We reject H_0.

(v). There is **sufficient** evidence that the mean length that pet owners have owned their pets is less than 7.2 years.

IX.18. (i). $H_0: \mu = 7$ vs. $H_A: \mu \neq 7$

(ii). $n = 50$, $\overline{X} = 6.45$, $s = 1.7$

We have a simple random sample and the sample size is large enough for the central limit theorem to apply, so the assumptions are satisfied. We use a t distribution with 49 degrees of freedom.

$t = \dfrac{\overline{X} - \mu}{s/\sqrt{n}} = \dfrac{6.45 - 7}{1.7/\sqrt{50}} = \dfrac{-0.55}{.2404} = -2.288$

(iii). P-value $= 2\, P(t_{49} \geq |-2.288|) = 2\, P(t_{49} \geq 2.288)$

Since $.01 < P(t_{49} \geq 2.288) < .02$, then $.02 < $ p-value $< .04$

(iv). $\alpha = .05$ Since p-value $< .05$ we reject the null hypothesis

(v). There is **sufficient** evidence that the mean number of shoots per rhizome for all *Phagmites australis* rhizomes is different from 7.

IX.19. (a).

89 •	3
89 *	7, 5
90 •	1
90 *	6, 5, 6, 8, 6, 7
91 •	4, 3
91 *	6, 8, 8
92 •	1

This distribution is roughly symmetric with no outliers.
Use of the t procedures is justified.

where 92 | 1 = 912

(b). $n = 16$ so d.f. $= n - 1 = 16 - 1 = 15$ so $t_{15} = 2.131$

From the data, $\overline{X} = 907.75$ and $s = 8.48$.

$$\overline{X} \pm t_{15} \frac{s}{\sqrt{n}} = 907.75 \pm 2.131 \, (8.48/\sqrt{16}) = 907.75 \pm 4.52 = (903.23, 912.27)$$

We have 95% confidence that the mean potency of all crystals is between 903.23 and 912.27.

(c). $H_0: \mu = 910$ vs $H_A: \mu \neq 910$

$$t = \frac{\overline{X} - \mu}{s/\sqrt{n}} = \frac{907.75 - 910}{8.48/\sqrt{16}} = -1.061$$

d.f. $= n - 1 = 16 - 1 = 15$

p-value $= 2 \, P(t_{15} \geq |-1.061|)$ Since $.15 < P(t_{15} \geq 1.061) < .20$, then $.30 < $ p-value $< .40$.

$\alpha = .05$ Since p-value $> \alpha$ we fail to reject H_0.

Therefore, there is **insufficient** evidence to conclude that the mean potency is not equal to the standard release potency of 910.

IX.20. Parameter of interest $= \mu =$ mean age of all contributors to the YMCA Annual Giving campaign

(i) $H_0: \mu = 48.3$ vs. $H_A: \mu \neq 48.3$

(ii) $n = 29$, $\overline{X} = 45.4$ and $s = 6.2$

$$t = \frac{\overline{X} - \mu}{s/\sqrt{n}} = \frac{45.4 - 48.3}{6.2/\sqrt{29}} = \frac{-2.9}{1.1513} = -2.519$$

(iii) d.f. $= n - 1 = 29 - 1 = 28$

p-value $= 2 \, P(t_{28} \geq |-2.519|)$ Since $.005 < P(t_{28} \geq 2.519) < .01$, then $.01 < $ p-value $< .02$.

(iv) Since p-value $< .10$ the test is significant and we reject H_0.

(v) Therefore, there is **sufficient** evidence that the mean age of all contributors to the YMCA Annual Giving campaign is different from 48.3 years.

IX.21. Parameter of interest $= \mu =$ mean number of questions that each student got correct

(a). $n = 30$, $\overline{X} = 12$, $s = 3.05$, df $= 29$ so for a 90% CI $t^* = 1.699$

$$\overline{X} \pm t^* \frac{s}{\sqrt{n}} = 12 \pm 1.699 \left(\frac{3.05}{\sqrt{30}}\right) = 12 \pm 1.699(.5569) = 12 \pm .946 = (11.054, 12.946)$$

We have 90% confidence that the mean number of questions that all high school students get correct is between 11.054 and 12.946.

(b). (i) $H_0: \mu = 10$ versus $H_a: \mu \neq 10$

(ii) $t = \dfrac{\overline{X} - \mu}{s/\sqrt{n}} = \dfrac{12 - 10}{3.05/\sqrt{30}} = 3.592$

(iii) P-value $= 2 \, P(t_{29} \geq |3.592|) = 2 \, P(t_{29} \geq 3.592)$

$.0005 < P(t_{29} \geq 3.592) < .001$ so $.001 < $ p-value $< .002$

(iv) $\alpha = .10$ Since p-value $< .10$ we reject the null hypothesis.

(v) There is **sufficient** evidence that the mean number of questions that all high school students get correct is different from 10.

(c). Since the hypothesized value, 10, is not in the confidence interval calculated in part (a), then 10 is not a reasonable value and rejecting 10 makes sense. They do give the same information.

IX.22. (a). The population of interest is all the flights that did not arrive on time during 2001, and the parameter of interest = μ = is the mean delay time of all flights that did not arrive on time during 2001.

(b). n = 35, $\overline{X}$ = 14.2, s = 6.4, df = 34 so for a 90% CI t* = 1.697

$$\overline{X} \pm t^* \frac{s}{\sqrt{n}} = 14.2 \pm 1.697(\frac{6.4}{\sqrt{35}}) = 14.2 \pm 1.697(1.082) = 14.2 \pm 1.84 = (12.36, 16.04)$$

We have 90% confidence that the mean delay time of all flights that did not arrive on time during 2001 is between 12.36 and 16.04.

(c). (i) H_0: μ = 15   versus H_a: μ < 15

(ii) $t = \dfrac{\overline{X} - \mu}{s/\sqrt{n}} = \dfrac{14.2 - 15}{6.4/\sqrt{35}} = -0.740$

(iii) P-value = $P(t_{34} \geq |-0.740|) = P(t_{34} \geq 0.740) =$
.20 < $P(t_{34} \geq 0.740)$ < .25 , so .20 < p-value < .25

(iv) α = .10 Since p-value > .10 we fail to reject the null hypothesis.

(v) There is **insufficient** evidence that the mean delay time of all flights that did not arrive on time during 2001 is less than 15.

IX.23. Parameter of interest = μ = mean number of religious and charitable organizations to which all members of Congress have made contributions

(a).   n = 30, $\overline{X}$ = 17, s = 7.405, df = 29 so for a 99% CI t* = 2.756

$$\overline{X} \pm t^* \frac{s}{\sqrt{n}} = 17 \pm 2.756(\frac{7.405}{\sqrt{30}}) = 17 \pm 2.756(1.352) = 17 \pm 3.726 = (13.274, 20.726)$$

We have 99% confidence that the mean number of religious and charitable organizations to which all members of Congress have made contributions is between 13.274 and 20.726.

(b). (i) H_0: μ = 20   versus H_a: $\mu \neq$ 20

(ii) n= 30, $\overline{X}$ = 17, s = 7.405, df = n – 1 = 30 – 1 = 29

$t = \dfrac{\overline{X} - \mu}{s/\sqrt{n}} = \dfrac{17 - 20}{7.405/\sqrt{30}} = -2.219$

(iii) P-value = $2\ P(t_{29} \geq |-2.219|) = 2\ P(t_{29} \geq 2.219)$
Since .01 < $P(t_{29} \geq 2.219)$ < .02 , then .02 < p-value < .04

(iv) α = .01 Since p-value > .01 we fail to reject the null hypothesis.

(v) There is **insufficient** evidence that the mean number of religious and charitable organizations to which all members of Congress have made contributions is different from 20.

(c). The hypothesized value 20 is contained in the confidence interval computed in part (a). Hence 20 is a reasonable value and not rejecting 20 makes sense.

IX.24. (a.). We have a simple random sample, the sample of size 51 is large enough for the central limit theorem to apply, and the population standard deviation is <u>not</u> known.

(b). For a 95% confidence interval $t^* = 2.009$, so the 95% confidence interval is:

$$\overline{X} \pm t^* \frac{s}{\sqrt{n}} = 18.7 \pm 2.009(\frac{2.4}{\sqrt{51}}) = 18.7 \pm 0.675 = (18.025, 19.375)$$

(c). (i). This is the correct interpretation of the interval.

(ii). When interpreting confidence intervals we should not talk about individual values, but instead about the parameter of interest (the population mean in this case).

(iii). This is not appropriate- we are making inferences about the population mean, not the sample mean.

(iv). The population mean will likely be close to the sample mean but it will most likely not equal it exactly.

(v). This is the correct definition of the 95% confidence interval.

(vi). When interpreting confidence intervals, we should use the term confidence, not the term probability.

(d). H_0: $\mu=20$ versus H_a: $\mu \neq 20$.

The confidence interval is (18.025, 19.375), and the hypothesized value 20 is not in the interval. Hence it is not a reasonable number and hence the null hypothesis would be rejected. Hence we would conclude that there is sufficient evidence that the mean weight of all Butterball turkeys sold by the local store for Thanksgiving 2009 is different from 20 pounds.

IX.25. Parameter of interest = μ = the mean amount of time it took all fans to park one they were within one mile of the RIR complex

$n = 31$, $\overline{X} = 69$, $s = 11.4$, $df = 30$ so for a 98% CI $t^* = 2.457$

$$\overline{X} \pm t^* \frac{s}{\sqrt{n}} = 69 \pm 2.457(\frac{11.4}{\sqrt{31}}) = 69 \pm 2.457(2.048) = 69 \pm 5.03 = (63.97, 74.03)$$

We have a 98% confidence that the mean amount of time it took all fans to park one they were within one mile of the RIR complex is between 63.97 and 74.03 minutes.

IX.26. Parameter of interest = μ = mean miles per gallon in all new Hummer H3 SUT's

(i) H_0: $\mu = 18$ versus H_a: $\mu \neq 18$
   $n = 20$, $\overline{X} = 17.84$, $s = .29$, $df = 19$

(ii) $t = \dfrac{\overline{X} - \mu}{s/\sqrt{n}} = \dfrac{17.84 - 18}{0.29/\sqrt{20}} = -2.467$

(iii) P-value = 2 $P(t_{19} \geq |-2.467|) = 2 P(t_{19} \geq 2.467)$
   Since $.01 < P(t_{19} \geq 2.467) < .02$, then $.02 < $ p-value $ < .04$

(iv) $\alpha = .05$ Since p-value $< .05$ we reject the null hypothesis.

(v) There is **sufficient** evidence that the mean miles per gallon in all new Hummer H3 SUT's is different from 18 mpg.

X.1. Community College R: $\mu_1 = 2.85$, $\sigma_1 = 0.63$, $n_1 = 37$
Community College T: $\mu_2 = 2.91$, $\sigma_2 = 0.58$, $n_2 = 42$

(a). We have independent, simple random samples and since the distributions are not known to be heavily skewed then the sample sizes are large enough for the central limit theorem to apply. Therefore, the sampling distribution can be described, as follows.

$$\mu_{\overline{x}_1 - \overline{x}_2} = \mu_1 - \mu_2 = 2.85 - 2.91 = -0.06$$

$$\sigma_{\overline{x}_1 - \overline{x}_2} = \sqrt{\frac{\sigma_1^2}{n_1} + \frac{\sigma_2^2}{n_2}} = \sqrt{\frac{0.63^2}{37} + \frac{0.58^2}{42}} = .1369$$

So the sampling distribution is $\overline{X}_1 - \overline{X}_2 \sim N(-0.06, .1369)$.

(b). $P(\overline{X}_1 - \overline{X}_2 > 0) = P\left(Z > \dfrac{0 - (-0.06)}{.1369} \right) = P(Z > 0.44) = 1 - P(Z < 0.44) = 1 - .6700 = .3300$

X.2. First book company: $\mu_1 = 121.25$, $\sigma_1 = 32.89$, $n_1 = 43$
Second book company: $\mu_2 = 118.32$, $\sigma_2 = 38.15$, $n_2 = 50$

(a). We have independent, simple random samples and since the distributions are not known to be heavily skewed then the sample sizes are large enough for the central limit theorem to apply. Therefore, the sampling distribution can be described, as follows.

$$\mu_{\overline{x}_1 - \overline{x}_2} = \mu_1 - \mu_2 = 121.25 - 118.32 = 2.93$$

$$\sigma_{\overline{X}_1 - \overline{X}_2} = \sqrt{\frac{\sigma_1^2}{n_1} + \frac{\sigma_2^2}{n_2}} = \sqrt{\frac{32.89^2}{43} + \frac{38.15^2}{50}} = 7.3665$$

So the sampling distribution is $\overline{X}_1 - \overline{X}_2 \sim N(2.93, 7.3665)$.

(b). $P(5 < \overline{X}_1 - \overline{X}_2 < 10) = P\left(\frac{5 - 2.93}{7.3665} < Z < \frac{10 - 2.93}{7.3665}\right) = P(0.28 < Z < 0.96)$

$= P(Z < 0.96) - P(Z < 0.28) = .8315 - .6103 = .2212$

X.3. μ_1 = mean age of Florida voters

μ_2 = mean age of voters from the other 49 states

(1) $H_0: \mu_1 = \mu_2$ versus $H_a: \mu_1 > \mu_2$

(2) $n_1 = 29$ $\overline{X}_1 = 47.9$ $\sigma_1 = 11.4$

      $n_2 = 267$ $\overline{X}_2 = 47.5$ $\sigma_2 = 12.7$

We have independent simple random samples and the sample sizes are large enough for the central limit theorem to apply.

$$Z = \frac{(\overline{X}_1 - \overline{X}_2) - \mu_0}{\sqrt{\frac{\sigma_1^2}{n_1} + \frac{\sigma_2^2}{n_2}}} = \frac{(47.9 - 47.5) - 0}{\sqrt{\frac{11.4^2}{29} + \frac{12.7^2}{267}}} = \frac{0.4}{2.255} = 0.18$$

(3)   p-value = $P(Z \geq 0.18) = 1 - P(Z < 0.18) = 1 - .5714 = .4286$

(4) $\alpha = .05$ Since p-value > .05 we fail to reject the null hypothesis

(5)   There is insufficient evidence that the mean age of Florida voters is greater than the mean age of voters from the other 49 states.

X.4. (a).   This is not a controlled experiment - the mothers choose which method to use, so no treatment is applied. Since this is an observational study, the results may be confounded with other factors that affect the choice of the mothers. The inferences made in the work below may be misleading.

(b).   Let BF = breast fed, FO = formula

(1) $H_0: \mu_{BF} = \mu_{FO}$ $(\mu_{BF} - \mu_{FO} = 0)$

      $H_a: \mu_{BF} \neq \mu_{FO}$ $(\mu_{BF} - \mu_{FO} \neq 0)$

(2) $t = \frac{(\overline{X}_{BF} - \overline{X}_{FO}) - \mu_0}{\sqrt{\frac{s_{BF}^2}{n_{BF}} + \frac{s_{FO}^2}{n_{FO}}}} = \frac{(13.3 - 12.4) - 0}{\sqrt{\frac{1.7^2}{23} + \frac{1.8^2}{19}}} = \frac{0.9}{.544} = 1.654$

(3)   df = min (23-1=22, 19-1=18) = 18

      p-value = $2\, P(t_{18} \geq |1.654|) = 2\, P(t_{18} \geq 1.654)$

      $.05 < P(t_{18} \geq 1.654) < .10$

      $.10 < $ p-value $< .20$

(4)   Since p-value > .10 the test is insignificant and we fail to reject H_0

(5)   There is insufficient evidence that the mean hemoglobin level is different among breast fed babies than formula babies.

(c).   df = min (23 - 1=22, 19 - 1=18) = 18   95% CI $\Rightarrow t_{18} = 2.101$

$$(\overline{X}_{BF} - \overline{X}_{FO}) \pm t_{18}^* \sqrt{\frac{s_{BF}^2}{n_{BF}} + \frac{s_{FO}^2}{n_{FO}}} = (13.3 - 12.4) \pm 2.101 \sqrt{\frac{1.7^2}{23} + \frac{1.8^2}{19}} = 0.9 \pm 2.101(.544)$$

$= 0.9 \pm 1.143 = (-0.243, 2.043)$

We have 95% confidence that the mean difference in hemoglobin levels between the two populations is between -0.243 and 2.043. Since 0 is contained within this interval, there is not sufficient evidence that there is a difference between the two groups.

X.5. (a). $n_1 = 100$ $\overline{X}_1 = 16.5$ $s_1 = 14.2$

$n_2 = 100$ $\overline{X}_2 = 7.0$ $s_2 = 13.1$

$df = \min(100 - 1, 100 - 1) = 99 \; t^* = 1.660$

$$\left(\overline{X}_1 - \overline{X}_2\right) \pm t^* \sqrt{\frac{s_1^2}{n_1} + \frac{s_2^2}{n_2}} = (16.5 - 7.0) \pm 1.660 \sqrt{\frac{14.2^2}{100} + \frac{13.1^2}{100}} = 9.5 \pm 1.660(1.932) = 9.5 \pm 3.2$$

$= (6.3, 12.7)$

We have 90% confidence that the difference in the mean IQ gain for all students in the experimental group and mean IQ gain for all students in the control group is between 6.3 and 12.7.

(b). The mean IQ gain for all students in the experimental group and the mean IQ gain of all students in the control group are not known so <u>we do not know</u> if their difference is in the interval or not.

X.6. $\mu_1 =$ mean wait-time to ride using regular stand-by line

$\mu_2 =$ mean wait-time to ride using FASTPASS

$n_1 = 73$ $\overline{X}_1 = 84$ $s_1 = 17$

$n_2 = 41$ $\overline{X}_2 = 9.5$ $s_2 = 3$

$df = 40$, 95% CI implies $t^* = 2.021$

$$\left(\overline{X}_1 - \overline{X}_2\right) \pm t^* \sqrt{\frac{s_1^2}{n_1} + \frac{s_2^2}{n_2}} = (84 - 9.5) \pm 2.021 \sqrt{\frac{17^2}{73} + \frac{3^2}{41}} = 74.5 \pm 2.021(2.044) = 74.5 \pm 4.13$$

$= (70.37, 78.63)$

We have 95% confidence that the difference in the mean wait times of stand-by riders versus FASTPASS riders is between 70.37 and 78.63 minutes.

X.7. $\mu_1 =$ mean number of traffic violations for men

$\mu_2 =$ mean number of traffic violations for women

$n_1 = 61$ $\overline{X}_1 = 8.4$ $s_1 = 3.9$

$n_2 = 65$ $\overline{X}_2 = 6.8$ $s_2 = 3.7$

(1) H_0: $\mu_1 = \mu_2$ $(\mu_1 - \mu_2 = 0)$

       H_a: $\mu_1 \neq \mu_2$ $(\mu_1 - \mu_2 \neq 0)$

(2) $t = \dfrac{\left(\overline{X}_1 - \overline{X}_2\right) - \mu_0}{\sqrt{\dfrac{s_1^2}{n_1} + \dfrac{s_2^2}{n_2}}} = \dfrac{(8.4 - 6.8) - 0}{\sqrt{\dfrac{3.9^2}{61} + \dfrac{3.7^2}{65}}} = \dfrac{1.6}{.678} = 2.359$

(3) $df = \min(61 - 1 = 60, 65 - 1 = 64) = 60$

       p-value $= 2P(t_{60} \geq |2.359|) = 2P(t_{60} \geq 2.359)$

       $.01 < P(t_{60} \geq 2.359) < .02 \Rightarrow .02 < $ p-value $< .04$

(4)   Since the p-value $< .05$ we reject H_0

(5)   There is sufficient evidence that the mean number of traffic violations for men and women are different.

X.8. $\mu_1 =$ mean number of strokes at Carambola Golf Course

$\mu_2 =$ mean number of strokes at Mahogany Run Golf Course

$n_1 = 70$ $\overline{X}_1 = 79.4$ $s_1 = 7.2$

$n_2 = 41$ $\overline{X}_2 = 83.2$ $s_2 = 6.8$

$df = 40$, 95% CI implies $t^* = 2.021$

$$\left(\overline{X}_1 - \overline{X}_2\right) \pm t^* \sqrt{\frac{s_1^2}{n_1} + \frac{s_2^2}{n_2}} = (79.4 - 83.2) \pm 2.021 \sqrt{\frac{7.2^2}{70} + \frac{6.8^2}{41}} = -3.8 \pm 2.021(1.367) = -3.8 \pm 2.76$$

= (-6.56, -1.04)

We have 95% confidence that the difference in the mean number of strokes at the Carambola Golf Course and the Mahogany Run Golf Course is between -6.56 and -1.04 (or 1.04 and 6.56) strokes.

X.9. μ_1 = mean credit card debt for all American male adults

μ_2 = mean credit card debt for all American female adults

$n_1 = 66 \qquad \overline{X}_1 = 3254 \qquad s_1 = 893$

$n_2 = 41 \qquad \overline{X}_2 = 3667 \qquad s_2 = 917$

(1) $H_0: \mu_1 = \mu_2 \quad (\mu_1 - \mu_2 = 0)$

$H_a: \mu_1 < \mu_2 \quad (\mu_1 - \mu_2 < 0)$

(2) $t = \dfrac{(\overline{X}_1 - \overline{X}_2) - \mu_0}{\sqrt{\dfrac{s_1^2}{n_1} + \dfrac{s_2^2}{n_2}}} = \dfrac{(3254 - 3667) - 0}{\sqrt{\dfrac{893^2}{66} + \dfrac{917^2}{41}}} = \dfrac{-413}{180.53} = -2.288$

(3) df = min(66 - 1 = 65, 41 - 1 = 40) = 40

p-value = $P(t_{40} \le -2.288) = P(t_{40} \ge 2.288)$

$.0025 < P(t_{40} \ge 2.288) < .005$

(4) Since the p-value < .05 we reject H_0

(5) There is sufficient evidence that the mean credit card debt for all American male adults is less than the mean credit card debt for all American female adults.

X.10. μ_1 = mean verbal SAT score for all students taking STAT 208

μ_2 = mean verbal SAT score for all students taking STAT 210

$n_1 = 41 \qquad \overline{X}_1 = 515 \qquad s_1 = 33$

$n_2 = 77 \qquad \overline{X}_2 = 506 \qquad s_2 = 28$

(a). df = 40, 90% CI implies t* = 1.684

$$\left(\overline{X}_1 - \overline{X}_2\right) \pm t^* \sqrt{\dfrac{s_1^2}{n_1} + \dfrac{s_2^2}{n_2}} = (515 - 506) \pm 1.684 \sqrt{\dfrac{33^2}{41} + \dfrac{28^2}{77}} = 9 \pm 1.684(6.061) = 9 \pm 10.2$$

= (-1.2, 19.2)

We have 90% confidence that the difference in the mean verbal SAT score for all students taking STAT 208 and the mean verbal SAT score for all students taking STAT 210 is between -1.2 and 19.2.

(b). $H_0: \mu_1 = \mu_2$ versus $H_A: \mu_1 \ne \mu_2$

Since 0 is contained in the 90% confidence interval then it is a reasonable value and we would fail to reject the null hypothesis. Hence there is insufficient evidence that there is a difference between the mean verbal SAT score for all students taking STAT 208 and the mean verbal SAT score for all students taking STAT 210.

X.11. White-collar $\qquad n_1 = 30 \qquad \overline{X}_1 = 57.2 \qquad s_1 = 4.9$

Blue-collar $\qquad n_2 = 34 \qquad \overline{X}_2 = 61.4 \qquad s_2 = 4.6$

(1) $H_0: \mu_1 = \mu_2 \quad (\mu_1 - \mu_2 = 0)$

$H_a: \mu_1 < \mu_2 \quad (\mu_1 - \mu_2 < 0)$

(2) $t = \dfrac{(\overline{X}_1 - \overline{X}_2) - \mu_0}{\sqrt{\dfrac{s_1^2}{n_1} + \dfrac{s_2^2}{n_2}}} = \dfrac{(57.2 - 61.4) - 0}{\sqrt{\dfrac{4.9^2}{30} + \dfrac{4.6^2}{34}}} = \dfrac{-4.2}{1.19276} = -3.521$

(3) df = min(30 - 1 = 29, 34 - 1 = 33) = 29

p-value = $P(t_{29} \le -3.521) = P(t_{29} > 3.521) \Rightarrow .0005 < $ p-value $ < .001$

(4) Since the p-value < .05 we reject H_0

(5) There is sufficient evidence that the mean retirement age of white-collar workers is lower than the mean retirement age of blue-collar workers.

X.12. UVA $\quad n_1 = 11 \qquad \overline{X}_1 = 3.41 \qquad s_1 = 0.53$

VCU $\quad n_2 = 9 \qquad \overline{X}_2 = 3.17 \qquad s_2 = 0.59$

(1) H_0: $\mu_1 = \mu_2$ $(\mu_1 - \mu_2 = 0)$
H_a: $\mu_1 \neq \mu_2$ $(\mu_1 - \mu_2 \neq 0)$

(2) Since the sample sizes are 11 and 9, the populations must be known to be normal. This is not the case, so the test cannot be completed using the t-test procedure described in this chapter.

X.13. (a). One might want the population of interest to be all American adults. However, the sample consists of only 20 healthy nonsmoking American males, so inferences can only be made to the population of all healthy nonsmoking American males.

(b). The answer would depend on how the drugs are assigned to the males. If the subject gets to choose which drug is used first, then it would be an observational study. If the experimenter controls which drug each male uses first (the more likely scenario) then it would be a controlled experiment. In either case the treatment is the "name" drug versus the generic drug, and the response the absorption extent.

(c). For each of the 20 subjects the differences can be computed, as below.

4108	1755	2353
2526	**1138**	1388
2779	**1613**	1166
3852	2254	1598
1833	1310	523
2463	**2120**	343
2059	1851	208
1709	1878	-169
1829	1682	147
2594	**2613**	-19
2344	**2738**	-394
1864	2302	-438
1022	**1284**	-262
2256	**3052**	-796
938	**1287**	-349
1339	**1930**	-591
1262	1964	-702
1438	2549	-1111
1735	**3340**	-1605
1020	3050	-2030

The mean difference is $\overline{X}_d = -37$ and the standard deviation of the differences is $s_d = 1070.622$. Then the test is as follows.

(1) H_0: $\mu_1 - \mu_2 = 0$ versus H_A: $\mu_1 - \mu_2 \neq 0$

(2) $t = \dfrac{\overline{X}_d - \mu_0}{s_d / \sqrt{n}} = \dfrac{-37 - 0}{1070.622 / \sqrt{20}} = \dfrac{-37}{239.4} = -0.155$

(3) p-value $= 2\, P(t_{19} \geq 0.155)$. From the t-table, $P(t_{19} \geq 0.155) > .25$, so p-value $> .50$.

(4) Since p-value $> .10$ we fail to reject the null hypothesis.

(5) There is insufficient evidence that the mean absorption for the two drugs is different.

X.14. The mean difference is $\overline{X}_d = 5.8$ and the standard deviation of the differences is $s_d = 24.6$. The assumptions are satisfied, so the paired t-test is as follows.

(1) $H_0: \mu_1 - \mu_2 = 0$ versus $H_A: \mu_1 - \mu_2 \neq 0$

(2) $t = \dfrac{\overline{X}_d - \mu_0}{s_d / \sqrt{n}} = \dfrac{5.8 - 0}{24.6 / \sqrt{40}} = \dfrac{5.8}{3.89} = 1.491$

(3) p-value $= 2\, P(t_{39} \geq 1.491)$. From the t-table, $.05 < P(t_{39} \geq 1.491) < .10$, so $.10 <$ p-value $< .20$.

(4) Since p-value $> .05$ we fail to reject the null hypothesis.

(5) There is insufficient evidence that the mean number of days using Duracell batteries and the mean number of days using Energizer batteries are different.

Glossary

Alternative (or research) hypothesis - usually denoted by H_a or H_1, is a conjecture about a population parameter that the researcher suspects or hopes is true.

Bias - anything, such as a factor not considered, that systematically favors certain outcomes over others and which causes the experimenter to question the validity of the results.

Bimodal – a distribution with two significant peaks to the curve.

Blinding – occurs when the experimental units do not know to which group they have been assigned.

Boxplot - a graphical display that uses the numerical measures in a five-number summary to give information on the symmetry or skewness of a distribution, on the central location and variability (spread) in a distribution, and on the concentrations of data values in the tails of a distribution (outliers).

Central limit theorem - if the sample size is sufficiently large, it states that the distribution of $\overline{X}$ will be approximately normal, regardless of the population distribution.

Class frequency - the number of observations falling in a particular class interval

Class intervals – the divisions of the possible measurements of a quantitative variable.

Coefficient of determination - the square of the correlation coefficient and represents the proportion (fraction) of the total variation in the Y values that is explained by the X variable.

Conditional distributions – the distribution of the categories of one variable given a specific category of a second variable.

Confidence interval – uses sample data to estimate an unknown population parameter with an indication of how accurate the estimate is and of how confident we are that the result is correct.

Confidence level C - implies that if repeated simple random samples of the same size are taken from the same population and a confidence interval is computed for each sample, then 100 x C% of these confidence intervals would contain the true value of the parameter (in the current case the parameter is μ) and 100 x (1 – C)% of these confidence intervals would not contain the true value of the parameter.

Confounding - the existence of some factor other than the treatment that makes the treatment and control groups different.

Constant - when the measurements of some characteristic do not change in repeated trials over time.

Continuous quantitative variable - a variable whose measurements can assume any one of a countless number of values in a line interval.

Control Group - group of experimental units who do not receive the treatment.

Correlation coefficient - a numerical measure of the direction and strength of the linear relationship between two variables.

Degrees of freedom – a quantity associated with the variability of a statistic that is used to specify the distribution of the statistic.

Dependent variable – (or response variable) the measurement variable Y, that measures an outcome of a process that is the effect or consequence of the independent variable.

Descriptive statistics - (or exploratory data analysis) the branch of statistics concerned with numerical and graphical techniques for describing one or more characteristics of a population and for comparing characteristics among populations.

Discrete quantitative variable - a variable whose measurements can assume only a <u>countable</u> number of possible values.

Dispersion parameter - measures the amount of spread or variability around this center.

Distribution - a listing of all the possible values that a characteristic can take and the number (or percentage) of times that each value occurs.

Double-blinding – occurs when the experimental units, as well as, those people who are conducting the experiment and have contact with the experimental units also do not know to which group the experimental units have been assigned.

Experimental units - the subjects (individuals, units) on which the measurements are made.

Extrapolation - predicting Y values for X values outside the range of the original values.

Five-number summary – consists of the smallest observation, the first quartile, the median, the third quartile, and the largest observation, written in order from smallest to largest.

Frequency histogram – a histogram that displays the class frequencies on the vertical axis.

Frequency table – for a histogram, a listing of the class intervals, class frequencies, and relative frequencies.

Haphazard sample - involves selecting a sample by some convenient mechanism that does not involve randomization.

Histogram – a graphical procedure that breaks the range of values of a quantitative variable into class intervals and displays the number of (or percentage of) the observations in that interval

Independent variable – (or explanatory variable) is the measurement variable X, that has no restraints placed on it and that attempts to explain the observed outcomes of another variable

Inference - a statement about a population based on the data collected in a sample.

Inferential statistics - the branch of statistics in which we use data and statistics computed from a sample to make inferences (statements) about a population.

Influential observations – with two variables, observations that are separated in the X (horizontal) direction from the other observations and have an unusually large influence on the position of the regression line.

Intercept - the value of Y when X = 0 (location where the line crosses the Y - axis)

Interquartile range (IQR) - a measure of the dispersion around the median that is resistant to outliers.

Location parameter - a measurement of where the center of a distribution lies.

Lower adjacent value - the smallest observation that remains in the data set after removing outliers.

Lower one-sided test - a significance test in which evidence against the null hypothesis requires a statistic less than the hypothesized parameter value.

Lower quartile - denoted Q_1, the measurement that is larger than 25% of the data and that is smaller than 75% of the data.

Lurking variable – a variable that has an important effect on the relationship among the variables in a study but is not included among the variables studied.

Marginal distribution - lists the categories of the variable together with either the frequency (count) or relative frequency (percentage) of observations in each category.

Margin of error - derived from the sampling distribution of the point estimate, the quantity subtracted from and added to the point estimate to create a confidence interval.

Mean – a measure of central location that involves averaging the observations and which is influenced by outliers.

Median - a measure of central location that is larger than half of the data and smaller than the other half of the data, also resistant to outliers.

Method of least squares – determines the values for the intercept and slope and involves minimizing the sum of the squared residuals.

Middle quartile - the central measurement that is larger than 50% of the data and that is smaller than the other 50% of the data.

Multistage random sampling – sampling in which the population is divided into clusters (groups) of individuals and simple random sampling is used to randomly select several of these clusters.

Negative association - when small values of X are associated with large values of Y, and large values of X are associated with small values of Y.

Nonresponse bias - exists when individuals chosen for the sample cannot be contacted or fail (or refuse) to respond.

Normal distribution - an example of a continuous distribution which has the same symmetric shape, and is completely specified by the population mean μ and the population standard deviation σ of the distribution.

Null hypothesis - usually denoted by H_0, is a conjecture about a population parameter that is presumed to be true and is usually a statement of no effect or no change.

Observational study - a procedure in which we <u>cannot</u> (or do not) control which experimental units are assigned to the two groups and hence only observe anecdotal evidence.

Outlier - with a single variable, an observation that stands out from the other observations (an extreme value). With two variables, an observation that lies far above or below the regression line and hence produces a large residual.

Parameter - some characteristic of the population that the researcher wants to measure

Placebo - a fake treatment, such as a sugar pill, that is given to the experimental units in the control group which (hopefully) prevents them from knowing if they received the treatment or not.

Point estimate – a single value estimate of a parameter.

Population - the entire group of individuals (subjects) about which the researcher wants information.

Population density curve - a smoothed version of a relative frequency histogram

Population mean - denoted by the Greek letter μ and is the sum of all the measurements divided by how many measurements there are.

Population standard deviation - denoted by σ and usually estimated by the sample standard deviation.

Population variance - denoted by the Greek symbol σ^2, it is a measure of variability about the population mean that is influenced by outliers

Positive association - when small values of X are associated with small values of Y and if large values of X are associated with large values of Y.

P-value - the probability, assuming the null hypothesis is true, that the test statistic takes a value as extreme or more extreme than the value actually observed.

Qualitative - (or categorical) **variable** is a variable whose measurements vary in kind or name but not in degree, meaning that they cannot be arranged in order of magnitude.

Quantitative variable - is a variable whose measurements vary in magnitude from trial to trial, meaning some order or ranking can be applied.

Randomization – the use of impersonal chance to assign experimental units to treatments.

Range - the simplest measure of data variation, being the difference between the smallest and largest observations, can also be heavily influenced by outliers.

Relative frequencies - the percentages of observations in each interval of a histogram.

Relative frequency histogram - a histogram that displays the relative frequencies on the vertical axis.

Replication – repetition of the experiment on many units to reduce chance variation in the results.

Regression line – a straight line that describes how a response variable y changes as an explanatory variable x changes.

Rejection region – a range of values that the test statistic can take that would lead us to reject the null hypothesis in favor of the alternative hypothesis.

Residual – the difference between an observed value of the response variable and the value predicted by the regression line.

Response bias - exists when the respondents give inaccurate information or if the interviewer influences the subject to respond in a certain way due to the wording of the question.

Sample - a subset of the population

Sample mean - denoted by $\overline{X}$, it is the sum of all the measurements in the sample divided by the sample size.

Sample standard deviation - the square root of the variance ($s = \sqrt{s^2}$), which measures spread by looking at how far the observations are from their mean.

Sample variance - denoted by s^2, it is a measure of variability about the sample mean that is influenced by outliers.

Sampling distribution - the distribution of values taken by the statistic in a large number of simple random samples of the same size n from the same population.

Scatterplot – the graphical display of the relationship between two quantitative variables.

Selection bias - exists when one or more types of subjects are systematically excluded from the sample.

Significance level - denoted by α, the probability of rejecting the null hypothesis when it is actually true that a researcher is willing to risk.

Significance test – a statistical test to assess the amount of evidence against a null hypothesis in favor of an alternative (research) hypothesis.

Simple random sampling – listing all possible individuals in the population and randomly choosing n of the subjects in such a way that every set of n subjects has an equal chance to be in the sample.

Simpson's Paradox – with categorical variables, the existence of a lurking variable that results in the reversal of the direction of the relationship when data from several groups are combined to form a single group.

Skewed – a distribution with the general bell-shape but which has one tail that is longer than the other.

Slope - the amount that Y changes when X is increased by one unit.

Standard deviation – a measure of spread around the mean that is influenced by outliers and which measures a typical deviation from the mean.

Standard error - when the standard deviation of a statistic is estimated from the sample data.

Standard normal distribution – usually denoted by Z, the normal distribution $N(0,1)$ with mean = 0 and standard deviation = 1.

Statistic - a descriptive measure, usually computed from a sample, which can be expressed or evaluated numerically

Statistical hypothesis - a statement about a population parameter

Statistical inference - involves using statistics computed from a sample to estimate unknown population parameters.

Statistics - a science that involves the extraction of information from numerical data obtained during an experiment or from a sample.

Stem-and-leaf plot - used to help sort a large list of data and to graphically display the distribution of the data.

Stratified random sampling – sampling in which the population is naturally divided into two or more groups of similar subjects, called strata, and a representative number of subjects are selected from each strata.

Student's t distributions – the sampling distribution of Student's t statistic that is specified by the appropriate degrees of freedom and that has a mean of 0 and a standard deviation that depends on the degrees of freedom.

Symmetric – when the right and left sides of a distribution are approximately mirror images of each other.

Table of Random Digits – a randomly generated set of digits used to randomly select subjects for a sample

Table of Standard Normal Probabilities - gives the probability that Z falls below some specified value z.

Test statistic - a quantity calculated from the data that we have collected that we use to assess the strength of the evidence against the null hypothesis

Treatment group(s) - the group or groups of experimental units who receive the treatment(s).

Trimodal - a distribution with three significant peaks to the curve

Two-sided test - a significance test in which evidence against the null hypothesis requires either a statistic greater than the hypothesized parameter value or less than the hypothesized parameter value.

Upper adjacent value - the largest observation that remains in the data set after removing outliers.

Upper one-sided test – a significance test in which evidence against the null hypothesis requires a statistic greater than the hypothesized parameter value.

Upper quartile - denoted Q_3, the measurement that is larger than 75% of the data and that is smaller than the other 25%.

Variable - when the measurements of some characteristic vary from trial to trial

Variance - a measure of variability about the mean that is influenced by outliers

Volunteer response sample - exists when people volunteer to be part of a study.

Z-score – a standardized value that tells us how many standard deviations the original observation falls away from the mean, and in which direction.

Z-score transformation – a method for converting any normal distribution to a standard normal distribution by subtracting the mean and dividing by the standard deviation.

Table of Random Digits

Line								
101	03316	88692	53340	64121	93600	58636	08900	12724
102	81868	52573	87151	50490	84552	49367	46816	24178
103	95761	90056	04312	31893	02384	16925	90656	53372
104	51025	36290	18132	02938	02150	88741	55300	12428
105	11937	82853	31685	11486	59505	35119	57067	51717
106	84826	32337	45195	84898	16953	96758	53791	06928
107	86382	45403	87201	27649	44575	33063	85848	14592
108	75532	22725	00795	76688	65194	75186	29485	92454
109	61181	19909	81982	83485	81940	47052	42648	32160
110	32592	90597	85117	87964	56934	35435	12531	68508
111	70915	43163	48409	94383	33586	66979	84569	09547
112	11776	69680	62103	50211	15373	90785	72460	97150
113	45785	88604	27611	17297	08563	26185	20903	96565
114	39950	24870	41842	48767	19876	62253	47500	97245
115	08708	50842	87136	82226	37741	14526	60705	08727
116	41979	00360	62224	82425	93623	56202	09931	87209
117	18883	48394	43742	42514	93739	22553	46109	36071
118	14893	79177	98624	79367	85576	73089	61762	41903
119	47487	98481	65956	27601	06489	71238	77919	39244
120	59335	79140	41448	62371	54303	42006	94591	91596
121	03547	28918	63553	27001	16703	35101	81973	35797
122	48501	85475	09429	09763	83946	81953	27022	99730
123	88006	89579	10365	91576	35006	81899	19924	20542
124	76630	96301	07119	17955	20206	10493	66321	58727
125	69618	99562	51085	46503	64202	68379	31935	25417
126	90449	77921	02368	92157	76384	00358	46949	56307
127	98253	37570	01011	14577	19474	67412	99324	98420
128	25280	42167	52162	98427	33609	52210	83197	40836
129	95725	24130	07056	34914	33278	29515	02050	25832
130	94953	85393	48663	70060	00913	54914	29820	42878
131	18510	25595	54164	53976	12426	28277	26504	80059
132	22851	46573	32639	76072	08002	63976	87025	83765
133	44592	22368	29334	90725	40742	07523	20795	92351
134	32812	10480	02488	64364	57802	62765	43972	35648
135	58104	15011	81525	08962	78095	89634	57047	54328
136	35749	01536	29676	95012	66999	18584	23632	81652
137	64951	02011	00742	15664	84979	56349	17403	92350
138	55157	81647	05366	16408	21199	42595	14349	24822
139	40719	91646	91921	18629	38140	83473	42559	71013
140	90707	69179	00582	73115	50001	73577	85900	41035
141	89868	14194	00725	57491	91227	27958	23792	19792
142	74952	62590	69011	30405	91340	90994	23167	69298
143	90322	36207	23306	16631	44657	18845	47498	54224
144	78188	20969	69884	96773	55612	94824	05520	35552
145	64952	99570	65795	38935	21581	35605	04153	75366
146	56941	91291	25972	31624	21457	33362	20492	20801
147	32307	90700	29576	78919	16153	87820	93526	39908
148	12952	99505	20591	03931	04711	39475	31662	73823
149	42880	58629	57392	44268	42238	06990	33339	11052
150	54613	16379	50421	37926	41847	40980	83974	63318

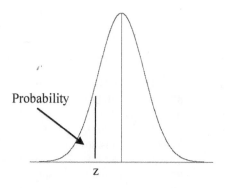

Probability

Probabilities in the body of the table are the probabilities of being <u>less than</u> the given value of z.

Standard Normal Probabilities

z	.00	.01	.02	.03	.04	.05	.06	.07	.08	.09
-3.4	.0003	.0003	.0003	.0003	.0003	.0003	.0003	.0003	.0003	.0002
-3.3	.0005	.0005	.0005	.0004	.0004	.0004	.0004	.0004	.0004	.0003
-3.2	.0007	.0007	.0006	.0006	.0006	.0006	.0006	.0005	.0005	.0005
-3.1	.0010	.0009	.0009	.0009	.0008	.0008	.0008	.0008	.0007	.0007
-3.0	.0013	.0013	.0013	.0012	.0012	.0011	.0011	.0011	.0010	.0010
-2.9	.0019	.0018	.0018	.0017	.0016	.0016	.0015	.0015	.0014	.0014
-2.8	.0026	.0025	.0024	.0023	.0023	.0022	.0021	.0021	.0020	.0019
-2.7	.0035	.0034	.0033	.0032	.0031	.0030	.0029	.0028	.0027	.0026
-2.6	.0047	.0045	.0044	.0043	.0041	.0040	.0039	.0038	.0037	.0036
-2.5	.0062	.0060	.0059	.0057	.0055	.0054	.0052	.0051	.0049	.0048
-2.4	.0082	.0080	.0078	.0075	.0073	.0071	.0069	.0068	.0066	.0064
-2.3	.0107	.0104	.0102	.0099	.0096	.0094	.0091	.0089	.0087	.0084
-2.2	.0139	.0136	.0132	.0129	.0125	.0122	.0119	.0116	.0113	.0110
-2.1	.0179	.0174	.0170	.0166	.0162	.0158	.0154	.0150	.0146	.0143
-2.0	.0228	.0222	.0217	.0212	.0207	.0202	.0197	.0192	.0188	.0183
-1.9	.0287	.0281	.0274	.0268	.0262	.0256	.0250	.0244	.0239	.0233
-1.8	.0359	.0351	.0344	.0336	.0329	.0322	.0314	.0307	.0301	.0294
-1.7	.0446	.0436	.0427	.0418	.0409	.0401	.0392	.0384	.0375	.0367
-1.6	.0548	.0537	.0526	.0516	.0505	.0495	.0485	.0475	.0465	.0455
-1.5	.0668	.0655	.0643	.0630	.0618	.0606	.0594	.0582	.0571	.0559
-1.4	.0808	.0793	.0778	.0764	.0749	.0735	.0721	.0708	.0694	.0681
-1.3	.0968	.0951	.0934	.0918	.0901	.0885	.0869	.0853	.0838	.0823
-1.2	.1151	.1131	.1112	.1093	.1075	.1056	.1038	.1020	.1003	.0985
-1.1	.1357	.1335	.1314	.1292	.1271	.1251	.1230	.1210	.1190	.1170
-1.0	.1587	.1562	.1539	.1515	.1492	.1469	.1446	.1423	.1401	.1379
-0.9	.1841	.1814	.1788	.1762	.1736	.1711	.1685	.1660	.1635	.1611
-0.8	.2119	.2090	.2061	.2033	.2005	.1977	.1949	.1922	.1894	.1867
-0.7	.2420	.2389	.2358	.2327	.2296	.2266	.2236	.2206	.2177	.2148
-0.6	.2743	.2709	.2676	.2643	.2611	.2578	.2546	.2514	.2483	.2451
-0.5	.3085	.3050	.3015	.2981	.2946	.2912	.2877	.2843	.2810	.2776
-0.4	.3446	.3409	.3372	.3336	.3300	.3264	.3228	.3192	.3156	.3121
-0.3	.3821	.3783	.3745	.3707	.3669	.3632	.3594	.3557	.3520	.3483
-0.2	.4207	.4168	.4129	.4090	.4052	.4013	.3974	.3936	.3897	.3859
-0.1	.4602	.4562	.4522	.4483	.4443	.4404	.4364	.4325	.4286	.4247
-0.0	.5000	.4960	.4920	.4880	.4840	.4801	.4761	.4721	.4681	.4641

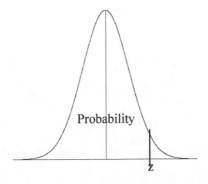

Probability

Probabilities in the body of the table are the probabilities of being <u>less than</u> the given value of z.

Standard Normal Probabilities

z	.00	.01	.02	.03	.04	.05	.06	.07	.08	.09
0.0	.5000	.5040	.5080	.5120	.5160	.5199	.5239	.5279	.5319	.5359
0.1	.5398	.5438	.5478	.5517	.5557	.5596	.5636	.5675	.5714	.5753
0.2	.5793	.5832	.5871	.5910	.5948	.5987	.6026	.6064	.6103	.6141
0.3	.6179	.6217	.6255	.6293	.6331	.6368	.6406	.6443	.6480	.6517
0.4	.6554	.6591	.6628	.6664	.6700	.6736	.6772	.6808	.6844	.6879
0.5	.6915	.6950	.6985	.7019	.7054	.7088	.7123	.7157	.7190	.7224
0.6	.7257	.7291	.7324	.7357	.7389	.7422	.7454	.7486	.7517	.7549
0.7	.7580	.7611	.7642	.7673	.7704	.7734	.7764	.7794	.7823	.7852
0.8	.7881	.7910	.7939	.7967	.7995	.8023	.8051	.8078	.8106	.8133
0.9	.8159	.8186	.8212	.8238	.8264	.8289	.8315	.8340	.8365	.8389
1.0	.8413	.8438	.8461	.8485	.8508	.8531	.8554	.8577	.8599	.8621
1.1	.8643	.8665	.8686	.8708	.8729	.8749	.8770	.8790	.8810	.8830
1.2	.8849	.8869	.8888	.8907	.8925	.8944	.8962	.8980	.8997	.9015
1.3	.9032	.9049	.9066	.9082	.9099	.9115	.9131	.9147	.9162	.9177
1.4	.9192	.9207	.9222	.9236	.9251	.9265	.9279	.9292	.9306	.9319
1.5	.9332	.9345	.9357	.9370	.9382	.9394	.9406	.9418	.9429	.9441
1.6	.9452	.9463	.9474	.9484	.9495	.9505	.9515	.9525	.9535	.9545
1.7	.9554	.9564	.9573	.9582	.9591	.9599	.9608	.9616	.9625	.9633
1.8	.9641	.9649	.9656	.9664	.9671	.9678	.9686	.9693	.9699	.9706
1.9	.9713	.9719	.9726	.9732	.9738	.9744	.9750	.9756	.9761	.9767
2.0	.9772	.9778	.9783	.9788	.9793	.9798	.9803	.9808	.9812	.9817
2.1	.9821	.9826	.9830	.9834	.9838	.9842	.9846	.9850	.9854	.9857
2.2	.9861	.9864	.9868	.9871	.9875	.9878	.9881	.9884	.9887	.9890
2.3	.9893	.9896	.9898	.9901	.9904	.9906	.9909	.9911	.9913	.9916
2.4	.9918	.9920	.9922	.9925	.9927	.9929	.9931	.9932	.9934	.9936
2.5	.9938	.9940	.9941	.9943	.9945	.9946	.9948	.9949	.9951	.9952
2.6	.9953	.9955	.9956	.9957	.9959	.9960	.9961	.9962	.9963	.9964
2.7	.9965	.9966	.9967	.9968	.9969	.9970	.9971	.9972	.9973	.9974
2.8	.9974	.9975	.9976	.9977	.9977	.9978	.9979	.9979	.9980	.9981
2.9	.9981	.9982	.9982	.9983	.9984	.9984	.9985	.9985	.9986	.9986
3.0	.9987	.9987	.9987	.9988	.9988	.9989	.9989	.9989	.9990	.9990
3.1	.9990	.9991	.9991	.9991	.9992	.9992	.9992	.9992	.9993	.9993
3.2	.9993	.9993	.9994	.9994	.9994	.9994	.9994	.9995	.9995	.9995
3.3	.9995	.9995	.9995	.9996	.9996	.9996	.9996	.9996	.9996	.9997
3.4	.9997	.9997	.9997	.9997	.9997	.9997	.9997	.9997	.9997	.9998

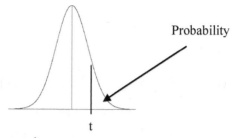

Probability

t

Table entry for p and C is the critical value t* with probability p lying to its <u>right</u> and probability C lying between –t* and t*.

t Distribution Critical Values

df	.25	.20	.15	.10	.05	.025	.02	.01	.005	.0025	.001	.0005
1	1.000	1.376	1.963	3.078	6.314	12.71	15.89	31.82	63.66	127.3	318.3	636.6
2	0.816	1.061	1.386	1.886	2.920	4.303	4.849	6.965	9.925	14.09	22.33	31.60
3	0.765	0.978	1.250	1.638	2.353	3.182	3.482	4.541	5.841	7.453	10.21	12.92
4	0.741	0.941	1.190	1.533	2.132	2.776	2.999	3.747	4.604	5.598	7.173	8.610
5	0.727	0.920	1.156	1.476	2.015	2.571	2.757	3.365	4.032	4.773	5.893	6.869
6	0.718	0.906	1.134	1.440	1.943	2.447	2.612	3.143	3.707	4.317	5.208	5.959
7	0.711	0.896	1.119	1.415	1.895	2.365	2.517	2.998	3.499	4.029	4.785	5.408
8	0.706	0.889	1.108	1.397	1.860	2.306	2.449	2.896	3.355	3.833	4.501	5.041
9	0.703	0.883	1.100	1.383	1.833	2.262	2.398	2.821	3.250	3.690	4.297	4.781
10	0.700	0.879	1.093	1.372	1.812	2.228	2.359	2.764	3.169	3.581	4.144	4.587
11	0.697	0.876	1.088	1.363	1.796	2.201	2.328	2.718	3.106	3.497	4.025	4.437
12	0.695	0.873	1.083	1.356	1.782	2.179	2.303	2.681	3.055	3.428	3.930	4.318
13	0.694	0.870	1.079	1.350	1.771	2.160	2.282	2.650	3.012	3.372	3.852	4.221
14	0.692	0.868	1.076	1.345	1.761	2.145	2.264	2.624	2.977	3.326	3.787	4.140
15	0.691	0.866	1.074	1.341	1.753	2.131	2.249	2.602	2.947	3.286	3.733	4.073
16	0.690	0.865	1.071	1.337	1.746	2.120	2.235	2.583	2.921	3.252	3.686	4.015
17	0.689	0.863	1.069	1.333	1.740	2.110	2.224	2.567	2.898	3.222	3.646	3.965
18	0.688	0.862	1.067	1.330	1.734	2.101	2.214	2.552	2.878	3.197	3.611	3.922
19	0.688	0.861	1.066	1.328	1.729	2.093	2.205	2.539	2.861	3.174	3.579	3.883
20	0.687	0.860	1.064	1.325	1.725	2.086	2.197	2.528	2.845	3.153	3.552	3.850
21	0.686	0.859	1.063	1.323	1.721	2.080	2.189	2.518	2.831	3.135	3.527	3.819
22	0.686	0.858	1.061	1.321	1.717	2.074	2.183	2.508	2.819	3.119	3.505	3.792
23	0.685	0.858	1.060	1.319	1.714	2.069	2.177	2.500	2.807	3.104	3.485	3.768
24	0.685	0.857	1.059	1.318	1.711	2.064	2.172	2.492	2.797	3.091	3.467	3.745
25	0.684	0.856	1.058	1.316	1.708	2.060	2.167	2.485	2.787	3.078	3.450	3.725
26	0.684	0.856	1.058	1.315	1.706	2.056	2.162	2.479	2.779	3.067	3.435	3.707
27	0.684	0.855	1.057	1.314	1.703	2.052	2.158	2.473	2.771	3.057	3.421	3.690
28	0.683	0.855	1.056	1.313	1.701	2.048	2.154	2.467	2.763	3.047	3.408	3.674
29	0.683	0.854	1.055	1.311	1.699	2.045	2.150	2.462	2.756	3.038	3.396	3.659
30	0.683	0.854	1.055	1.310	1.697	2.042	2.147	2.457	2.750	3.030	3.385	3.646
40	0.681	0.851	1.050	1.303	1.684	2.021	2.123	2.423	2.704	2.971	3.307	3.551
50	0.679	0.849	1.047	1.299	1.676	2.009	2.109	2.403	2.678	2.937	3.261	3.496
60	0.679	0.848	1.045	1.296	1.671	2.000	2.099	2.390	2.660	2.915	3.232	3.460
80	0.678	0.846	1.043	1.292	1.664	1.990	2.088	2.374	2.639	2.887	3.195	3.416
100	0.677	0.845	1.042	1.290	1.660	1.984	2.081	2.364	2.626	2.871	3.174	3.390
1000	0.675	0.842	1.037	1.282	1.646	1.962	2.056	2.330	2.581	2.813	3.098	3.300
z*	0.674	0.841	1.036	1.282	1.645	1.960	2.054	2.326	2.576	2.807	3.091	3.291
	50%	60%	70%	80%	90%	95%	96%	98%	99%	99.5	99.8	99.9

Confidence Level C